TREASURY OF
SNAKE LORE

Other Books By
BRANDT AYMAR

The Complete Cruiser
Cruising Is Fun

Co-editor of
The Deck Chair Reader

Treasury of Snake Lore

edited by Brandt Aymar

From the Garden of Eden to Snakes of Today
in Mythology, Fable, Stories, Essays, Poetry,
Drama, Religion, and Personal Adventures

New York
Greenberg: Publisher

To Johnny, a wonderful lifelong companion

ACKNOWLEDGMENTS

No treasury such as this could be compiled without the generous assistance of the authors and publishers of many of the works contained herein. SNAKE DOCTOR by Irvin S. Cobb is reprinted from *Snake Doctor* (a collection of short stories) by Irvin S. Cobb, published and copyrighted 1923 by George H. Doran Co., renewed 1950 by Laura Baker Cobb, used by permission of Laura Baker Cobb, c/o Buhler, King & Buhler, 274 Madison Avenue, New York, N.Y.

To the late Arthur Richmond I am deeply indebted for his kind advice and help in suggesting ideas for this treasury, and for his permission to use two selections from *The Encircled Serpent* by M. Oldfield Howey, THE SERPENT AS AMULET AND CHARM and THE SERPENT AS PHALLIC EMBLEM.

THE HOPI SNAKE DANCE is reprinted from *Mornings in Mexico* by D. H. Lawrence by permission of Alfred A. Knopf, Inc., copyright 1927 by Alfred A. Knopf, Inc. THE ANCIENT ENMITY from *Cross Creek* by Marjorie Kinnan Rawlings, copyrighted 1942 by Marjorie Kinnan Rawlings is reprinted by permission of the publishers, Charles Scribner's Sons. SNAKES AS PETS from *The Book of Wild Pets* by Clifford Moore, copyright 1937, is used here by permission of G. P. Putnam's Sons. THE SERPENT WORLD is from *Snakes of the World* by Raymond L. Ditmars and used by permission of The Macmillan Company.

My thanks to Ellen C. Masters for her kind permission to include BEETHOVEN'S NINTH SYMPHONY AND THE KING COBRA by Edgar Lee Masters. To *Popular Science Monthly* for allowing me to reprint SNAKE MYTHS SMASHED BY SCIENCE, an interview with C. B. Perkins from their March 1940 issue. To Holiday House for KNUTE, THE GIANT BULLSNAKE from the 1949 edition of *Ol' Paul* by Glen Rounds. To Grove Press for the fable of PRINCE ALBERIC AND THE SNAKE LADY by Vernon Lee. To Indiana University Press for Rolfe Humphries' translation of AESCULAPIUS from Ovid's *Metamorphoses*. To Richard R. Smith Publisher, Inc., of West Rindge, N. H., for Arthur F. Kraetzer's 1950 translation of the poem THE SERPENT THAT DANCES from *The Flowers of Evil* by Charles Baudelaire. To the Naylor Company for THE FENCE THAT MOVED from *Cowboy Lore* by Jules Verne Allen. To James T. White and Co., for the poem SNAKE by John Russell McCarthy.

The Alistair MacCrae short story SERPENT VERSUS DONOVAN is copyright 1946 by The Atlantic Monthly Company, Boston 16, Mass. The Robert Bordner story THE PENINSULA PYTHON is copyright 1945 by The Atlantic Monthly Company, Boston 16, Mass. Both are used by their kind permission.

EVERY STICK A SNAKE is taken from the book *Kingdom of the Elephant* by E. Temple-Perkins and published 1955 by Andrew Melrose Ltd., London, England.

To all the above and to the many other authors included in this volume I am indebted for their interest and inspiration in using the serpent and the snake as the subject of their writings.

PREFACE

It was in the writings of W. H. Hudson that I found the excuse to compile a treasury of snake lore. The idea struck me while reading *The Book of the Naturalist* where I came across this passage: "If we have known the creature, at home or abroad, and wish in reading to recover the impression of a sweet summer-hot Nature that invites our caresses, always with a subtle serpent somewhere concealed in the folds of her garments, we must go to literature rather than to science. The poet has the secret, not the naturalist."

So saying, in this present volume we go to the poets, to the story-tellers, to the essayists, and leave the scientific aspect of the snake to those whose life-work with these ophidians speaks with fuller authority on that score.

Just as in the art of painting, the great masters turned first to the Bible for their subject matter, so in the literature of the snake it seemed only logical for me to begin this treasury with the role of the serpent in the Garden of Eden, and to take my opening selection from Genesis itself. This is later followed up in the poetry section with John Milton's lofty exposition of the Adam and Eve theme in pertinent passages from *Paradise Lost*. In such a beginning I had no choice, of course, but to present the subject of this work as the deadliest kind of a culprit, the destroyer of all moral values, a hellion incarnate.

But if the serpent is the arch-villain to those whose religion is based on the Bible, not at all so to those who worshipped the Egyptian, Greek and Roman deities. To them the serpent was hero, savior, and healer. For example, Ovid recounts in his *Metamorphoses* how Apollo sends his son, Aesculapius, in the form of an enormous serpent to drive the pestilence from Rome and save the populace from the dreaded plague. All through mythology and serpent worship, the snake is endowed with such curative powers. Even today the symbol of healing is still the serpent-form of Aesculapius, god of medicine.

Our fableists, almost without exception from Aesop on, treat the snake with considerably less respect—one might say with none at all—and attribute to him only a deadly cunning. It is interesting to note that their universal agreement on this subtle yet evil wisdom of the snake reflects a somewhat different attitude from that of Jesus Christ in one of the opening passages of this volume. When Jesus admonishes his disciples, upon sending them forth to preach his gospel: "Be ye wise as serpents," while not being deliberately laudatory to the serpent, he was realistically advising his followers to combat the craftiness of men with the inborn cleverness of the snake.

In the section on serpent worship I picked four representative selections from a mass of material that could fill many a library shelf. From these works of James Fergusson, M. Oldfield Howey, and Catherine C. Hopley, emerges, I hope, a short if necessarily sketchy picture of the who-how-and-why of serpent worship, just enough, perhaps, to influence you to delve deeper into the fascinating mysteries of this subject.

The essayists look upon the snake with a somewhat different feeling. To them the snake is an object for wonder. They marvel at the physical grace embodied in his elongated, limbless form. They question man's reason for horror and revulsion at the mere thought of the creature. "Why that horror?" asks Ruskin. "We all feel it, yet how imaginative it is, how disproportioned to the real strength of the creature! . . . That horror is of the myth, not of the creature." They admire the poets' imaginative intertwining of serpent and human emotions.

By far the longest sections of this treasury are those devoted to the snake in fiction. Rather than lumping them all together in one group, I thought it more appropriate to divide them into four: short stories, mystery stories, tall tales, and selections from novels which form complete units in their own right. There is not room in a preface to comment on each; suffice it to say that in most of them the snake comes off the worse, by far. About two of them, Ambrose Bierce's "The Man and the Snake" and Irvin S. Cobb's prize-winning short story "Snake Doctor," I would like to incite your curiosity by mentioning a more than cursory similarity of climax.

I wish I could have included many more personal adventures with snakes. Physical limitations on the size of a treasury sorely try the conscience of any editor. I am happy, however, to include Marjorie Kinnan Rawlings' first snake hunt, during which Ross Allen taught her gradually to lose her inborn fear of snakes. It is from *Cross Creek,* and entitled "The Ancient Enmity." And Clifford B. Moore's "Snakes as Pets" may even inspire some of you to enlarge your domestic households.

I am loath to admit that I know of only one famous scene in world drama in which the snake plays a leading part, and this is included as "The Death of Cleopatra" from Act V of William Shakespeare's *Antony and Cleopatra.* There may be others from which I might have chosen, but neither I nor my drama-authority friends knew of them. Anyway, until a better one comes along, Shakespeare will suffice.

The snake dance is a vital part of North American folklore. Stories, myths, and legends involving this Indian ceremony abound in all the folklore journals and other periodicals—a great many of them being about the Hopis. Luckily my choice in this direction was made simple through the fact that D. H. Lawrence had written a superb description of America's most famous Indian ceremony, "The Hopi Snake Dance." Others tried but were no match for Lawrence. Even Theodore Roosevelt's description of it showed he was better at politics than the pen.

It might seem implausible that snakes, having the connotation so many people attach to them, should be a fit subject for the poets. Nothing could be farther from the facts. Of all the sections of this treasury, my most difficult task was to select for this last one. I again thank Hudson for introducing me to Matthew Arnold's beautiful "Cadmus and Harmonia." "How the immemorable fable" he writes, "is freshened into life by the poet's genius, and the heart stirred as by a drama of the day we live in! . . . To those who are familiar with the serpent, and have been profoundly impressed by it, there is a rare beauty and truth in that picture of its breathless quiet, its endless placid dumb existence amid the flowery brakes."

So, you see, the snake is not all venom and vice.

Brandt Aymar

TABLE OF CONTENTS

xiii

THE BIBLE

Adam, Eve, and the Serpent

NOW THE SERPENT WAS MORE SUBTLE THAN ANY BEAST of the field which the Lord God had made. And he said unto the woman, Yea, hath God said, Ye shall not eat of every tree of the garden?

And the woman said unto the serpent, We may eat of the fruit of the trees of the garden:

But of the fruit of the tree which is in the midst of the garden, God hath said, Ye shall not eat of it, neither shall ye touch it, lest ye die.

And the serpent said unto the woman, Ye shall not surely die:

For God doth know that in the day ye eat thereof, then your eyes shall be opened: and ye shall be as gods, knowing good and evil.

And when the woman saw that the tree was good for food, and that it was pleasant to the eyes, and a tree to be desired to make one wise, she took of the fruit thereof, and did eat; and gave also unto her husband with her, and he did eat.

And the eyes of them both were opened, and they knew that they were naked: and they sewed fig leaves together, and made themselves aprons.

And they heard the voice of the Lord God walking in the garden in the cool of the day: and Adam and his wife hid themselves from the presence of the Lord God, amongst the trees of the garden.

And the Lord God called unto Adam, and said unto him, Where art thou?

And he said, I heard thy voice in the garden, and I was afraid, because I was naked: and I hid myself.

And he said, Who told thee that thou wast naked? Hast thou eaten of the tree, Whereof I commanded thee that thou shouldest not eat?

And the man said, The woman whom thou gavest to be with me, she gave me of the tree, and I did eat.

And the Lord God said unto the woman, What is this that thou hast done? And the woman said, the serpent beguiled me, and I did eat.

And the Lord God said unto the serpent, Because thou hast done this, thou art cursed above all cattle, and above every beast of the field: upon thy belly shalt thou go, and dust shalt thou eat all the days of thy life:

And I will put enmity between thee and the woman, and between thy seed and her seed; it shall bruise thy head, and thou shalt bruise his heel.

Unto the woman he said, I will greatly multiply thy sórrow, and thy conception: in sorrow thou shalt bring forth children; and thy desire shall be to thy husband, and he shall rule over thee.

And unto Adam he said, Because thou hast hearkened unto the voice of thy wife, and hast eaten of the tree of which I commanded thee, saying, Thou shalt not eat of it: cursed is the ground for thy sake; in sorrow shalt thou eat of it all the days of thy life:

Thorns also and thistles shall it bring forth to thee and thou shalt eat the herb of the field:

In the sweat of thy face shalt thou eat bread, till thou return unto the ground; for out of it wast thou taken: for dust thou are, and unto dust shalt thou return.

And Adam called his wife's name Eve; because she was the mother of all living.

Unto Adam also, and to his wife, did the Lord God make coats of skins, and clothed them.

And the Lord God said, Behold, the man is become as one of us, to know good and evil: and now, lest he put forth his hand, and take also of the tree of life, and eat, and live for ever:

Therefore the Lord God sent him forth from the garden of Eden to till the ground from whence he was taken.

So he drove out the man: and he placed at the east of the garden of Eden, cherubims, and a flaming sword which turned every way, to keep the way of the tree of life.

(Genesis, Chap. 3:1–24)

Changing the Rods to Serpents

AND THE LORD SAID UNTO MOSES, SEE, I HAVE MADE THEE a god to Pharaoh; and Aaron thy brother shall be thy prophet.

Thou shalt speak all that I command thee; and Aaron thy brother shall speak unto Pharaoh, that he send the children of Israel out of his land.

And I will harden Pharaoh's heart, and multiply my signs and my wonders in the land of Egypt.

But Pharaoh shall not hearken unto you, that I may lay my hand upon

Egypt, and bring forth mine armies, and my people the children of Israel, out of the land of Egypt by great judgments.

And the Egyptians shall know that I am the Lord, when I stretch forth mine hand upon Egypt, and bring out the children of Israel from among them.

And Moses and Aaron did as the Lord commanded them, so did they.

And Moses was fourscore years old, and Aaron fourscore and three years old, when they spake unto Pharaoh.

And the Lord spake unto Moses and unto Aaron, saying,

When Pharaoh shall speak unto you, saying, Shew a miracle for you; then thou shalt say unto Aaron, Take thy rod, and cast it before Pharaoh, and it shall become a serpent.

And Moses and Aaron went in unto Pharaoh, and they did so as the Lord had commanded: and Aaron cast down his rod before Pharaoh, and before his servants, and it became a serpent.

Then Pharaoh also called the wise men and the sorcerers: now the magicians of Egypt, they also did in like manner with their enchantments.

For they cast down every man his rod, and they became serpents; but Aaron's rod swallowed up their rods.

(Exodus, Chap. 7: 1–12)

God tells Moses to Make a Fiery Serpent

AND THE PEOPLE SPAKE AGAINST GOD, AND AGAINST Moses, Wherefore have ye brought us up out of Egypt, to die in the wilderness? for there is no bread, neither is there any water, and our soul loatheth this light bread.

And the Lord sent fiery serpents among the people, and they bit the people, and much people of Israel died.

Therefore the people came to Moses, and said, We have sinned, for we have spoken against the Lord, and against thee, pray unto the Lord, that he take away the serpents from us. And Moses prayed for the people.

And the Lord said unto Moses, Make thee a fiery serpent, and set it upon a pole and it shall come to pass, that every one that is bitten, when he looketh upon it, shall live.

And Moses made a serpent of brass, and put it upon a pole: and it came to pass, that if a serpent had bitten any man, when he beheld the serpent of brass, he lived.

(Numbers, Chap. 21: 5–9)

Hezekiah Destroys the Serpent of Moses

NOW IT CAME TO PASS, IN THE THIRD YEAR OF HOSHEA, son of Elah king of Israel, that Hezekiah, the son of Ahaz king of Judah began to reign.

Twenty and five years old was he when began to reign: and he reigned twenty and nine years in Jerusalem. His mother's name also was Abi, the daughter of Zachariah.

And he did that which was right in the sight of the Lord, according to all that David his father did.

He removed the high places, and brake the images, and cut down the groves, and brake in pieces the brazen serpent that Moses had made: for unto those days the children of Israel did burn incense to it: and he called it Nehushtan.

(Kings, Chap. 18: 1–4)

Paul and the Viper

AND WHEN THEY HAD TAKEN UP THE ANCHORS, THEY committed themselves unto the sea, and loosed the rudder bands, and hoisted up the mainsail to the wind, and made toward shore.

And falling into a place where two seas met, they ran the ship aground;

and the forepart stuck fast, and remained unmoveable, but the hinder part was broken with the violence of the waves.

And the soldiers' counsel was to kill the prisoners, lest any of them should swim out, and escape.

But the centurion, willing to save Paul, kept them from their purpose; and commanded that they which could swim should cast themselves first into the sea, and get to land:

And the rest, some on boards, and some on broken pieces of the ship. And so it came to pass, that they escaped all safe to land.

And when they were escaped, then they knew that the island was called Meilita.

And the barbarous people shewed us no little kindness; for they kindled a fire, and received us every one, because of the present rain, and because of the cold.

And when Paul had gathered a bundle of sticks, and laid them on the fire, there came a viper out of the heat, and fastened on his hand.

And when the barbarians saw the venomous beast hang on his hand, they said among themselves, No doubt this man is a murderer, whom, though he hath escaped the sea, yet vengeance suffereth not to live.

And he shook off the beast into the fire, and felt no harm.

Howbeit, they looked when he should have swollen, or fallen down dead suddenly: but after they had looked a great while, and saw no harm come to him, they changed their minds, and said that he was a god.

(The Acts, Chap. 27: 41–44, Chap. 28: 1–6)

Wise as Serpents

THESE TWELVE JESUS SENT FORTH, AND COMMANDED them, saying, Go not into the way of the Gentiles, and into any city of the Samaritans enter ye not:

But go rather to the lost sheep of the house of Israel.

And, as ye go, preach, saying, The kingdom of heaven is at hand.

And whosoever shall not receive you, nor hear your words, when ye depart out of that house or city, shake off the dust of your feet.

Verily I say unto you, It shall be more tolerable for the land of Sodom and Gomorrha in the day of judgment, than for that city.

Behold, I send you forth as sheep in the midst of wolves: be ye therefore wise as serpents, and harmless as doves.

(Matthew, Chap. 10: 5–7, 14–16)

Aesculapius

by OVID
(translated by Rolfe Humphries)

And now, O Muses, helpers of the poets,
You knowers and rememberers, aid the telling
Of how an island in the Tiber's channel
Brought the god Aesculapius to Rome.

In the old days a deadly pestilence
Infected Latium's air, and bodies wasted
Pale with a bloodless sickness. Men were weary
Of caring for the dead, and saw their efforts
All came to nothing, found the arts of healers
Of no avail, and so they went to Delphi,
Earth's center, there to beg the god to help them,
To heal them in their misery, and end
The ills of their great city. All things trembled,
The shrine, the laurel, and Apollo's quiver,
And from the innermost tripod came the words
That shook them all with fear: "What you are seeking
In Delphi, Romans, you should have sought for nearer.
Go, seek it nearer home, Apollo cannot
Lessen your troubles, but Apollo's son
Has power to help you. Go, with all good omens,
And call upon him." The wise senate listened,
Heard the injunction, and inquired what city
Held the young god, and sent to Epidaurus
By ship to find him. When they beached their vessel
On that curved shore, they went to meet the fathers,
The council of the Greeks, prayed for the gift
Of that one deity to end their troubles,
According to the oracle. The elders
Differed among themselves: some were for giving
The gift outright, but there were more who favored
Keeping their god, their wealth, their aid and guardian.
And while they sat in doubt, the dusk of evening

Banished the lingering day, and darkness shadowed
The light of the world. Then Aesculapius seemed,
In dream, to stand before the Roman's couch,
Even as in his temple, with the staff
In his left hand, his right forefinger stroking
His flowing beard. He spoke, or seemed to, calmly:
"Be not afraid; I shall come, and leave my statues,
But see this serpent, as it twines around
The rod I carry: mark it well, and learn it,
For I shall be this serpent, only larger,
Like a celestial presence." And he vanished,
And with his voice the slumber died, and day
Dawned calm upon that sleep, and the bright morning
Had driven out the stars, when all the elders,
Uncertain still, assembled at the temple
And prayed their god to give a sign, an omen,
Where he would have his dwelling-place. And silence
Had hardly fallen, when the god, all crested
With gold, in serpent-form, uttered a warning,
Hissed terribly, a sign that he was coming,
And all the altars, all the doors, the pavement,
The roof of gold, the statue, shook and trembled.
Reared high, he stood there, and he gazed about him
With fiery eyes, and as the people shuddered,
The priest, in ceremonial headdress, knew him,
Calling: "The god! Behold the god! Bow down
To him in word and spirit, all who stand here!
That we may see his beauty as our blessing,
Here at his shrine!" And all the people worshipped,
Made their responses, and the Romans also
Gave sign of deep devotion, and the god
Was gracious, signified his lasting favor,
Hissed, glided down the marble stairs, and turned
To gaze once more on those familiar altars
For the last time, and then he wound his way,
Looping and coiling, over the ground where flowers
Were scattered in his honor, and so came
To the harbor with its curving walls, and halted,
And seemed to say farewell to all his people,
And went aboard the ship, which under the burden
Of the god's weight, seemed to be heavy laden.
And joy filled all the Romans; on the shore
They slew a bull for sacrificial offering
And wreathed the ship with flowers, and loosed
        the moorings.

Soft breezes blew the vessel on: the god
Looked down from the high stern on the blue waters,
And the winds held fair through the Ionian sea,
Five days to Italy, on by Lacinium,
Famous for Juno's temple, past Scylaceum,
Beyond Iapygia, skirting crags and rocks,
Skirting Romethium, Caulon, and Narycia,
Past Sicily and Pelorus' straits, beyond
The island of the winds, the copper-mines,
On toward Leucosia and Paestum's headland
Whose roses love the warmth; then by Capri
Minerva's cape, Sorrento's hilly vineyards,
Past Herculaneum, Stabiae, and Naples
Founded for leisure, famous for the temple
Of the Cumaean Sibyl. On and on
By the hot springs of Baiae, by Linternum,
Where grow the mastic-trees, beyond Volturnus,
The whirling sandy river, by Sinuessa
And all its snowy doves, beyond Minturnae,
A pestilential town, beyond Caieta
Named for Aeneas' nurse, whose funeral
Was held there long ago, past Formiae,
Past marshy Terracina and Circe's island,
Past Antium and the shore of hard-packed sand.
Here the sea roughened, and the sailors altered
Their course to landward, and the god unfolded
His coils and came in looping curving motion
To his father's temple on that yellow shore.
And the sea calmed, and once again he left
His father's altars, a guest there, for a little,
In blood-relationship, and turned, and made a furrow
Along the beach, and the scales rasped like metal,
Until he came to the ship, wound upward, slowly,
The rudder's length, and rested by the tiller.
He came to Castrum, to the mouth of Tiber,
Lavinium's holy place, and here the people
Came thronging down to meet him, men and matrons
And maids, the Vestals, and they cried Hosannas,
As the swift ship rode on upstream, and incense
Crackled on altars on both sides of the river
And air was fragrant with the smoke of incense
And victim beasts made the knife warm with blood.
He had entered Rome, the capital of the world,
And climbed the mast, and swung his head about
As if to seek his proper habitation.

Just at this point the river breaks and flows,
A double stream, around a mole of land
Men call The Island. Here the serpent-son,
Apollo's offspring, came to land, put on
His heavenly form again, and to the people
Brought health and end of mourning.

Apollo and Python

by BULLFINCH

THE SLIME WITH WHICH THE EARTH WAS COVERED BY the waters of the flood produced an excessive fertility, which called forth every variety of production, both bad and good. Among the rest, Python, an enormous serpent, crept forth, the terror of the people, and lurked in the caves of Mount Parnassus. Apollo slew him with his arrows—weapons which he had not before used against any but feeble animals, hares, wild goats, and such game. In commemoration of this illustrious conquest he instituted the Pythian games, in which the victor in feats of strength, swiftness of foot, or in the chariot race was crowned with a wreath of beech leaves; for the laurel was not yet adopted by Apollo as his own tree.

The famous statue of Apollo called the Belvedere represents the god after this victory over the serpent Python.

Cadmus

by BULLFINCH

JUPITER, UNDER THE DISGUISE OF A BULL, HAD CARRIED away Europa, the daughter of Agenor, king of Phœnicia. Agenor commanded his son Cadmus to go in search of his sister, and not to return without her. Cadmus went and sought long and far for his sister, but could not find her, and not daring to return unsuccessful, consulted the oracle of Apollo to know what country he should settle in. The oracle informed him that he should find a cow in the field, and should follow her wherever she might wander, and where she stopped, should build a city and call it Thebes. Cadmus had hardly left the Castalian cave, from which the oracle was delivered, when he saw a young cow slowly walking before him. He followed her close, offering at the same time his prayers to Phœbus. The cow went on till she passed the shallow channel of Cephisus and came out into the plain of Panope. There she stood still, raising her broad forehead to the sky, filled the air with her lowings. Cadmus gave thanks, and stooping down kissed the foreign soil, then lifting his eyes, greeted the surrounding mountains. Wishing to offer a sacrifice to Jupiter, he sent his servants to seek pure water for a libation. Near by there stood an ancient grove which had never been profaned by the axe, in the midst of which was a cave, thick covered with the growth of bushes, its roof forming a low arch, from beneath which burst forth a fountain of purest water. In the cave lurked a horrid serpent with a crested head and scales glittering like gold. His eyes shone like fire, his body was swollen with venom, he vibrated a triple tongue, and showed a triple row of teeth. No sooner had the Tyrians dipped their pitchers in the fountain, and the in-gushing waters made a sound, than the glittering serpent raised his head out of the cave and uttered a fearful hiss. The vessels fell from their hands, the blood left their cheeks, they trembled in every limb. The serpent, twisting his scaly body in a huge coil, raised his head so as to overtop the tallest trees, and while the Tyrians from terror could neither fight nor fly, slew some with his fangs, others in his folds, and others with his poisonous breath.

Cadmus, having waited for the return of his men till midday, went in search of them. His covering was a lion's hide, and besides his javelin he carried in his hand a lance, and in his breast a bold heart, a surer reliance than either. When he entered the wood, and saw the lifeless bodies of his men, and the monster with his bloody jaws, he exclaimed, "O faithful friends, I will avenge you, or share your death." So saying he lifted a huge stone and threw it with all his force at the serpent. Such a block would have shaken the wall of a fortress, but it made no impression on the monster. Cadmus next threw his javelin, which met with better success, for it penetrated the serpent's scales, and pierced through to his entrails. Fierce with pain, the monster turned back his head to view the wound, and attempted to draw out the weapon with his mouth, but broke it off, leaving the iron point rankling in his flesh. His neck swelled with rage, bloody foam covered his jaws, and the breath of his nostrils poisoned the air around. Now he twisted himself into a circle, then stretched himself out on the ground like the trunk of a fallen tree. As he moved onward, Cadmus retreated before him, holding his spear opposite to the monster's opened jaws. The serpent snapped at the weapon and attempted to bite its iron point. Cadmus, watching his chance, thrust the spear at a moment when the animal's head thrown back came against the trunk of a tree, and succeeded in pinning him to its side. His weight bent the tree as he struggled in the agonies of death.

While Cadmus stood over his conquered foe, contemplating its vast size, a voice was heard (from whence he knew not, but he heard it distinctly) commanding him to take the dragon's teeth and sow them in the earth. He obeyed. He made a furrow in the ground, and planted the teeth, destined to produce a crop of men. Scarce had he done so when the clods began to move, and the points of spears to appear above the surface. Next helmets with their nodding plumes came up, and next the shoulders and breast and limbs of men with weapons, and in time a harvest of armed warriors. Cadmus, alarmed, prepared to encounter a new enemy, but one of them said to him, "Meddle not with our civil war." With that he who had spoken smote one of his earth-born brothers with a sword, and he himself fell pierced with an arrow from another. The latter fell victim to a fourth, and in like manner the whole crowd dealt with each other till all fell, slain with mutual wounds, except five survivors. One of these cast away his weapons and said, "Brothers, let us live in peace!" These five joined with Cadmus in building his city, to which they gave the name of Thebes.

Cadmus obtained in marriage Harmonia, the daughter of Venus. The gods left Olympus to honour the occasion with their presence, and Vulcan presented the bride with a necklace of surpassing brilliancy, his own workmanship. But a fatality hung over the family of Cadmus in consequence of his killing the serpent sacred to Mars. Semele and Ino, his daughters, and Actæon and Pentheus, his grandchildren, all perished unhappily, and Cadmus and Harmonia quitted Thebes, now grown odious to them, and emigrated to the country of the Enchelians, who received them with honour and made Cadmus their king. But the misfortunes of their children still weighed upon their minds; and one day Cadmus exclaimed, "If a serpent's life is so dear to the gods, I would I were myself a serpent." No sooner had he uttered the words than he began to change his form. Harmonia beheld it and prayed to the gods to let her share his fate. Both became serpents. They live in the woods, but mindful of their origin, they neither avoid the presence of man nor do they ever injure any one.

The Fate of Laocoön

by VIRGIL
(translated by Christopher Pearse Cranch from the Aeneid)

Here another dire event
More dreadful far befalls, disturbing us,
Wretched and unprepared, with gloomy thoughts.
Laocoön, chosen Neptune's priest by lot,
A huge bull at the solemn altars there
Was sacrificing, when behold, two snakes—
I shudder as I tell—from Tenedos
Come gliding upon the sea, and side by side
Toward the shore they move with necks erect,
And bloody crests that tower above the waves;
Their other parts behind sweeping the sea,
With huge backs winding on in sinuous folds.
A noise of foaming brine is heard. And now
They reach the shores, their burning eyes suffused
With blood and fire, and lick their hissing mouths
With quivering tongues. We, pale with terror, fly.
But they with steady pace Laocoön seek.
First the two bodies of his little sons
Each serpent twines about, with tightening folds,
And bites into their miserable limbs.
Then him, as he with help and weapons comes,
They seize, and bind him in their mighty spires;
Twice round the middle, twice around his neck,
Twisting, with scaly backs, they raise on high
Their heads and lofty necks. He with his hands
Strains to untwine the knots, his fillets wet

With gore and poison black. His dreadful shrieks
Rise to the stars,—such groans as when a bull
Flies from the altar wounded, and shakes free
His forehead from the ill-aimed axe. But they,
The dragons, slip away to the lofty shrine
And citadel of cruel Pallas. There,
Beneath the goddess' feet and orbèd shield
They hide. Then verily a new fear creeps
Into the trembling hearts of all. They said
Laocoön paid the penalty deserved
Of crime, for having with his steel profaned
The sacred wood, when he had hurled his spear
Against the horse. And now all cry aloud
To take the image to its rightful seat,
And supplicate the goddess.

Perseus and Medusa

by BULLFINCH

PERSEUS WAS THE SON OF JUPITER AND DANAË. HIS
grandfather Acrisius, alarmed by an oracle which had told him that his
daughter's child would be the instrument of his death, caused the mother
and child to be shut up in a chest and set adrift on the sea. The chest
floated towards Seriphus, where it was found by a fisherman who conveyed the mother and infant to Polydectes, the king of the country, by
whom they were treated with kindness. When Perseus was grown up
Polydectes sent him to attempt the conquest of Medusa, a terrible monster who had laid waste the country. She was once a beautiful maiden
whose hair was her chief glory, but as she dared to vie in beauty with
Minerva, the goddess deprived her of her charms and changed her beautiful ringlets into hissing serpents. She became a cruel monster of so
frightful an aspect that no living thing could behold her without being
turned into stone. All around the cavern where she dwelt might be seen
the stony figures of men and animals which had chanced to catch a
glimpse of her and had been petrified with the sight. Perseus, favoured
by Minerva and Mercury, the former of whom lent him her shield and
the latter his winged shoes, approached Medusa while she slept and taking
care not to look directly at her, but guided by her image reflected in the

bright shield which he bore, he cut off her head and gave it to Minerva, who fixed it in the middle of her Ægis.

Milton, in his "Comus," thus alludes to the Ægis:

"What was that snakyheaded Gorgon-shield
That wise Minerva wore, unconquered virgin,
Wherewith she freezed her foes to congealed stone,
But rigid looks of chaste austerity,
And noble grace that dashed brute violence
With sudden adoration and blank awe!"

Perseus, continuing his flight, arrived at the country of the Æthiopians, of which Cepheus was king. Cassiopeia his queen, proud of her beauty, had dared to compare herself to the Sea-Nymphs, which roused their indignation to such a degree that they sent a prodigious sea-monster to ravage the coast. To appease the deities, Cepheus was directed by the oracle to expose his daughter Andromeda to be devoured by the monster. As Perseus looked down from his aerial height he beheld the virgin chained to a rock, and waiting the approach of the serpent. She was so pale and motionless that if it had not been for her flowing tears and her hair that moved in the breeze, he would have taken her for a marble statue. He was so startled at the sight that he almost forgot to wave his wings. As he hovered over her he said, "O virgin, underserving of those chains, but rather of such as bind fond lovers together, tell me, I beseech you, your name, and the name of your country, and why you are thus bound." At first she was silent from modesty, and, if she could, would have hid her face with her hands; but when he repeated his questions, for fear she might be thought guilty of some fault which she dared not tell, she disclosed her name and that of her country, and her mother's pride and beauty. Before she had done speaking, a sound was heard off upon the water, and the sea-monster appeared, with his head raised above the surface, cleaving the waves with his broad breast. The virgin shrieked, the father and mother who had now arrived at the scene, wretched both, but the mother more justly so, stood by, not able to afford protection, but only pour forth lamentations and to embrace the victim. Then spoke Perseus: "There will be time enough for tears; this hour is all we have for rescue. My rank as the son of Jove and my renown as the slayer of the Gorgon might make me acceptable as a suitor; but I will try to win her by services rendered, if the gods will only be propitious. If she be rescued by my valour, I demand that she be my reward." The parents consent (how could they hesitate?) and promise a royal dowry with her.

And now the monster was within range of a stone thrown by a skilful slinger, when with a sudden bound the youth soared into the air. As an eagle, when from his lofty flight he sees a serpent basking in the sun, pounces upon him and seizes him by the neck to prevent him from turning his head round and using his fangs, so the youth darted down upon the back of the monster and plunged his sword into its shoulder. Irritated by the wound, the monster raised himself into the air, then plunged into the depth; then, like a wild boar surrounded by a pack of barking dogs, turned swiftly from side to side, while the youth eluded its attacks by means of his wings. Wherever he can find a passage for his sword between the scales he makes a wound, piercing now the side, now the flank, as it slopes towards the tail. The brute spouts from his nostrils water mixed with blood. The wings of the hero are wet with it, and he dares no longer trust to them. Alighting on a rock which rose above the waves, and holding on by a projecting fragment, as the monster floated near he gave him a death stroke. The people who had gathered on the shore shouted so that the hills reëchoed with the sound. The parents, transported with joy, embraced their future son-in-law, calling him their deliverer and the saviour of their house, and the virgin, both cause and reward of the contest, descended from the rock.

Scylla and Charybdis

by BULLFINCH

ULYSSES HAD BEEN WARNED BY CIRCE OF THE TWO MONsters Scylla and Charybdis. We have already met with Scylla in the story of Glaucus, and remember that she was once a beautiful maiden and was changed into a snaky monster by Circe. She dwelt in a cave high up on the cliff, from whence she was accustomed to thrust forth her long necks (for she had six heads), and in each of her mouths seize one of the crew of every vessel passing within reach. The other terror, Charybdis, was a gulf, nearly on a level with the water. Thrice each day the water rushed into a frightful chasm, and thrice was disgorged. Any vessel coming near the whirlpool when the tide was rushing in must inevitably be ingulfed; not Neptune himself could save it.

On approaching the haunt of the dread monsters, Ulysses kept strict watch to discover them. The roar of the waters as Charybdis ingulfed them, gave warning at a distance, but Scylla could nowhere be discerned. While Ulysses and his men watched with anxious eyes the dreadful whirlpool, they were not equally on their guard from the attack of Scylla, and the monster, darting forth her snaky heads, caught six of his men, and bore them away, shrieking, to her den. It was the saddest sight Ulysses had yet seen; to behold his friends thus sacrificed and hear their cries, unable to afford them any assistance.

FABLE

The Boy and the Snake

by GOTTHOLD LESSING

A BOY WAS PLAYING WITH A TAME SNAKE. "MY DEAR little creature," said he, "I should not be so familiar with you, had you not been deprived of your venom. You snakes are the most malignant, unthankful reptiles! I well remember reading what happened to a poor countryman, who picked up a snake, perhaps one of your ancestors, from beneath a hedge, where it lay almost frozen to death, and compassionately put it into his bosom, that it might be restored by the warmth. Scarcely had the wicked creature recovered, than she bit her benefactor; and the good, kind-hearted man gave up the ghost."

"I am astonished," said the snake. "How partial your historians must be! Ours relate this story quite differently. Your kind-hearted countryman thought the snake was really frozen to death; and it being a handsome specimen, he picked it up in order to skin it when he arrived home. Was that correct?"

"Be silent," replied the boy, "what ungrateful wretch ever lacked an excuse?"

"True, my son," interrupted the boy's father, who had been listening to this conversation. "At the same time, whenever you hear of any remarkable instance of ingratitude, examine strictly every circumstance, before branding a person with so ignominious a blemish. True benefactors have seldom conferred favours on the ungrateful; for the honour of mankind I will hope never. But those benefactors possessed with narrow-minded selfish views, deserve, my son, to meet with ingratitude instead of thankful acknowledgement."

The Dog Gellert

from GESTA ROMANORUM

FOLLICULUS, A KNIGHT, WAS FOND OF HUNTING AND tournaments. He had an only son, for which three nurses were provided. Next to this child, he loved his falcon and his greyhound. It happened that one day he was called to a tournament, whither his wife and domestics went also, leaving the child in the cradle, the greyhound lying by him, and the falcon on his perch. A serpent that inhabited a hole near the castle, taking advantage of the profound silence that reigned, crept from his habitation, and advanced toward the cradle to devour the child. The falcon perceiving the danger, fluttered with his wings till he woke the dog, who instantly attacked the invader, and after a fierce conflict, in which he was sorely wounded, killed him. He then lay down on the ground to lick and heal his wounds. When the nurses returned, they found the cradle overturned, the child thrown out, and the ground covered with blood, as was also the dog, who they immediately concluded had killed the child.

Terrified at the idea of meeting the anger of the parents, they determined to escape; but in their flight fell in with their mistress, to whom they were compelled to relate the supposed murder of the child by the greyhound. The knight soon arrived to hear the sad story, and, maddened with fury, rushed forward to the spot. The poor wounded and faithful animal made an effort to rise and welcome his master with his accustomed fondness, but the enraged knight received him on the point of his sword, and he fell lifeless to the ground. On examination of the cradle, the infant was found alive, and unhurt, with the dead serpent lying by him. The knight now perceived what had happened, lamented bitterly over his faithful dog, and blamed himself for having too hastily depended on the words of his wife. Abandoning the profession of arms, he broke his lance in pieces, and vowed a pilgrimage to the Holy Land, where he spent the rest of his days in peace.

The Eagle and the Serpent

from GESTA ROMANORUM

PLINY MENTIONS THE STORY OF AN EAGLE THAT HAD built her nest upon a lofty rock, whose young a kind of serpent called Perna attempted to destroy. But finding that they were beyond her reach, she stationed herself to windward and emitted a large quantity of poisonous matter, so as to infect the atmosphere and poison the young birds.

But the eagle, led by the unerring power of instinct, took this precaution. She fetched a peculiar sort of stone called agate which she deposited in that quarter of the nest which was against the wind; and the stone by virtue of certain occult properties which it possessed, prevented the malicious intentions of the serpent from taking effect.

The Farmer and the Snake

by AESOP

A FARMER FOUND IN THE WINTER TIME A SNAKE STIFF and frozen with cold. He had compassion on it, and taking it up placed it upon his bosom. The snake on being thawed by the warmth quickly revived, when, resuming its natural instincts, he bit his benefactor, inflicting on him a mortal wound. The farmer said with his last breath, "I am rightly served for pitying a scoundrel!" The greatest benefits will not bind the ungrateful.

The Fowler and the Viper

by AESOP

A FOWLER, TAKING HIS BIRD-LIME AND HIS TWIGS, WENT out to catch birds. Seeing a thrush sitting upon a tree, he wished to capture it, and fitting his twigs to a proper length, he watched intently, having his whole thoughts directed towards the sky. While thus looking upwards, he unawares trod upon a Viper asleep just before his feet. The Viper, turning towards him, stung him; and he, falling into a swoon, said to himself; "Woe is me! that while I purposed to hunt another, I am myself fallen unawares into the snares of death."

The Head and Tail of the Serpent

by LEO TOLSTOI

THE SERPENT'S TAIL WAS DISPUTING WITH THE SER-pent's head as to which should go first.

The Head said: "You cannot go first; you have no eyes or ears."

The Tail replied: "But at all events I have the strength to make you go. If I wanted, I could twine around a tree, and you could not stir."

The Head said: "Let us part company."

And the Tail tore itself free from the Head, and crawled away in its own direction.

But as soon as it had left the Head, it came upon a cranny and fell stupidly into it.

Killing a Serpent

by P'U SUNG-LING

AT KU-CHI ISLAND IN THE EASTERN SEA, THERE WERE
camellias of all colours which bloomed throughout the year. No one, however lived there, and very few people ever visited the spot. One day, a
young man of Têng-chou, named Chang, who was fond of hunting and
adventure, hearing of the beauties of the place, put together some wine
and food, and rowed himself across in a small open boat. The flowers were
just then even finer than usual, and their perfume was diffused for a mile
or so around; while many of the trees he saw were several armfuls in
circumference. So he roamed about and gave himself up to enjoyment
of the scene; and by-and-by he opened a flask of wine, regretting very
much that he had no companion to share it with him, when all of a sudden
a most beautiful young girl, with extremely bright eyes and dressed in red,
stepped down from one of the camellias before him. "Dear me!" said she
on seeing Mr. Chang; "I expected to be alone here, and was not aware
that the place was already occupied." Chang was somewhat alarmed
at this apparition, and asked the young lady whence she came; to which
she replied that her name was Chiao-ch'ang, and that she had accompanied thither a Mr. Hai, who had gone off for a stroll and had left her
to await his return. Thereupon Chang begged her to join him in a cup of
wine, which she very willingly did, and they were just beginning to enjoy
themselves when a sound of rushing wind was heard and the trees and
plants bent beneath it. "Here's Mr. Hai!" cried the young lady; and jumping quickly up, disappeared in a moment. The horrified Chang now beheld a huge serpent coming out of the bushes near by, and immediately
ran behind a large tree for shelter, hoping the reptile would not see him.
But the serpent advanced and enveloped both Chang and the tree in its
great folds, binding Chang's arms down to his sides so as to prevent him
from moving them; and then raising its head, darted out its tongue and bit
the poor man's nose, causing the blood to flow freely out. This blood it
was quietly sucking up, when Chang, who thought that his last hour had
come, remembered that he had in his pocket some fox poison; and managing to insert a couple of fingers, he drew out the packet, broke the paper,
and let the powder lie in the palm of his hand. He next leaned his hand
over the serpent's coils in such a way that the blood from his nose dripped

21

into his hand, and when it was nearly full the serpent actually did begin to drink it. And in a few moments the grip was relaxed; the serpent struck the ground heavily with its tail, and dashed away up against another tree, which was broken in half, and then stretched itself out and died. Chang was a long time unable to rise, but at length he got up and carried the serpent off with him. He was very ill for more than a month afterwards, and even suspected the young lady of being a serpent, too, in disguise.

The King, the Serpent, and the Philosopher

from GESTA ROMANORUM

AN EMPEROR RODE OUT IN THE AFTERNOON TO HUNT. Happening to pass a certain wood, he heard a serpent, which some shepherds had caught and bound firmly to a tree, making a most horrible clamour. Moved by pity, he loosed it, and warmed its frozen body in his own bosom. No sooner, however, did the animal find itself recovered, than it began to bite its benefactor, and shot a flood of poison into the wound.

"What have you done?" said the emperor. "Wherefore have you rendered evil for good?"

The serpent like the ass of Balaam, being suddenly endowed with voice, replied, "The tendencies which nature has implanted no one can destroy. You have done what you could; and I have only acted according to my nature. You exhibited towards me all the kindness in your power, and I have recompensed you as well as I might. I offered poison, because, except poison, I had nothing to offer. Moreover, I am an enemy to man; for through him I became punished with a curse."

As they thus contended, they entreated a philosopher to judge between them, and to state which was in the wrong.

"I know these matters," answered the umpire, "only by your relation; but I should like to see the thing itself upon which I am to pronounce judgment. Let the serpent, therefore, be bound to the tree, as he was in the first instance, and let my lord the emperor remain unbound; I shall then determine the matter between you." This was done accordingly.

"Now you are bound," said the philosopher, addressing the serpent, "loose yourself if you can."

"I cannot," said the serpent; "I am bound so fast that I can scarcely move."

"Then die," rejoined the philosopher, "by a just sentence. You were always ungrateful to man, and you always will be. My lord, you are now free; shake the venom from your bosom, and go your way: do not repeat your folly. Remember that the serpent is only influenced by his natural propensities."

The emperor thanked the philosopher for his assistance and advice, and departed.

The Labourer and the Snake

by AESOP

A SNAKE, HAVING MADE HIS HOLE CLOSE TO THE PORCH of a cottage, inflicted a severe bite on the Cottager's infant son, of which he died, to the great grief of his parents. The father resolved to kill the Snake, and the next day, on its coming out of its hole for food, took up his axe; but, making too much haste to hit him, missed his head, and cut off only the end of his tail.

After some time the Cottager, afraid lest the Snake should bite him also, endeavoured to make peace, and placed some bread and salt beside his hole. The Snake, slightly hissing, said; "There can henceforth be no peace between us; for whenever I see you I shall remember the loss of my tail, and whenever you see me you will be thinking of the death of your son."

No one truly forgets injuries in the presence of him who caused the injury.

Lion and Rattlesnake

by AMBROSE BIERCE

A MAN HAVING FOUND A LION IN HIS PATH UNDERTOOK to subdue him by the power of the human eye; and near by was a Rattlesnake engaged in fascinating a small bird.

"How are you getting on, brother?" the Man called out to the other reptile, without removing his eyes from those of the Lion.

"Admirably," replied the serpent. "My success is assured; my victim draws nearer and nearer in spite of her efforts."

"And mine," said the Man, "draws nearer and nearer in spite of mine. Are you sure it is all right?"

"If you don't think so," the reptile replied as well as he then could, with his mouth full of bird, "you'd better give it up."

A half-hour later the Lion, thoughtfully picking his teeth with his claws, told the Rattlesnake that he had never in all his varied experiences in being subdued, seen a subduer try so earnestly to give it up. "But," he added, with a wide significant smile, "I looked him into countenance."

The Man and the Adder
(As Told to the Raven by the Rat)

by PILPAY

A MAN MOUNTED UPON A CAMEL ONCE RODE INTO A thicket, and went to rest himself in that part of it from whence a caravan was just departed, and where the people having left a fire, some sparks of it, being driven by the wind, had set a bush, wherein lay an Adder, all in a flame. The fire environed the Adder in such a manner that he knew

24

not how to escape, and was just giving himself over to destruction, when he perceived the Man already mentioned, and with a thousand mournful conjurations begged of him to save his life.

The Man, on this, being naturally compassionate, said to himself; "It is true these creatures are enemies to mankind; however, good actions are of great value, even of the very greatest when done to our enemies; and whoever sows the seed of good works, shall reap the fruit of blessings."

After he had made this reflection, he took a sack, and tying it to the end of his lance, reached it over the flame to the Adder, who flung himself into it; and when he was safe in, the traveller pulled back the bag, and gave the Adder leave to come forth, telling him he might go about his business; but hoped he would have the gratitude to make him a promise, never to do any more harm to men, since a man had done him so great a piece of service.

To this the ungrateful creature answered; "You much mistake both yourself and me; think not that I intend to be gone so calmly; no, my design is first to leave you a parting blessing, and throw my venom upon you and your Camel."

"Monster of ingratitude!" replied the Traveller, "desist a moment at least, and tell me whether it be lawful to recompense good with evil."

"No," replied the Adder, "it certainly is not; but in acting in that manner I shall do no more than what yourselves do every day; that is to say, retaliate good deeds with wicked actions, and requite benefits with ingratitude."

"You cannot prove this slanderous and wicked aspersion," replied the Traveller; "nay, I will venture to say, that if you can show me any one other creature in the world that is of your opinion, I will consent to whatever punishment you think fit to inflict on me for the faults of my fellow-creatures."

"I agree to this willingly," answered the Adder; and at the same time spying a Cow, "let us propound our question," said he, "to this creature before us, and we shall see what answer she will make."

The Man consented; and so both of them accosting the Cow, the Adder put the question to her, how a good turn was to be requited. "By its contrary," replied the Cow, "if you mean according to the custom of men; and this I know by sad experience. I belong," said she, "to a man, to whom I have long been several ways extremely beneficial. I have been used to bring him a calf every year, and to supply his house with milk, butter, and cheese; but now I am grown old, and no longer in a condition to serve him as formerly I did, he has put me in this pasture to fat me, with a design to sell me to a butcher, who is to cut my throat, and he and his friends are to eat my flesh. And is not this requiting good with evil?"

On this, the Adder taking upon him to speak, said to the Man; "What say you now? are not your own customs a sufficient warrant for me to treat you as I intend to do?"

The Traveller, not a little confounded at this ill-timed story, was cunning enough, to answer; "This is a particular case only, and give me leave to say, one witness is not sufficient to convict me; therefore pray let me have another."

"With all my heart," replied the Adder; "let us address ourselves to this Tree that stands here before us."

The Tree, having heard the subject of their dispute, gave his opinion in the following words; "Among men, benefits are never requited but with ungrateful actions. I protect travellers from the heat of the sun, and yield them fruit to eat, and a delightful liquor to drink; nevertheless, forgetting the delight and benefit of my shade, they barbarously cut down my branches to make sticks, and handles for hatchets, and saw my body to make planks and rafters. Is not this requiting good with evil?"

The Adder, on this, looking upon the Traveller, asked if he was satisfied. But he was in such a confusion that he knew not what to answer. However, in hopes to free himself from the danger that threatened him, he said to the Adder; "I desire only one favour more; let us be judged by the next beast we meet; give me but that satisfaction, it is all I crave; you know life is sweet; suffer me therefore to beg for the means of continuing it." While they were thus parleying together, a Fox passing by was stopped by the Adder, who conjured him to put an end to their controversy.

The Fox, upon this, desiring to know the subject of their dispute, said the Traveller: "I have done this Adder a signal piece of service, and he would fain persuade me that, for my reward, he ought to do me a mischief." "If he means to act by you as you men do by others, he speaks nothing but what is true," replied the Fox, "but, that I may be better able to judge between you, let me understand what service it is that you have done him."

The Traveller was very glad of this opportunity of speaking for himself, and recounted the whole affair to him; he told him after what manner he had rescued him out of the flames with that little sack, which he showed him.

"How!" said the Fox, laughing outright, "would you pretend to make me believe that so large an Adder as this could get into such a little sack? It is impossible!" Both the Man and the Adder, on this, assured him of the truth of that part of the story; but the Fox positively refused to believe it. At length said he; "Words will never convince me of this monstrous improbability; but if the Adder will go into it again, to convince me of the truth of what you say, I shall then be able to judge of the rest of this affair."

"That I will do most willingly," replied the Adder, and, at the same time, put himself into the sack.

Then said the Fox to the Traveller; "Now you are the master of your enemy's life; and, I believe, you need not be long in resolving what treatment such a monster of ingratitude deserves of you." With that the Traveller tied up the mouth of the sack, and with a great stone, never left off beating it till he had pounded the Adder to death; and, by that means, put an end to his fears and the dispute at once.

"This Fable," pursued the Rat, "informs us, that there is no trusting to the fair words of an enemy, for fear of falling into the like misfortunes."

Prince Alberic and the Snake Lady

by VERNON LEE

NOW LISTEN, COURTEOUS PRINCE, TO WHAT BEFELL your ancestor, the valorous Alberic, returning from the Holy Land.

Already a year had passed since the strongholds of Jerusalem had fallen beneath the blows of the faithful, and since the Sepulchre of Christ had been delivered from the worshippers of Macomet. The great Godfrey was enthroned as its guardian, and the mighty barons, his companions, were wending their way homewards—Tancred, and Bohemund, and Reynold, and the rest.

The valorous Alberic, the honour of Luna, after many perilous adventures, brought by the anger of the Wizard Macomet, whom he had offended, was shipwrecked on his homeward way, and cast, alone of all his great army, upon the rocky shore of an unknown island. He wandered long about, among woods and pleasant pastures, but without ever seeing any signs of habitation; nourishing himself solely on berries and clear water, and taking his rest in the green grass beneath the trees. At length, after some days of wandering, he came to a dense forest, the like of which he had never seen before, so deep was its shade and so tangled were its boughs. He broke the branches with his iron-gloved hand, and the air became filled with the croaking and screeching of dreadful night-birds. He pushed his way with shoulder and knee, trampling the broken leafage under foot, and the air was filled with the roaring of monstrous lions and tigers. He grasped his sharp double-edged sword and hewed through the interlaced branches, and the air was filled with the shrieks and sobs of a vanquished city. But the Knight of Luna went on, undaunted, cutting his way through the enchanted wood. And behold! as he issued thence, there was before him a lordly castle, as of some great Prince, situate in a pleasant meadow among running streams. And as Alberic approached, the portcullis was raised, and the drawbridge lowered; and there arose sounds of fifes and bugles, but nowhere could he descry any living wight around. And Alberic entered the castle, and found therein guardrooms full of shining arms, and chambers spread with rich stuffs, and a banqueting-hall with a great table laid and a chair of state at the end. As he entered a concert of invisible voices and instruments greeted him sweetly, and called him by name, and bid him be welcome; but not a living soul did he see. So he sat him down at the table, and as he did so, invisible hands filled his cup and his plate, and ministered to him with delicacies of all sorts. Now, when the good knight had eaten and drunken his fill, he drank to the health of his unknown host, declaring himself the servant thereof with his sword and heart. After which, weary with wandering, he prepared to take rest on the carpets which strewed the ground; but invisible hands un-buckled his armour, and clad him in silken robes, and led him to a couch all covered with rose-leaves. And when he had lain himself down, the concert of invisible singers and players put him to sleep with their melodies.

It was the hour of sunset when the valorous Baron awoke, and buckled on his armour, and hung on his thigh the great sword Brillamorte; and in-visible hands helped him once more.

The Knight of Luna went all over the enchanted castle, and found all manner of rarities, treasures of precious stones, such as great kings possess, and stores of gold and silver vessels, and rich stuffs, and stables full of fiery coursers ready caparisoned; but never a human creature any-where. And, wondering more and more, he went forth into the orchard, which lay within the castle walls. And such another orchard, sure, was never seen, since that in which the hero Hercules found the three golden apples and slew the great dragon. For you might see in this place fruit-trees of all kinds, apples, and pears, and peaches and plums, and the goodly orange, which bore at the same time fruit and delicate and scented blossom. And all around were set hedges of roses, whose scent was even like heaven; and there were other flowers of all kinds, those into which the vain Narcissus turned through love of himself, and those which grew, they tell us, from the blood-drops of fair Venus's minion; and lilies of which that Messenger carried a sheaf who saluted the Meek Damsel, glorious above all womankind. And in the trees sang innumerable birds; and others, of unknown breed, joined melody in hanging cages and aviaries. And in the orchard's midst was set a fountain, the most wonder-ful e'er made, its waters running in green channels among the flowered grass. For that fountain was made in the likeness of twin naked maidens, dancing together, and pouring water out of pitchers as they did so; and the maidens were of fine silver, and the pitchers of wrought gold, and

the whole so cunningly contrived by magic art that the maidens really
moved and danced with the waters they were pouring out—a wonderful
work, most truly. And when the Knight of Luna had feasted his eyes upon
this marvel, he saw among the grass, beneath a flowering almond-tree,
a sepulchre of marble, cunningly carved and gilded, on which was written,
'Here is imprisoned the Fairy Oriana, most miserable of all fairies, condemned for no fault, but by envious powers, to a dreadful fate,'—and as
he read, the inscription changed, and the sepulchre showed these words:
'O Knight of Luna, valorous Alberic, if thou wouldst show thy gratitude
to the hapless mistress of this castle, summon up thy redoubtable courage,
and, whatsoever creature issue from my marble heart, swear thou to kiss
it three times on the mouth, that Oriana may be released.'

And Alberic drew his great sword, and on its hilt, shaped like a cross,
he swore.

Then wouldst thou have heard a terrible sound of thunder, and seen
the castle walls rock. But Alberic, nothing daunted, repeats in a loud
voice, 'I swear,' and instantly that sepulchre's lid upheaves, and there
issues thence and rises up a great green snake, wearing a golden crown,
and raises itself and fawns towards the valorous Knight of Luna. And
Alberic starts and recoils in terror. For rather, a thousand times, con-
front alone the armed hosts of all the heathen, than put his lips to that
cold, creeping beast! And the serpent looks at Alberic with great gold
eyes, and big tears issue thence, and it drops prostrate on the grass; and
Alberic summons courage and approaches; but when the serpent glides
along his arm, a horror takes him, and he falls back, unable. And the
tears stream from the snake's golden eyes, and moans come from its
mouth.

And Alberic runs forward, and seizes the serpent in both arms, and
lifts it up, and three times presses his warm lips against its cold and slippery skin, shutting his eyes in horror. And when the Knight of Luna
opens them again, behold! O wonder! in his arms no longer a dreadful
snake, but a damsel, richly dressed and beautiful beyond compare.

The Slanderer and the Snake

by IVAN KRILOFF

ON THE OCCASION OF SOME TRIUMPHAL PROCESSION IN the realms below, the Snake and the Slanderer refused to yield each other precedence, and began a noisy quarrel as to which of the two had the best right to go first.

Now, in the infernal regions, as is well known, he takes precedence who has done most harm to his fellow-creatures. So in this hot and serious dispute, the Slanderer showed his tongue to the Snake; and the Snake boastingly talked to the Slanderer about its sting, hissed out that it was unable to put up with an affront, and strove hard to crawl past him. The Slanderer actually found himself being left behind. But Beelzebub could not allow this; he himself took the Slanderer's part, and drove the Snake back, saying,

"Although I recognise your merit, yet I justly assign precedence to him. You are excessively venomous, and dangerous in the extreme to everything which is near you; your sting is fatal, and you sting—which is no small merit—without provocation. But can you wound from afar, like the deadly tongue of the Slanderer, from whom there is no escape, even though mountains or oceans intervene? It is clear, then, that he is more deadly than you; so give place to him, and in future behave more quietly."

Since that time, Slanderers have been honoured more than Snakes in hell.

The Subtle Serpent

from GESTA ROMANORUM

IN THE REIGN OF THE EMPEROR FULGENTIUS, A CERTAIN Knight named Zedechias, married a very beautiful but imprudent wife. In a certain chamber of their mansion a serpent dwelt.

Now, the knight's passionate inclination for tournaments and jousting brought him to extreme poverty; he grieved immoderately, and, like one who was desperate, walked backward and forward, ignorant of what he should do.

The serpent, beholding his misery, like the ass of Balaam, was on that occasion miraculously gifted with a voice, and said to the knight, "Why do you lament? Take my advice, and you shall not repent it. Supply me every day with a certain quantity of sweet milk, and I will enrich you."

This promise pleased the knight, and he faithfully followed the instructions of his subtle friend. The consequence was that he had a beautiful son, and became exceedingly wealthy.

But it happened that his wife one day said to him, "My lord, I am sure that serpent has great riches hidden in the chamber where he dwells. Let us kill him and get possession of the whole."

The advice pleased the knight, and at the request of his wife he took a hammer and a vessel of milk to destroy the serpent. Allured by the milk, it put its head out of the hole, as it had been accustomed, and the knight lifted the hammer to strike it. The serpent, observing his intention, suddenly drew back its head; and the blow fell upon the vessel. No sooner had he done this, than his offspring died, and he lost everything that he formerly possessed.

The wife, grieved by their common loss, said to him, "Alas! I have ill counselled you; but go now to the hole of the serpent, and humbly acknowledge your offence. Perhaps you may find grace."

The knight complied, and standing before the dwelling-place of the serpent, shed many tears, and entreated that he might once more be made rich.

"I see," answered the serpent, "I see now that you are a fool, and will always be a fool. For how can I forget that blow of the hammer which you designed for me, for which reason I slew your son and took away your wealth? There can be no real peace between us."

31

The knight, full of sorrow, replied thus: "I promise the most unshaken fidelity, and will never think the slightest injury, provided I may this once obtain your grace."

"My friend," said the serpent, "It is the nature of my species to be subtle and venomous. Let what I have said suffice. The blow offered at my head is fresh upon my recollection; get you gone before you receive an injury."

The knight departed in great affliction, saying to his wife, "Fool that I was to take thy counsel!" But ever afterwards they lived in the greatest poverty.

The Viper and the File

by AESOP

A VIPER ENTERING INTO A SMITH'S SHOP BEGAN LOOKING about for something to eat. At length, seeing a File, he went up to it and commenced biting at it; but the File bade him leave him alone, saying, "You are likely to get little from me, whose business it is to bite others."

The Wasp and the Snake

by AESOP

A WASP SEATED HIMSELF UPON THE HEAD OF A SNAKE, and, striking him again and again with his stings, wounded him to death. The Snake, being in great torment, and not knowing how to rid himself of his enemy, or to scare him away, saw a wagon heavily laden with wood, and went and purposely placed his head under the wheels, and said; "My enemy and I shall thus perish together."

Why There Is Evil in the World

by LEO TOLSTOI

A HERMIT LIVED IN THE FOREST, AND THE ANIMALS WERE not afraid of him. He and the wild animals used to talk together, and they understood one another.

Once the Hermit lay down under a tree, and a Raven, a Dove, a Stag, and a Snake came to the same place to sleep. The animals began to reason why evil should exist in the world.

The Raven said; "It is all owing to hunger that there is evil in the world. When we have as much as we wish to eat, we sit by ourselves on the bough and caw, and everything is good and gay, and we are in every respect well off; but some other day we are famished, and everything is quite the opposite, so that we can see no brightness in God's world, and we feel full of unrest; we fly about from place to place, and there is no rest for us. And even if we see some meat afar off, then it becomes still worse; for if we fly down to get it, either sticks and stones are thrown at us, or wolves and dogs chase us, and we are absolutely destroyed. How much trouble comes upon us from hunger! All evil is caused by it."

The Dove said; "In my opinion, evil does not arise from hunger, but it all comes from love. If we only lived alone, we should have little trouble. Wretchedness shared makes one doubly wretched. And so we always live in pairs. And if we love our mates there is no peace for us at all. We are always thinking, 'Has she had enough to eat? is she warm?' And when our mate is away from us anywhere, then we are wholly lost; we cannot help worrying all the time, 'If only the hawk does not carry her off, or men make away with her'; and we ourselves fly off in pursuit of her, and perhaps find the poor thing either in the hawk's claws or in the snare. And if our mate is lost, then there is no more comfort for us. We cannot eat, we cannot drink; we can only fly about and mourn. How many of us have perished in this way! No; evil comes not from hunger, but from love."

The Snake said; "No; evil arises neither from hunger nor from love, but from ill-temper. If we lived peacefully, we should not do so much harm; everything would be delightful for us. But now if anything is done to us, we fall into a rage, and then there is nothing gentle about us; we only think how we can avenge the wrong on some one. We lose control of ourselves and hiss, and try to bite some one. We would not have pity on any one,

33

we would bite our own father and mother! It seems as if we could eat our own selves. The moment we begin to lose our temper we are undone. All the evil in the world arises from ill-temper."

The Stag said; "No; not from ill-temper, and not from love, and not from hunger arises all the evil that is in the world, but evil arises from fear. If it were possible for us to live without fear, all would be well with us. We are swift-footed, and have great strength. With our antlers we can defend ourselves from little animals; and we can run from the large ones. But it is impossible to escape fear. If it is only the twigs creaking in the forest, or the leaves rustling, we are all of a tremble with fear, our heart beats, we instinctively start to run, and fly with all our might. Another time a hare runs by or a bird flutters, or a dry twig crackles, and we think it is a wild beast, and in running away we really run into danger. And again we are running from a dog, and we come upon a man. Oftentimes we are frightened and start to flee, we don't know whither, and we roll over a precipice and perish. And we have to sleep with one eye open, with one ear alert, and we are always in alarm. There is no peace. All evil comes from fear."

Then the Hermit said; "Not from hunger, nor from love, nor from ill-temper, nor from fear come all our troubles; but all the evil that is in the world is due to our different natures. Hence come hunger and love, ill-temper and fear."

SERPENT WORSHIP

The Serpent as Amulet and Charm

by M. OLDFIELD HOWEY

THE HISTORY OF MANKIND SHOWS A STRIKING TENDENCY among primitive peoples to regard the animate and inanimate objects around them as vehicles used by the gods to reveal their will, and possessed of innate occult powers which can be employed to control the evil forces so continually threatening man's life or well-being.

Civilised man, after centuries of materialistic teaching, has almost lost sight of the fact which is so evident to the child of Nature,—that the appearances and phenomena surrounding him are all miraculous, magical, inscrutable, unaccountable, unprovable, and, under proper conditions are resolvable into invisibility and apparent nothingness. It is indeed little less than a miracle that thinking beings accept their own and the world's existence in the matter-of-fact unquestioning manner so many of them do, taking everything for granted as the merest matter of course, and showing real interest only in the things affecting their immediate material environment.

But this blindness to the wonder of things is an acquired, not a natural characteristic of humanity. The prophet Isaiah attributed it to the curse of Jehovah (or Ialdabaoth), and tells us how Jehovah bade him "Go, and tell this people, Hear ye indeed, but understand not; and see ye indeed, but perceive not. Make the heart of this people fat, and make their ears heavy, and shut their eyes; lest they see with their eyes, and hear with their ears, and understand with their heart, and convert, and be healed" (Isa. vi. 9 and 10).

Upon the soul of man fell the dark night of materialistic science, and long enshrouded him with its gloomy negation. But night does not last for ever, and the dawn is breaking anew with promise of a far fairer day than that to which he so sadly said farewell. It will help us to realise our gain if we look back upon that earlier day, for although its light enabled man to recognise himself as a spiritual being living in a spiritual world, yet so faint was it that the gods were dim, whilst the shadows of evil loomed black and tremendous and menacing above his head, and charms, and incantations, and horrid bloody sacrifice of all he held most dear, seemed the only means of propitiating the forces that threatened his destruction.

35

And now the serpent, so sinister, yet so subtly attractive, appeared to man as a sort of link between the two worlds that pressed upon his growing consciousness. Consequently it became the principal figure in a large number of ancient charms and amulets, and the constant companion of the physician, the soothsayer and the magician; besides which it was regarded as the means by which usually invisible spirits, and sometimes even the gods, made known their will and manifested themselves to poor blind man in a form which he could understand and appreciate.

Among the ancient Egyptians this was especially the case, and they naturally esteemed the serpent very highly as an amulet, because of the importance it assumed in their eyes as a religious emblem. Mr. Wynn Westcott tells us that serpent's head amulets, "made of stone, red jasper, or paste to imitate jasper, and of cornelian," were in common use. These images have been found with mummies, and the Egyptians appear to have believed that their presence prevented the dead from being bitten by the serpents of evil in the underworld. Numerous papyri have been found full of magical charms intended to repel the attacks of Apophis and Set, during a time when these were regarded as evil deities in serpent form.

Among the collection of Egyptian amulets at University College are several models of serpents' heads which were worn to give protection from snake bite. Professor Flinders Petrie, referring to these, says that "Chapter thirty-three of the 'Book of the Dead' reads: 'Chapter whereby all serpents are kept back'; Chapter 34. 'Chapter whereby a person is not devoured by the dweller in the shrine'; Chapter 35. 'Chapter whereby the person is not devoured by a serpent in the underworld.' There is nothing in these chapters to explain the amulets further."

One example represents a finger-ring intended to preserve that wearer from serpents, which is said by Professor Petrie to belong to the prehistoric period. It is made of yellow-brown limestone. At a later date serpent amulets of glass and faïence were worn as necklets by the Egyptian women.

Mr. Wake says that "the reference in Hebrew history to the *seraphim* of Jacob's family recalls the fact that Abrahams' father was *Terah,* a 'maker of images.' The *teraphim* were doubtless the same as the *seraphim,* which were serpent images (the serpent-symbol of the Exodus is called 'Seraph'), and probably the household charms or idols of the Semitic worshippers of the Sun-god, to whom the serpent was sacred."

The Jewish people, as will be seen from the above, were deeply impregnated with these ideas, even before their residence in Egypt, and were continually returning to ophiolatrous practices, which the most terrible threats failed to make them abandon.

In confirmation of this statement, we may refer to the discovery at Taanach in Palestine of many serpents' heads, which had been used in incantations, and two serpent-like bronze knives intended as amulets to ward off the evil eye.

According to Ewing, the word *lehāshim,* which occurs in Isaiah iii. 20, and is there translated tablets, with an alternative reading in the margin "houses of the soul," is derived from *lāhash,* which means "enchantments," and also the objects by which enchantments are averted.

Jahn thinks these were the figures of serpents carried in the hand by Hebrew women, as "Arab women, before Mohammed, wore golden serpents between their breasts." The marginal reading certainly confirms this idea, for it was as "houses of the soul" that serpents were specially regarded. Isaiah said that Ialdabaoth would take these "tablets" from the daughters of Zion, together with "their cauls, and their round tires like the moon," and the other charms and ornamentations which decorated their persons. "And it shall come to pass that instead of sweet smell there shall be stink; and instead of a girdle a rent; and instead of well-set hair baldness; and instead of a stomacher a girding of sackcloth; and burning instead of beauty."

We have referred above to the golden serpents worn as charms by Arabian women. The following interesting paragraph from the "Daily News" of November 30th, 1869, throws light on the meaning attached to serpent amulets by modern Arabs:

"A curious picture of Arab life has just been exhibited before the Court of Assizes at Constantina in Algeria. A native, named Ben-Kem-mari, was accused of mutilating his wife by cutting off her nose and upper lip in a fit of jealousy. The mother of the victim said that to cure her son-in-law of his jealousy she had consulted a much-venerated marabout, who had given her as a charm for her daughter a serpent's head wrapped up in hemp-leaves which was to be placed in the folds of the husband's turban. The woman appealed to the public present to prove that by this method she would have cured the man of his suspicions, and several Arabs at once showed the same talisman, while a native officer of the coast, without being consulted, called out to the judge, 'Yes, I have also a serpent's head; it gives strength to the man and fidelity to the woman.' "

In India also, to this day, the serpent is regarded as a talisman and bringer of good fortune to those in whose dwelling it takes up its abode, and Sir Edwin Arnold writes of

> ". . . the sky black snake, that gives
> Fortune to households."

> ("Light of Asia.")

Elizabeth Villiers tells us that the sacred Hindu talisman of the Bamboo with Seven Knots, consists of a circle "inscribed with triangles, and across the circle, forming the spokes of the wheel as it were, lie the seven-knotted bamboo and a serpent. Every part of the device has a mystic significance. The circle is the symbol of Eternity, the triangles stand for the Hindu Trinity (Brahma the Creator, Vishnu the Preserver, Siva the Destroyer),

the serpent for wisdom, the bamboo for the seven degrees of learning the
devout must possess."

Regina Bloch, commenting on this in the "Occult Review," says that
"there is another aspect of this beautiful symbol. The circle is Infinitude,
with the Masters or triangles shining as Pyramids within it. In it rests the
Bamboo (the human spine) with the seven knots or centres governed by
the seven archangels, which are awakened by that mysterious and celestial
fire—the Serpent Coil. It is an Orientalised form of the *caduceus* of
Hermes, the messenger (the Hebrew for *angel* is messenger) of the gods.
The central rod is the spine, the cone the pineal gland of Man, the two
Serpents the turning inspirational ray of the Lord."

Rings and bracelets and other ornaments in Eastern countries were
often made in the form of serpents in primeval days, and served rather
for amulets and charms than as ornaments. They were thought to ensure
good health, strength, and long life, and were also believed to possess
great protective powers, probably as securing the favour of the god whose
emblem they were, or symbolising his presence.

Bracelets in the form of serpents were worn by the Grecian women in
the time of Clemens Alexandrinus, as we may learn from his ignorant re-
proof of this custom. He says: "The women are not ashamed to place
about them the most manifold symbols of the evil one; for as the serpent
deceived Eve, so the golden trinket in the fashion of a serpent misleads the
women." The Grecian children wore chaplets of the same kind.

Hurd tells us that in the island of Amboyna (in the Asiatic archipelago)
the women wear jewels set in gold, in the form of serpents. They look
upon these as sacred, and never touch them but with the most reverential
awe.

The serpent's connection with Æsculapius of course made it a potent
charm in every kind of illness or injury, and many allusions to this belief
may be found in the works of ancient authors. Not only the flesh of the
reptile, but even its skin, though long parted from the original owner,
was thought to possess a magical healing power.

No doubt it was because of this that Hannibal's Amazonian cavalry
women used shields made of serpent's skins.

In an old version of the life of Merlin, we read that "hadde not ben
the doublet that he hadde of a serpent's skyn, deed hadde he ben with
oute recouer" ("Merlin," II, 336, E.E.T.S.).

Pliny, writing about A.D. 77, said that a snake's skin eased delivery
(XXX, 44), and Palladius, a Roman author of the fourth century A.D.
who wrote a work on Agriculture, considered the serpent-skin's life-giving
power extended even to trees. According to an old translation he wrote:

> "A serpent skynne doon on this tree men lete
> Avaylant be to save it in greet hete."
>
> ("Husbondrie," E.E.T.S., p. 211.)

Lawson, in his "History" (1714), says that the cast skins of the rattle-snake "are used in physic, and the rattles are reckoned good to expedite the birth. The gall is made up into pills with clay, and kept for use, being given in pestilential fevers and the small-pox. It is accounted a noble remedy, known to few, and held as a great *arcanum*."

The gipsies of Southern Europe practise a ceremonial charm in which the serpent takes a prominent place, believing that they thereby dispel all the maladies that otherwise would have afflicted them throughout the year. They take a wooden box which rests upon two cross pieces of wood, and in it they put herbs and simples along with the dried body of a snake, or lizard, which everyone present must first have touched with his fingers. They then wrap the box in white and red wool, and the oldest man carries it from tent to tent. Everyone spits into it once, and the sorceress utters spells over it. Finally it is cast into running water. If anyone finds it, and opens it from curiosity, he and his will be the victims of all the troubles those who made the charm have escaped.

It is interesting to compare this charm with the Grecian myth of the serpent-man Erechtheus. This hero was brought up by Athena, who placed him in a chest which was confided to the care of Agraulus, Pandrosos, and Herse, the daughters of Cecrops, with strict injunctions that it was not to be opened. But unable to curb their curiosity, they opened the chest, and found within the child entwined with serpents. As soon as they saw him they were seized with madness, and cast themselves down the most precipitous part of the Acropolis. Is this myth the origin of the charm?

Goldsmith says that viper's flesh "has long been celebrated as a noble medicine. A broth, made by boiling one viper in a quart of water till it comes to a pint, is the usual method in which it is given at present; and it is said to be a very powerful restorative in battered constitutions: the salt of vipers is also thought to exceed any other animal salt whatever, in giving vigour to the languid circulation, and prompting to venery."

The "Penny Cyclopædia" notes that: "Even the last generation witnessed the great demand for these poisonous serpents in consequence of the virtues supposed to reside in their flesh. The lingering belief in the wonderfully invigorating qualities of 'viper broth' is not yet quite extinct in some places. Pliny, Galen, and others praise the efficacy of viper flesh in the cure of ulcers, elephantiasis, and other disorders arising from a corrupt state of the system. By the ancients the animal was generally served to the patient boiled like fish, as being more efficacious than when taken in the form of a powder or other dried state. Sir Kenelm Digby's beautiful wife was fed on capons fattened with the flesh of vipers."

According to both Gælic and German folklore, the white snake, when boiled, has the property of conferring medical wisdom. The white snake is venerated as the king of serpents by the Scottish Highlanders, but other serpents are also thought by them to have curative powers in their bodies, when these have been specially treated.

For instance, the Rev. Kenneth Macdonald tells us that in the Scottish Highlands the ancient treatment of epilepsy was as follows:

"A live snake was caught and placed in a bottle, which was then filled with pure water and corked. After standing for a short time, the infusion was given to the patient, who was kept ignorant of the nature of the drug."

The famous Nicholas Culpeper prescribes the following remedy for dropsy: "A water snake, a string being thrust through her tail, and she hung up, a vessel ful of water being set underneath, into which she may thrust her head, after certain hours or days she will vomit up a stone, which being received in the vessel ful of water, will drink it all up; which stone being tied about the middle of the one that hath the dropsie wil dry up all the water."

Our national patron saint and hero, St. George, apart from his famous exploit in slaying the dragon, seems to have had some curious sympathetic and occult link with serpents. Mr. Frazer has given us several instances. For example, in Bohemia and Moravia, serpents are believed to be innocuous up to the 23rd of April, but obtain their poison on the saint's day, and various charms may be affected by means of serpents on this day. Thus, in Bulgaria, a wife who wishes to have a baby will cut off a snake's head on St. George's Day, and place a bean inside its mouth. Then she will either lay the head in a hollow tree, or carry it so far from her village that the crowing of the cocks is no longer audible, and there bury it in the ground. Her wish will be obtained if the bean buds.

Again, on the eve of St. George's Day witches are thought by the herdsmen and shepherds of Eastern Europe to be specially active, and all sorts of precautions are taken to guard against their knavish tricks. The Ruthenians drive their cattle out to pasture for the first time after their long drear winter on St. George's Day, and as the farmers know how busy the witches have been the preceding night casting their spells on the cows, they naturally take precautionary measures to evade the effect of these, and thwart the fell purposes of the witches. A favourite charm is to catch a snake, skin it, and fumigate the cows with the skin, on St. George's Eve, whilst to rub the udders and horns of the cows with serpents' fat is said to be equally potent to keep the witches from the cows.

Lewis Spence says, "Many kinds of amulets or talismans were used by the Breton peasantry to neutralise the power of sorcerers. Thus if a person carried a snake with him, enchanters would be unable to harm his sight, and all objects would appear to him in their natural forms."

We have seen in how many instances serpents have been (and are) used in charms against witches and the forces of evil, but we find them also used by witches to aid in effecting their fell purposes; another instance of the meeting of the seemingly antagonistic meanings of this amazing symbol.

When the witches in Macbeth make the horrible mixture in their black cauldron in order to obtain from it sinister presages, among other maleficent ingredients is the

> "Fillet of a fenny snake"

and

> "Adder's fork and blind worm's sting"

is added to make it thoroughly effective.

Goats used to be considered as specially proof against adders, and the minister of Kirkmichael, Banff, in 1794, quotes a Gadhelic saying, implying that the goat eats the serpent or adder. "Like the goat eating the adder or serpent."

A favourite method of charming away vermin which did not hurt their feelings nor show them disrespect was to make metal images of them. The good bishop, Gregory of Tours, has told us how the city of Paris used to be free from dormice and serpents, but that in his lifetime, whilst a sewer was being cleansed, a bronze serpent and bronze dormouse were discovered, and removed. "Since then," says the bishop, "dormice and serpents without number have been seen in Paris."

As we have noted in another chapter, this was the method employed by Moses when the swarm of serpents afflicted Israel in the wilderness, and probably even at that date it was an ancient one.

A similar idea is embodied in the Celtic folk remedies for serpent bite, one of which is to bathe the wound with water in which a serpent's head had been boiled, whilst another is an ointment made from snake's tongues.

Dr. Carmichael describes a charm which consisted of pounding the embers from a peat fire in one's stocking at the threshold, or the outer doorstep, on St. Bride's Day, the ritualist concluding with the words, "I shall not injure the serpent nor shall the serpent injure me."

George Henderson says that "in Skye at least," he has heard the charm "On St. Brigit's Day the serpent will say from off the knoll: 'I will not injure Nic Imheair, neither will Nic Imheair injure me,' repeated on St. Brigit's Day, the woman doing so having placed a burning peat in one of her stockings, and pounding at it while on the threshold of the outer door (a specially sacred place) as a precaution against the entrance of evil spirits. . . . It is proper to add that another variant of the serpent rhyme typifies the serpent as queen. . . . 'On St. Bride's (Brigit's) Day the queen will come from the knoll,' and its association with the act of pounding a burning peat on the threshold involuntarily reminds one of the Siberian 'Fiery Snake,' or *zagovor* (invoked for kindling amorous longing), with which has been compared the folk belief that with the beginning of every January—i.e. at the end of the festival in honour of the return of the sun towards summer—the Fiery Snake begins to fly, enters into the *izba* through the chimney, turns into a brave youth and steals by magic the

hearts of fair maidens. In a Servian song a girl who has been carried off
by a 'fiery snake' calls herself his 'true love,' and it is thought that in mythical language the 'Fiery Snake' is one of the forms of the lightning. 'The
blooming earth, fructified by the rains poured forth during the first spring
storms, is turned in the myth into the bride of the Fiery Snake. But the
wedder of nature became looked upon at a later period as the patron of
weddings among the children of men, and so the inducing of love-pangs
naturally became ascribed to the Fiery Snake' (Ralston)."

In Africa the Bakongo who desires that his dog should be a good
hunter uses the following charm. He sends for the special medicine-man
for dogs, who takes the head of a viper, some chalk, various leaves, and
mint, which he mixes and makes into a bundle. A small portion of this
he encloses in a leaf twisted like a funnel. Next, he catches a wasp and
presses its juice into the funnel, then, adding a little palm wine he squeezes
the moisture from this mixture into the dog's nose, and thereafter it is a
good hunter and trekker.

Whittier in his description of the home of an American Indian chief
says:

> "Loosely on a snake-skin strung,
>   In the smoke his scalp-locks swung
>   Grimly to and fro."
>
>   ("Bridal of Pennacook," II.)

Here we have the snake-skin—the emblem of life, supporting the symbols of death,—in short, the Encircled Serpent.

Endless other instances of the use of this all-embracing symbol as a
charm of everywhere respected potency for good or ill, might easily be
adduced; but enough to illustrate the subject have now been given.

The Serpent as Phallic Emblem

by M. OLDFIELD HOWEY

ALTHOUGH MANY WRITERS UNHESITATINGLY ATTRIBUTE
a Phallic origin to the serpent as a religious emblem, this theory is not
supported by all. Mr. C. S. Wake says, "So far as I can make out the serpent-symbol has not a direct phallic reference, nor is its attribute of wisdom the most essential. The idea most intimately associated with this

animal, was that of life, not present merely, but continued, and probably everlasting. Thus the snake *Bai* was figured as Guardian of the doorways of the Egyptian Tombs which represented the mansions of heaven. A sacred serpent would seem to have been kept in all the Egyptian temples, and we are told that many of the subjects, in the tombs of the kings at Thebes in particular, show the importance it was thought to enjoy in a future state. Crowns, formed of the Asp or sacred *Thermuthis,* were given to sovereigns and divinities, particularly to Isis, and these no doubt were intended to symbolise eternal life. Isis was goddess of life and healing and the serpent evidently belonged to her in that character, seeing that it was the symbol also of other deities with the like attributes. Thus, on papyri, it encircles the figure of Harpocrates, who was identified with Æsculapius, while not only was a great serpent kept alive in the great temple of Serapis, but on later monuments this god is represented by a great serpent with or without a human head.

"Mr. Fergusson, in accordance with his peculiar theory as to the origin of serpent worship, thinks this superstition characterised the old Turanaian (or rather let us say Akkadian) empire of Chaldea, while tree-worship was more a characteristic of the later Assyrian Empire.

"This opinion is no doubt correct, and it means really that the older race had that form of faith with which the serpent was always indirectly connected—adoration of the male principle of generation, the principle phase of which was probably ancestor worship, while the latter race adored the female principle, symbolised by the sacred tree, the Assyrian 'grove.' The 'tree of life,' however, undoubtedly had reference to the male element, and we may well imagine that originally the fruit alone was treated as symbolical of the opposite element."

According to Layard, during the researches of M. Botta in the ruins of Kouyunjik, a curious representation of an Assyrian ceremony was discovered. It seems fairly evident that this had a Phallic significance. It shows two eunuchs standing before an altar, on which burns the sacred fire, and two serpents attached to poles, suggesting by their attitude the popular representation of the brazen serpent set up by Moses in the wilderness. A bearded figure leads a goat (symbol of sexual uncleanness), but the form and size of the altar do not suggest that a sacrifice is intended. The eunuchs and the uplifted serpents seem to suggest that it has already been made.

Dr. Donaldson considers that the serpent has always had a Phallic significance, and General Forlong from close and independent "observation in Eastern lands unaided by books or teachers, from thousands of stories and conversations with Eastern priests and people" arrived at the same deduction. He even asserts his opinion that phallic worship enters so closely into union with all faiths to the present hour, that it is impossible to exclude it from view. He says, "So imperceptibly arose the serpent on pure Phallic faiths, fire on these, and sun on all, and so intimately did all blend with one another, that even in the ages of true history it was often impossible to descry that exact God alluded to."

The intimate blending of the several symbols of ancient worship alluded to above is strongly marked in the Semitic languages, where, as Mr. Gliddon has pointed out, the same root signifies serpent and phallus. Both, in different senses, are of course solar emblems.

A further contribution to this subject is made by Brown, in his "Great Dionysiak Myth." He says, "The Serpent has six principal points of connection with Dionysos: (1) As a symbol of, and connected with, wisdom. (2) As a solar emblem. (3) As a symbol of time and eternity. (4) As an emblem of the earth, life. (5) As connected with fertilising moisture. (6) As a phallic emblem." Enlarging on the last of these points our author continues: "The serpent being connected with the sun, the earth life and fertility must needs be also a phallic emblem, and so appropriate to the cult of Dionysus Priapos. Mr. Cox, after a review of the subject, observes, 'Finally, the symbol of the Phallos suggested the form of the serpent, which thus became the emblem of life and healing. There then we have the key to that tree and serpent worship which has given rise to much ingenious speculation.' The myth of the serpent and the tree is not, I apprehend, exhausted by any merely phallic explanation, but the phallic element is certainly one of the most prominent features in it, as it might be thought any inspection of the carvings connected with the Topes of Sanchi and Amravati would show. It is hard to believe, with Mr. Fergusson, that the usefulness and beauty of trees gained them the payment of divine honours. Again the Asherah or Grove-cult (Exod. xxxiv. 13, 1 Kings xvii. 16; Jer. xvii. 2; Micah v. 14) was essentially Phallic, Asherah being the Upright. It seems also to have been in some degree connected with that famous relic, the brazen serpent of Nehushtan (2 Kings xvii. 4). Donaldson considers that the Serpent is the emblem of desire. It has also been suggested that the creature symbolised sensation generally."

The Rev. G. W. Cox (whom Brown refers to in the paragraph quoted above), in his "Mythology of Aryan Nations," says "If there is one point more certain than another it is that wherever tree and serpent worship has been found, the cultus of the Phallos and the Ship, of the Linga and Yoni, in connection with the worship of the sun, has been found also. It is impossible to dispute the fact, and no explanation can be accepted for one part of the cultus which fails to explain the other. It is unnecessary, therefore, to analyse theories which profess to see it in the worship of the creeping brute or the wide-spreading tree. A religion based on the worship of the venomous reptile must have been a religion of terror; in the earliest glimpses which we have of it, the serpent is a symbol of life and of love.

"Nor is the Phallic cultus in any respect a cultus of the full-grown and branching tree. In its earliest form the symbol is everywhere a mere stauros or pole; and although this stock or rod budded in the shape of the thyrsus and the shepherd's staff, yet, even in its latest developments, the worship is confined to small bushes and shrubs and diminutive plants of a particular kind. Nor is it possible again to dispute the fact that every nation at some stage or other of its history has attached to this cultus precisely that meaning which the Brahman now attaches to the Linga and the Yoni.

"That the Jews clung to it in this special sense with vehement tenacity is the bitter complaint of the prophets; and the crucified serpent adored for its healing powers stood untouched in the Temple until it was removed and destroyed by Hezekiah. This worship of serpents, 'void of reason,' condemned in the Wisdom of Solomon, probably survived even the Babylonish captivity. Certainly it was adopted by the Christians who were known as Ophites, Gnostics and Nicolaitans. In Athenian mythology the serpent and the tree are singularly prominent. Kekrops, Erechtheus, and Erichthonios, are each and all serpentine in the lower portion of their bodies. The sacred snake of Athene had its abode in the Akropolis, and her olive trees secured for her the victory in her rivalry with Poseidôn. The health-giving serpent lay at the feet of Asklêpios and snakes were fed in his temple at Epidauros and elsewhere. That the ideas of mere terror and death suggested by the venomous or the crushing reptile could never have given way thus completely before those of life, healing, and safety, is obvious enough; and the latter ideas alone are associated with the serpent as the object of adoration. The deadly beast always was, and has always remained, the object of the horror and loathing which is expressed for Ahi, the choking and throttling snake, the Vritra whom Indra smites with his unerring lance, the dreadful Azidahaka of the Avesta, the Zohak of Biter of modern Persian mythology, the serpents whom Heraktes strangles in his cradle, the Python, or Fafnir, or Grendel, or Sphinx whom Phoibos, or Sigurd, or Beowulf, or Oidipous smite and slay. That the worship of the serpent has nothing to do with these evil beasts is abundantly clear from all the Phallic monuments of the East or West. In the topes of Sanchi, and Amravati the discs which represent the Yoni predominate in every part of the design; the emblem is worn with unmistakable distinctness by every female figure, carved within these discs, while above the multitude are seen, on many of the discs, a group of women with their hands resting on the linga which they uphold. It may indeed be possible to trace out the association which connects the Linga with the bull in Sivaison, as denoting more particularly the male power, while the serpent in Jainaison and Vishnavism is found with the female emblem, the Yoni. So again in Egypt, some may discern in the bull Apis or Mnevis the predominance of the male idea in that country, while in Assyria or Palestine the Serpent or Agathos Daimon is connected with the altar of Baal."

Mr. J. H. Rivett-Carnac, in his paper printed in the journal of the Asiatic Society of Bengal, entitled "The Snake Symbol in India," also upholds the opinion that the serpent is a symbol of the phallus. He says:

"The serpent appears on the prehistoric cromlechs and menhirs of Europe, on which I believe the remains of phallic worship may be traced. What little attention I have been able to give to the serpent-symbol has been chiefly in its connection with the worship of Mahádeo or Siva, with a view to ascertain whether the worship of the snake and that of Mahádeo or the phallus may be considered identical, and whether the presence of the serpent on the prehistoric remains of Europe can be shown to support my theory, that the markings on the cromlechs and menhirs are indeed the traces of this form of worship, carried to Europe from the East by the tribes whose remains are buried beneath the tumuli.

"During my visits to Benares, the chief centre of Siva-worship in India, I have always carefully searched for the snake-symbol. On the most ordinary class of 'Mahádeo,' a rough stone placed on end supposed to represent the phallus, the serpent is not generally seen. But in the temples, and in the better class of shrines which abound in the city and neighbourhood the snake is generally found encircling the phallus. . . . In the Benares bazaar I once came across a splendid metal cobra, the head erect and hood expanded, so made as to be placed around or above a stone or metal 'Mahádeo.' It is now in England. The attitude of the cobra when excited and the expansion of the head will suggest the reason for this snake representing 'Mahádeo' and the phallus.

"Although the presence of this snake in these models cannot be said to prove much, and although from the easy adaptability of its form the snake must always have been a favourite subject in ornament, still it will be seen that the serpent is prominent in connection with the conventional shape under which Mahádeo is worshipped at Benares and elsewhere, that it sometimes takes the place of the Linga, and that it is to be found entwined with almost every article connected with this worship."

As the author of "Ophiolatreia" points out, these symbols were "conceived in no obscene sense, but as representing regeneration, the new life, 'life out of death, life everlasting, which those buried in the tumuli, facing towards the sun in its meridian, were expected to enjoy in the hereafter. . . . 'a fitting ornament for the graves of the departed.' . . . The same idea in fact which . . . causes the rude Mahádeo and Yoni to be worshipped daily by hundreds of thousands of Hindus."

Frazer informs us that Sayids and Mussulmans of high rank in Northern India say that a snake should never be called by its real name, but should be described either as a tiger (*sher*), or as a string (*rassi*). Crooke says of the same district, that if you are bitten by a serpent, you must not mention its name, but may say, "A rope has touched me."

A curious sidelight is thrown on the reason of this mysterious paraphrasing by a remark of Jennings. "There is something strange about these cords, cordons, ropes, belts, bands, baldrics (also in the term 'belted earl'). These are always male accessories. . . . Many early Norman mouldings exhibit various examples of the cable. Thongs, ties and net-

work are seen to bind all the significant figures in the early English and
Irish churches. Is there any connection between these bonds, or ties, or
lacings with the 'cable-tow' of the initiates among the Masons? Perhaps
the 'tow' in this 'cable-tow' means the 'Tau,' or stood for it originally.
Reference may here be made to the snake which forms the girdle of the
Gnostic 'Good Shepherd' in the illustration later in our book. . . . The
Good Shepherd bearing upon his shoulder the Lost Lamb, as he seems to
the uninitiated eye: but on close inspection he becomes the double-headed
Anubis; having one head human, the other a jackal's whilst his girdle
assumes the form of a serpent, rearing aloft its crested head."

Anubis bore the title of Ap-hera, "opener of the roads" or "paths,"
which lead to heaven, and in this character he was often presented as a
jackal seated on a pylon or gateway.

Samuel Birch says: "This may be considered as the type of the celestial
Anubis, and as such he was styled lord of the heaven, and opener of the
solar disc."

Anubis is identified with Mercury, whose serpent-entwined rod we have
described in the chapter on the caduceus. He is "the mystic Mercurius
Trismegistus,—'Thrice-Master, Thrice-Mistress,'—for this personage is
double-sexed: Phœbe above, Diana on earth, Hecate below."

This description of Mercury at once recalls the fable of Tiresias, the
celebrated prophet of Thebes, and suggests that the double sex ascribed
to the god was not unconnected with the serpents that clung to his rod.
Our readers shall judge for themselves. The story of Tiresias is said by
Ovid to be as follows:

> "When Jove disposed to lay aside the Weight
> Of public Empire and the Cares of State,
>> As to his Queen in Nectar Bowls he quaff'd,
>> 'In troth,' says he, and as he spoke he laugh'd,
>> 'The Sense of Pleasure in the Male is far
>> More dull and dead, than what you Females share.'
> Juno the Truth of what was said deny'd;
> Tiresias therefore must the Cause decide,
> For he the pleasure of each sex had try'd.
> It happen'd once within a shady Wood,
> Two twisted Snakes he in Conjunction view'd,
> When with his staff their slimy Folds he broke,
> And lost his Manhood at the fatal Stroke.
> But after seven revolving Years, he view'd
> The self-same Serpents in the self-same Wood:
>> 'And if,' says he, 'such Virtue in you lie,
>> That he who dares your slimy Folds untie
>> Must change his Kind, a second stroke I'll try.'
> Again he struck the Snakes, and stood again
> New sex'd, and straight recover'd into Man;
> Him therefore doth both Deities create

The sov'reign Umpire in their grand Debate;
And he declar'd for Jove; when Juno fir'd
More than so trivial an Affair requir'd,
Depriv'd him in her Fury, of his Sight,
And left him groping round in sudden Night.
But Jove (for so it is in Heav'n decreed,
That no one God repeal another's Deed)
Irradiates all his Soul with inward Light,
And with the Prophet's Art relieves the Want of Sight."
                                        (Addison's Translation.)

Related to the serpents of the caduceus is the phallic serpent of the mystic Nehushtan, set up in the wilderness by the Hebrew lawgiver Moses. This consisted of a serpent coiled around the emblem of the phallus, the Tau or T.

Freemasons have perpetuated this ancient symbolism. Wynn West-cott writes: "The Tau is well known to all Freemasons as the design on the Master's apron; the Triple Tau is known in a higher grade, and in the 25th degree of the Ancient and Accepted Rite—the Knight of the Brazen Serpent—the jewel was a serpent creeping upon a Tau, with the words *nachustan*, 'serpent,' and *chethanu*, 'I have sinned.' This grade is said to be a revival of a military and monastic benevolent society founded by the Crusaders in the Holy Land."

The connection of the idea of sin with the creative act is reproved by Madame Blavatsky, who writes: "The first Christians never perceived that not only was there no sin in this disobedience [of Adam and Eve], but that actually the Serpent was the Lord God Himself, who, as the Ophis, the Logos, or the bearer of divine creative wisdom, taught mankind to be creators in their turn. They never realised that the cross was an evolution from the tree and the Serpent, and thus became the salvation of mankind. By this it would become the very first symbol of creative cause, applying to geometry, to numbers, to astronomy, to measure and to animal reproduction."

But the cross of Christ was an advancement on the Tau or male cross of the serpent of Moses. The latter is the symbol of negation; man's aspirations and desires represented by the ascending pole, abruptly terminated by the crushing horizontal. "Thou shalt not," thunders the law, in answer to all man's efforts of self-expression.

A new element is visible in the Christian cross. The upright pole has pierced and transcended the horizontal. The cross no longer represents negation. The divine uplifted "Serpent" has redeemed it, and man's aspirations may soar into infinity.

The union of the masculine Tau with the feminine circle produces the ankh or crux-ansata, the symbol of that physical life which is brought into being by the conjunction of the male and female principles. But such life, though it be the gift of the gods, is brief, and unsatisfying to its possessor, and serves but to arouse in him the longing for fuller expression. The nails of the crucifixion must replace the Tau, and the divine ideal of the Encircled Serpent, supercede the circle of desire and selfish gratification.

Serpent Worship and Snake Charming

by CATHERINE C. HOPLEY

IN REVIEWING THE GENERAL ORGANIZATION OF THE Ophidia, their marvellous powers and habits, can we wonder at the impressions they have created in untutored minds? Let us picture to ourselves our earliest ancestors with their dawning intellect contemplating the instantaneous coil of a constrictor; or the almost invisible action in a flash of time with which the death-dealing stroke of the poison fang is effected. From a source which was incomprehensible, like the burning, scathing fluid from the skies, came a 'sting,' an agony, death! Awe-struck and filled with sacred terror were the beholders, as before them lay the paralyzed, tortured victim. Can we wonder that the slender, gliding 'worm' which inflicted this mortal injury should have been regarded as an evil spirit, a devil, and invested with maleficence?

Add to the two great death-dealing powers of the serpent race—constriction and venom—those other peculiarities which have been faithfully recorded, the seeming renewal of life after the annual sleep, a mystery enhanced by the restored brilliancy and beauty of the reptile on its change of cuticle; let us picture to ourselves those wondering savages now watching the limbless creature as it glides into sight and is gone again, or as with fixed and glittering eyes it flicks that mysterious little tongue; let us imagine them crowding near to behold a serpent feeding, or to witness the still more amazing spectacle of a brood of young ones vanishing down their mother's throat. There is enough of the mysterious in an ophidian to excite the awe and wonder of even a present-day beholder, taking each one of these surprising doings singly; but considering that any one serpent may be endowed with nearly all of these phenomenal powers, let us imagine the effect produced by them in the savage mind. To worship such an incomprehensible creature was only consistent with all we know of the influences which first awakened faith in a supernatural Being.

Consequently we find that in every country where a serpent was known, it plays its part in the mythology and religion of that country. We may examine the antiquities of any nation which has left a monument of its history and beliefs, and a serpent will be represented. Scarcely an Egyptian sculpture (in its entirety) can be found in which the serpent does not appear. The same may be said of the Hindoo monuments, their temples, buildings, and sculptured caves; also of Mexican, Japanese, Chinese, and other ancient mythologies.

Singularly, too, no other object in nature—no birds or flowers or beautiful things—have been so universally adopted in personal ornaments as the serpent idea. And in times of remote antiquity—as relics prove—personal adornments, bracelets, coronets, and rings in the form of serpents were as much in favour as at the present day. We may, indeed, affirm that the modern bracelet is but a reproduction or a restoration of those of antiquity, dating as far back as artificers in metals can be traced. Rough and rude representations of still earlier times are extant. And where the human race in its savage state had no knowledge of art, the reptile itself, or such relics of it as could be preserved, were adopted as personal decorations. Thus were the American Indians found by the early colonists, with their belts of snake skins, with the rattles of the Crotalus strung in their ears, and with necklaces and chains of snake bones and *rattles*. Mackeney, Catlin, Schoolcraft, and other historians of the American Indians relate numerous instances in proof of the universal veneration and superstition with which the serpent is regarded by those savages. If they kill a rattlesnake, it is immediately skinned and distributed in small pieces among the tribe for their medicine bags, while the captor is pompously decorated with the skin. If on a journey they meet a rattlesnake in their direct path, this is taken to be a sign that they must go no further. Some of the Indian traditions bear a remarkable resemblance to the prophetic symbols of the Hebrew faith. 'If thou bruise its head, it shall bruise thy heel.' This in their eyes is regarded as 'destiny,' and they will on no account kill one that lies in their path, lest it should cause the death of the destroyer's relatives. The Indians are also supposed to possess the art of snake-taming to an extraordinary degree. We are assured by more than one writer that they also pet rattlesnakes, investing them with divine attributes, and sheltering them during the winter; though in this case the 'tameness' may be partially due to the inertness resulting from the season of the year. On returning spring they permit their *Penates* to issue forth again.

The ancient temples of Mexico were richly embellished with carvings of serpents. One of them represents a serpent idol of not less than seventy feet long, in the act of swallowing a human being. Also, there is the 'God of the Air,' a feathered rattlesnake; and an edifice known as the 'Wall of Serpents,' from the numerous reptilian forms crowded upon it. But it is not necessary to enumerate antiquities, with most of which the reader must be already acquainted, the object here being rather to endeavour to account for those other attributes which have grown out of serpent worship, such as 'fascinating,' taming, 'charming,' 'dancing to music,' etc.

Not that serpent worship is extinct by any means. In India it is still so strong as to amount to a fatality; for the high annual death-rate from snake bites there is not half so much because the natives can't be cured, as because they won't be cured of what they regard as a just punishment from their diety. That serpent superstitions are still rampant among the low-caste Hindoos, is borne out by all modern writers on the native faiths or customs. A. K. Forbes in his *Hindoo Annals,* or *Râs Mala,* tells us that cobras are looked upon as guardian angels. One cobra 'guarded' a cave in which treasures were deposited; another cobra, 'guarded' a garden; and very good guards we should say they were, as few persons would venture too near to such an 'angel.' One of the supposed 'Divinities' is the *Poorwug Dev,* or spirit personified by a snake, which is not allowed to be killed or injured; and if it bite a person, that individual is supposed to be justly punished for some fault. Fatalism forbids any attempt to cure that unhappy victim, and he swells the annual death-rate. Due honours are paid to these 'guardian angels' found in most hamlets. Periodical festivals are held to them: their retreats are then garlanded with flowers, and eggs and milk are placed as propitiatory offerings. One of the Bengalese traditions is, that a male infant auspiciously shaded by a cobra will come to the throne.

And is the reptile which brings such distinction and honour into a family to be ruthlessly destroyed? 'No Hindoo will willingly kill a cobra,' Colonel Meadows Taylor tells us, in his *People of India.* Should one be killed accidentally within the precincts of a guarded village, a piece of copper money is put into its mouth, and the body is burned with offerings to avert the anticipated evil. The *najas,* or hooded snakes, from their habit of erecting themselves on the approach of persons, are those especially regarded as guardians. It was the same in Egypt. In the *najas* are also supposed to dwell the spirits of highly-favoured persons, or those whose lives had been of remarkable purity and goodness,—another motive for their being protected. It is still the same in many parts of Africa, where the natives think ill luck follows the death of a python.

In works where medical statistics are given, such as Fayrer's *Thanatophidia,* we learn the fatal results of these superstitions. When the natives find a cobra in their houses, as is not unfrequently the case, says Fayrer, 'they will conciliate it, feed and protect it, as though to injure it were to invoke misfortune on the house and family. Even should the death of some relative, bitten by accident, occur, the serpent is not killed, but caught and deferentially deported to the field or jungle, where it is set free.' No one can peruse the above without seeing how largely the percentage of deaths is traceable to native superstition. Fayrer also shows us the fatal consequences of the confidence placed in the snake charmers, who are considered to be especially favoured by their deities, and endowed with curative powers. Much interesting reading, apart from medical science, will be found in the *Thanatophidia* on the Hindoo faith in the *müntras* or spells and incantations used by the charmers in cases of snake-bite. Out of some ninety such cases selected by Fayrer from returns sent in by medical officers in the Bengal Presidency, nearly half proved that either no remedies at all were tried, or that recourse was had to native nostrums or *müntras*. Briefly to enumerate a few of the reports: 'Boy bitten by *keautiah,* charms and incantations; died in half an hour.' 'Man keeping a krait (Bungarus) for "Poojah" (worship) was bitten, and died in seven hours, notwithstanding native nostrums.' A woman bitten died in three hours '*in spite of incantations!*' 'A man bitten while asleep had *leaves to smell,*" but nevertheless died in three hours!' 'Woman bitten at night, got up and had *müntras* (chantings) to expel the poison. She died four hours after the bite notwithstanding; and her infant at the breast died two hours after partaking the maternal nutriment.' And many similar cases. What wonder, then, with this miserable fatalism prevailing over that vast and densely-populated country, that death by snake-bites should amount to many thousands annually? One more case must be recorded to show how deeply rooted the faith. A tall, strong young man was bitten in the hand, while sleeping out of doors. No medicine was given, but *incantations* were muttered over him. In an hour he was a corpse: yet the village where this happened continues to do Poojah (adoration) to the cause of the evil. By far the largest percentage of deaths is attributable to the cobra, though this is not a proof that its numbers predominate so much above other snakes, as of the religious veneration in which it is everywhere held. It is found all over the peninsula, even as high as 8000 feet on the sunny slopes of the Himalayas. The names of castes, *Năg, Năgo, Năgojee, Năgowa,* etc., found among all classes of Hindoos, have all reference to the *Năg* or *Nâja* deities, says Colonel Meadows Taylor. Among many living and semi-barbarous tribes serpent superstitions exist, though, perhaps, more strongly in West Africa than elsewhere, excepting India at the present time. In Africa, not the venomous so much as the large constricting snakes are the objects of care and veneration. In *Dahomey and the Dahomeans,* F. E. Forbes relates some amusing instances of the sacred devotion of the Fetish women, or guardians and slaves of the python deities at Whydah. A Fetish house or temple devoted to the snakes was built round a large cotton-tree, and in this a number of pythons were permitted to roam about at their pleasure. When they ventured beyond the precincts, their Fetish attendants went in search of them, and by gentle persuasions (probably in the form of poultry or other dietetic arguments) induced them to go home: while all who met them bowed down and kissed the dust of their path. Morning and evening the devotees prostrated themselves before the sacred abode of these ophidian deities, either to worship the invisible god *Seh,* or his representatives in serpentine form.

From frequent and gentle handling, snakes thus protected naturally grow tame. The Fetish attendants become skilled in managing their reptile gods, and are not slow in investing themselves with especial powers for their office. And to this may the origin of the so-called 'charmers' be traced; for 'snake charming,' like snake worship, dates back to the very earliest ages. With a more intimate knowledge of the reptilian class which modern zoology has brought about, comes happily a clearer insight into the tricks of the snakemen, jugglers, and charmers of Egypt and the East. Snake-taming to-day is not confined to *Saadees* and *Samp Wallahs;* it is not even confined to non-venomous snakes, of which pythons have always proved very amenable pets. Mr. Mann's tame pythons were popular performers at the time they were introduced in Chancery, and his pet constrictor, 'Cleo,' was honoured with an obituary notice from the pen of Mr. Frank Buckland, in *Land and Water,* after she died 'of grief,' as was said, at the illness of her master. The amiable 'Cleo' (or Cleopatra) was the 'constant companion' of Mr. and Mrs. Mann for several years, and they soon learned her wishes when she 'asked' for either food, drink, or fresh air. 'A short time before her death she contracted a friendship for a young kitten,' was always 'fond of children,' who displayed no fear of that sociable ophidian. But she was shy of strangers; and this I myself realized on paying my respects to her; for not until she was fully convinced that I had no evil intentions, and not without much coaxing and persuasion on the part of her guardians, could Cleo be induced to approach me.

Several of the constricting snakes at the Zoological Gardens of even larger size than Cleo are exceedingly tame, permitting themselves to be handled. One of them, a temporary inmate during the winter of 1881–82, was introduced to the public by Dr. Stradling through the columns of *Land and Water,* April 3, 1880, as 'Totsey,' together with her brother 'Snap,' the latter named 'from a trifling infirmity of temper when young.' These two were the offspring of the Panama boa who gave birth to 20 live young at the Gardens, June 30, 1877. Of these twenty, Mr. Sclater notified, at one of the Zoological Society's meetings in the following November, that all but one were still alive. Of the two which became the property of Dr. Stradling and were tamed by him, he wrote, 'Any one can handle them with impunity'; and that they recognised him among others in the dark, permitting him only to touch them at such a time. 'Lolo' and 'Menina' are the pretty names of two other tame constrictors belonging to this ophiphilist, and whose amiable and interesting manners were recorded in the above journal. Of 'Totsey' the Dr. writes, 'She is the most gentle and affectionate snake I ever had.'

That some of the most venomous serpents are also capable of being tamed we have many proofs. They use their fangs in self-defence, actuated by fear or hunger; and where no fear exists, a serpent would not deliberately crawl about, expending its precious and only protective power, *venom,* on any object it met with. Would a cobra or a crotalus in its native woods approach any living thing it saw and indiscriminately strike it with its poison fangs? No. Its primary impulse would be to escape. It strikes only under provocation or hunger. Therefore if a venomous snake in captivity became so familiar with your presence as to cease to fear you, it would also abstain from biting you. Not that one would recommend Jararacas or cobras for pets, notwithstanding the assurance of some residents in India that the latter are capital guards to a dwelling, and in some are even encouraged instead of dogs, as the less liable to bite of the two! Miss Frere, in her interesting reminiscences of India, *Old Deccan Days,* gives instances of children playing with the cobra without injury. She mentions a Brahman boy who could without any other music than his own voice attract and handle with impunity any venomous serpents that might be within hearing. They would come out of a thicket or a dry stone wall—their favourite refuge. Such instances are sufficiently rare to be regarded as miraculous, adds the authoress, still they do occur. 'How much is due to gentleness of touch and fearlessness, how much to any personal peculiarity which pleases the senses of the snake, it is difficult to say.' The boy above alluded to was believed to be the incarnation of some divinity, and the magistrate took note of his proceedings.

But at last, through some inadvertency, he got bitten; when he died, notwithstanding the divinity he was supposed to enshrine, notwithstanding the spells and *müntras* which might be pronounced over him.

The cobra is supposed to have originally had seven heads, as we see represented on Hindoo temples. The 'hood' is believed to be the remains of these seven heads; and the *Gokurrah,* whose pattern of the double ocellus had gained it the name of the 'spectacled cobra,' is held in the highest esteem of all from the two spots being considered the footprints of the god *Krishna.* These are the especial favourites of the professional snake charmers.

When it is borne in mind that snakes have been tamed by persons of only slight experience, we can easily comprehend that with a life's practice, and with inherited facilities, the Oriental jugglers must acquire peculiar expertness in dealing with their 'charmed' specimens. Originally, no doubt, the office of the professed snake tamer was connected with the sacred rites of serpent-worshipping communities, but has now greatly degenerated into the trade of jugglers and tricksters. That some of these do acquire extraordinary skill in dealing with their dangerous captives cannot be denied. Profound faith is placed in their performances by the natives, who attribute to them supernatural agency. From being close observers of reptile character, they know how far to venture on familiarities. They thoroughly understand the movements of the sluggish and timid serpents with which they are toying; and while keeping up a perpetual gabble to divert the attention of the spectators, aggravated by the tum-tumming and so-called 'music' to which the snakes are supposed to 'dance,' they themselves keep just beyond striking reach, and provoke the snake to follow the waving motion of their hands. The true object or impulse of the snake is to bite the irritating cause, the pretended motive is 'dancing.' To follow the movement of the object which provokes them is instinctive, music or not; and without any din and cackle and jargon, the cobras would do this all the same. Long practice and an intimate acquaintance have given the jugglers confidence and dexterity, while on the part of the snake fear is the chief characteristic. Even the tamest cobra is only watching the opportunity to escape, and the moment the juggler ceases his performance, down it drops, and makes for its basket. Should the performance not be ended, the snakes are called to attention by being sharply pulled back by their tail, when up they rise with hood expanded, and with just enough of power and spirit left in them to recommence the 'dance,' more truly to make one more futile attempt to strike their tyrannical masters. It is only a repetition of the same kind of 'obedience' and 'intelligence' that was accredited to that first rattlesnake ever exhibited in England.

That showman had become well acquainted with crotalus idiosyncrasies, and knew how to turn them to account before an ignorant crowd.

Those who have to deal with venomous serpents tell us, that with caution and expertness they are not difficult to handle; and this is verified by all who describe the performances of Oriental snake-charmers. Not only cobras with fangs extracted, or mouths sewn up, or composition 'cerastes' with artificial horns fastened on to the heads of harmless snakes, but those with perfect fangs and well-filled poison glands, are handled with equal facility. By pressing down the snake's head gently with a stick and then seizing it firmly close behind the head, so close that it has no power to turn it, you fetter its movements. Or to snatch up a venomous snake by its tail and quickly support it festooned on a stick which you draw gently towards the head, and then secure that as above, is another method adopted; or, again, to seize the tail and pass the hand swiftly along the body till the head is reached, and *then* grasp the neck. These are among the various ways of handling poisonous serpents, according to the purposes required of them. Every movement must be carefully watched, and the head not released until the entire snake is free to be returned straight into its cage. Even wild and vicious cobras are thus fearlessly dealt with by experts; and those which are in process of taming are put through a daily training. They are made comfortable in a basket, conciliated with food and milk, soothed by softly stroking them with a brush and by kind and gentle handling.

I once stood by and looked on while the keeper unpacked a box of cobras. He took each one out by its tail, and dropped it into another box with such expedition that the fearful reptile had not time to turn and bite him. Not that he ventured to lower his hand into the midst of the writhing angry tangle of snakes, but first, at a respectful distance (the writer still more deferentially contemplating the transfer from afar), he, with a long-handled hook, contrived to draw out a snake tail first, and getting the tip over the edge of the box, this he seized, thus, one after the other, shifting eight of the dozen cobras. Both boxes had lids, of course—glass slides, which were cautiously but quickly drawn aside, and as sharply closed again. These deadly reptiles, after being some weeks, perhaps months, in a small close box, were not, as may be supposed, in a very lively condition, but sufficiently so to erect themselves and hiss like a flock of geese, striking at the lid and the glass, and doing their best to alarm the manipulator, and also to suspend the breath of my awe-struck self. Calmly and safely, however, Holland concluded his task.

By pressing down the head with a stick, or seizing it quickly by the tail, American Indians similarly manage the rattlesnakes. Not they alone, however, are skilled in taming these deadly reptiles. Here, at home in England, domesticated *Crotali* are not unknown. Dr. Stradling thinks they may be rendered as harmless as non-venomous kinds, by a gradual training; and has succeeded in so far taming one that he felt safe in offering it as a gift to even an unskilled non-charmer. 'I have a very *nice* tame rattlesnake between four and five feet long, in good condition and feeding well, which I shall be delighted to send you,' he wrote me, August 1881. 'It has got so tame that you might handle it without fear at any time you wished to investigate any part of it.' It is perhaps superfluous to add that this amiable and exemplary reptile was gratefully declined.

The reader's devoted servant had not undergone a course of prophylactics as the Doctor had. He is both an expert and to a certain extent venom-proof at the same time; but for all that the snake was, as he affirmed, tame enough to be handled with impunity by those who might have sufficient courage to venture. That interesting and accommodating rattlesnake is no more, but was even more honoured in death than in life. A true martyr to science, it was sacrificed that its friend and teacher might prosecute his experiments, and also swallow some of the contents of its poison gland, in order to convince two or three challenging skeptics that he could do this with impunity.

As in all other trades, there are various grades among the Oriental snake-tamers. The legitimate 'charmer' of India—the *Samp Wallah*—prides himself on being a descendant of the prophet, and the secret of his art is cherished as an heirloom in his family. This also is the case in Arabia and Egypt, where the astonishing feats which, without any doubt, are performed by professional 'snake men,' are attributed to special and secret powers, jealously guarded from age to age. It may be possible that, like the Psylli of old, they may have recourse to some drug which renders their person repugnant to the serpent, and thus provides immunity from a bite. Not yet altogether discarded, either, is the ancient belief that in the body of the viper itself is found a specific for its poison. Since the days of Æsculapius, decoctions of vipers and recipes enough to form an Ophidian cookery-book and pharmacopeia combined, have found favour not only among the 'faculty' of classic days, but among all our ancestral dames. We are told that vipers abound in volatile salts that are cures for many ills. Certain it is that 'viper wine,' viper broth, viperine salts, the powder of dried vipers, preparations from the dejecta, the oil, and even the slough have all enjoyed a high reputation, and I believe are—*some* of these at any rate—still in vogue in secluded districts where the refinements of medical science have not yet replaced them. It is remarkable too, that for skin affections their virtues chiefly commend themselves. The ancient belief that to devour vipers proved a specific for their bite, has to the present day prevailed among the snake-charmers of Egypt, who—whether or not from this practice—are said to assimilate their bodies that the venom does not harm them. The Bushmen of South Africa, it is asserted, swallow poison to render themselves proof against its effects; and history records many other tribes who have had such confidence in their own and an inherited immunity, that they hesitated not in exposing their infants to deadly serpents. The Persian word *Bezoar,* a popular drug, means counter-poison which persons who feed on venomous snakes are believed to enjoy.

Though much discredit has been thrown on these so-called 'immunities,' and though it is very difficult to know what to believe where a serpent is concerned, the possibility does appear to be borne out by some authentic writers of our own time. The late John Keast Lord, when in Egypt, had frequent opportunities of observing the tricks of the jugglers; and not only he, but, as he assures us, many intelligent and educated Europeans, fully believed that some secret power was practised by the 'high-caste' charmers, who really did exhibit astonishing feats with their snakes. Of these, the habit of devouring the reptiles alive can here admit only one of bare allusion.

In *Dahomey and the Dahomeans,* F. E. Forbes tells of the natives walking fearlessly bare legged in the grass where snakes abound, and that on one occasion on alluding to the danger, a boy said to him: 'No fear; if my father is bitten, he knows of an herb that will cure him.'

Another recent authority whom we are bound to respect is Schliemann. In his work *Troy and its Remains,* published in 1875, he writes: 'We still find poisonous snakes among the stones as far down as from thirty-three to thirty-six feet, and I have hitherto been astonished to see my workmen take hold of the reptiles with their hands and play with them: nay, yesterday I saw one of the men bitten twice by a viper, without seeming to trouble himself about it. When I expressed my horror, he laughed, and said that he and all his comrades knew there were a great many snakes in this hill, and they had therefore all drunk a decoction of the snake-weed, which grows in the district, and which renders the bite harmless. Of course I ordered a decoction to be brought to me, so that I also may be safe from these bites. I should, however, like to know whether this decoction would be a safeguard against the fatal effects of the bite of the hooded cobra, of which in India I have seen a man die within half an hour. If it were so, it would be a good speculation to cultivate snake-weed in India.'

A correspondent in *Land and Water,* signed 'R. C.,' quoting Schliemann, inquired the name of this snake-weed, but without eliciting information. Most of the countries in which snakes abound would seem to rejoice in 'snake-weeds' and 'snake-roots.' 'It has pleased nature that there should be nothing without this antidote,' said Pliny; and though 'the faculty' tell us that no antidote for snake venom has yet been discovered, it nevertheless appears to be certain that the Arabs, the Nubians, Egyptians, and other nations seek to procure immunity from snake-bite by the use of certain plants, of which the *Aristolochias* seem to be most frequent. The juice or a decoction is drunk, the root chewed, and an infusion used for washing the skin. The South American Indians are said to be able thus to protect themselves; and we have the high authority of Humboldt in support of the theory that the famous *huaco,* and other poisonous plants with which they inoculate themselves, may impart an odour to their bodies which is repugnant to the snakes.

It would be well to obtain definite information as to what the 'snake-weed' of Schliemann was, *botanically.* It is also important to ascertain the species of 'viper' that is there so abundant; then there would be a basis for investigation. The testimony of a traveller like Schliemann is not to be disregarded. Besides him, Livingstone, P. H. Gosse, and others have affirmed the same thing, viz. the existence of antidotal plants, but which, in the hands of science, seem never to disclose their virtues!

As a part of the present subject comes a serpent's supposed love of 'music,' and on this head again the evidence is contradictory. Setting aside the idea of 'music,' in the way of melody or harmony, we may be able to arrive at a clue to the undeniable fact that snakes do exhibit some consciousness of *noise.* 'Music,' properly so called, is certainly very far removed from the gourd-rapping and tum-tumming of the Oriental jugglers; yet the snakes display a consciousness of these uncouth sounds. Mr. Mann affirmed that Cleo and his other pet boas manifested undoubted feeling—let us call it consciousness—when the piano was being played. Dr. Arthur Stradling, on the contrary, tells us that his own snakes 'are almost always within hearing of a piano, and never show the slightest emotion at the sound.' His observations, I believe, refer chiefly to his life at sea, where his cabin did duty as concert-room, menagerie, and all else combined, and where, apart from piano, there would be ceaseless noise and jarring; or even if on shore, the 'always' would rather support my own theory or speculation as to any feasible solution of the fact that serpents are affected by *noise,* not 'music.' And my idea is, that it is the jarring or vibration *through solids,* and not the mere sound, that thus affects the snakes. Since first venturing to express his idea in the *Dublin University Magazine,* Jan. 1876, I have continued to observe the effect on snakes of what we may call *disturbing noises.* At the Gardens, where they become accustomed to noises of all kinds, it is less easy to arouse them; but when the place is unusually quiet, the experiment may be tried. The 'snake men' of the East, whose trade is to hunt out snakes by means of sound, effect this by *rapping* on the wall or ceiling, or by making loud, clucking noises with their tongue as much as by their so-called 'music'; and Pliny, —if we may cite Pliny to suit our purpose and discard him otherwise,— or whoever *he* quotes, affirms that snakes are more easily aroused by the *sound* of footsteps than by the sight of the approaching person. A custom is prevalent in Ceylon, we are told, of using a jingling stick in the dark to strike the ground in order to frighten snakes out of the path. The jingling 'music' here is disturbing, not alluring, but as regards the knocking it proves sensitiveness to vibration conveyed by the ground. The American Indians are *experts* in the way of ascertaining sounds as conveyed by the ground. They throw themselves prone upon the earth, pressing their ear close to it, and are able to decide with great accuracy the direction, the distance, and the nature of a far-off sound. May we not conclude, then, that the perception of sound to a serpent is through solids, a feeling more than a hearing of noises? The creature, always prone to the ground or other solids, and with an internal aural apparatus, must be peculiarly sensitive to vibrations thus conveyed.

As to *tune,* any sharp sound will answer; and as to time, it is not the 'music,' but, as we have already hinted, the waving hand or knee, or bright colours used by the *charmers,* to which the movements of the serpents respond. This is also a subject quite worth scientific investigation.

Tree and Serpent Worship

by JAMES FERGUSSON

THERE ARE FEW THINGS WHICH AT FIRST SIGHT APPEAR to us at the present day so strange, or less easy to account for, than that worship which was once so generally offered to the Serpent God. If not the oldest, it ranks at least among the earliest forms through which the human intellect sought to propitiate the unknown powers. Traces of its existence are found not only in every country of the world; but before the new was discovered by us, the same strange idolatry had long prevailed there, and even now the worship of the Serpent is found lurking in out-of-the-way corners of the globe, and startles us at times with the unhallowed rites which seem generally to have been associated with its prevalence.

Although the actual worship of Trees is nearly as far removed from our ordinary forms of faith as Serpent Worship, still it can hardly be considered as more than an exaggerated perversion of many of the ideas now current; and we can hardly wonder that in an early stage of human civilization, it may have assumed considerable importance. There is such wondrous beauty in the external form of trees, and so welcome a shelter beneath their over-arching boughs, that we should not feel surprise that in early ages groves were considered as the fittest temples for the gods. There are also, it must be remembered, few things in nature so pleasing to the eye as the form or the colour of the flowers which adorn at seasons the whole vegetable kingdom, and nothing so grateful to the palate of the rude man as the flavour of the fruits which trees afford. In addition to these were the multifarious uses to which their wood could always be applied. For buildings, for furniture, for implements of peace or war, or for ornament, it was indispensable. In ancient times it was from wood alone that man obtained that fire which enabled him to cook his food, to warm his dwelling, or to sacrifice to his gods. With all their poetry, and all their usefulness, we can hardly feel astonished that the primitive races of mankind should have considered trees as the choicest gift of the gods to men, and should have believed that their spirits still delighted to dwell among their branches, or spoke oracles through the rustling of their leaves.

On the other hand, when it comes to be more closely examined, the worship of the Serpent is not so strange as it might at first appear. As was well remarked by an ancient author, "The serpent alone of all animals without legs or arms, or any of the usual appliances for locomotion, still moves with singular celerity"; and he might have added—grace, for no one who has watched a serpent slowly progressing over the ground, with his head erect, and his body following apparently without exertion, can fail to be struck with the peculiar beauty of the motion. There is no jerk, no reflex motion, as in all other animals, even fishes, but a continuous progression in the most graceful curves. Their general form, too, is full of elegance, and their colours varied and sometimes very beautiful, and their eyes bright and piercing. Then, too, a serpent can exist for an indefinite time without food or apparent hunger. He periodically casts his skin, and, as the ancients fabled, by that process renewed his youth. Add to this the longevity, which, though not so great as was often supposed, is still sufficient to make the superstitious forget how long an individual may have been reverenced in order that they may ascribe to him immortality.

Though these qualities, and others that will be noted in the sequel, may have sufficed to excite curiosity and obtain respect, it is probable that the serpent never would have become a god but for his exceptional power.

The destructive powers of tigers or crocodiles are merely looked upon as ordinary exaggerations of a general law, but the poison fang of the serpent is something so exceptional, and so deadly in its action, as to excite dread, and when we find to how few of the serpent tribe it is given, its presence is only more mysterious. Even more terrible, however, than the poison of the Cobra is the flash-like spring of the Boa—the instantaneous embrace and the crushed-out life—all accomplished faster almost than the eye can follow. It is hardly to be wondered at that such power should impress people in an early stage of civilization with feelings of awe; and with savages it is probably true that most religions sprung from a desire to propitiate by worship those powers from whom they fear that injury may be done to themselves or their property. Although, therefore, fear might seem to suffice to account for the prevalence of the worship, on looking closely at it we are struck with phenomena of a totally different character. When we first meet Serpent Worship, either in the Wilderness of Sinaï, the Groves of Epidaurus, or in the Sarmatian huts, the Serpent is always the Agathodæmon, the bringer of health and good fortune. He is the teacher of wisdom, the oracle of future events. His worship may have originated in fear, but long before we become practically acquainted with it, it had passed to the opposite extreme among its votaries. Any evil that ever was spoken of the serpent, came from those who were outside the pale, and were trying to depreciate what they considered as an accursed superstition.

If fear were the only or even the principal characteristic of Serpent Worship, it might be sufficient, in order to account for its prevalence, to say, that like causes produce like effects all the world over; and that the serpent is so terrible and so unlike the rest of creation that these characteristics are sufficient to explain everything. When more narrowly examined, however, this seems hardly to be the case. Love and admiration, more than fear or dread, seem to be the main features of the faith, and there are so many unexpected features which are at the same time common to it all the world over, that it seems more reasonable to suspect a common origin. In the present state of our knowledge, however, we are not in a position to indicate the locality where it first may have appeared, or the time when it first became established among mankind.

In so far as such glimmerings as we possess enable us to guess the locality of its origin, I would feel inclined to say that it came from the mud of the Lower Euphrates, among a people of Turanian origin, and spread thence as from a centre to every country or land of the Old World in which a Turanian people settled. Apparently no Semitic, or no people of Aryan race, ever adopted it as a form of faith. It is true we find it in Judea, but almost certainly it was there an outcrop from the older underlying strata of the population. We find it also in Greece, and in Scandinavia, among people whom we know principally as Aryan, but there too it is like the tares of a previous crop springing up among the stems of a badly-cultivated field of wheat. The essence of Serpent Worship is as diametrically opposed to the spirit of the Veda or of the Bible as is possible to conceive two faiths to be; and with varying degrees of dilution the spirit of these two works pervades in a greater or less extent all the forms of the religions of the Aryan or Semitic races. On the other hand, any form of animal worship is perfectly consistent with the lower intellectual status of the Turanian races, and all history tells us that it is among them, and essentially among them only, that Serpent Worship is really found to prevail.

Human Sacrifices

The almost universal association of human sacrifices with the practice of Serpent Worship would render it extremely desirable to ascertain, if it were possible, how far the connexion between the two is real, or to what extent the juxtaposition may be only accidental. The subject is, however, very seriously complicated by the circumstance of the very different form which the rite took in various ages, and the different points of view from which it must consequently be at times regarded.

In its earliest and simplest form, human sacrifice seems merely to have been regarded in the nature of a tithe. A cannibal savage shared with his cannibal god the spoils of victory as he did the products of the chase, or he sought to sanctify his revenge or his sensuality by making his deity a participator in his crimes. Another form arose from the idea that death was only a change, and that the future state was little more than a continuation of this world. It became consequently necessary for his enjoyment of it, that a man should be accompanied by his cattle, and his slaves, male and female, and in its most refined form the wife voluntarily sacrificed herself to rejoin her beloved husband. A third form sprang from a higher and more religious motive: it arose from a conviction of man's own unworthy and sinful nature as compared with the greatness and goodness of God, and the consequent desire to atone for the one by the sacrifice of whatever was most dear, and to propitiate the favour of the deity by offering up whatever was most precious and most beloved—even one's own, and it might be only, child. A fourth form, equally compatible with the highest civilisation, was the national sacrifice of one to atone for the sins of the many. Serpent Worship is associated in a greater or less degree with all these forms of the human rite, and so much so that it is nearly correct to say that wherever human sacrifices prevailed, there Serpent Worship is found also, though the converse does not appear so capable of proof. Serpent Worship did continue to exist when, at least, human sacrifices had ceased to be performed, though even then it is not quite clear whether it was not only from the disuse of one part of what had once been associated.

In Egypt human sacrifices never assumed the position of a religious or domestic institution. The victorious king dedicated the prisoners taken in war to the gods, but beyond this it does not seem to have been carried; and Serpent Worship in Egypt seems likewise to have been sporadic and of little importance.

In Judea, so long as any traces of Serpent Worship prevailed, the idea of human sacrifices seems to have been familiar, but after Hezekiah's time we simultaneously lose all traces of either.

So long as Greece was Pelasgic, Serpent Worship and human sacrifices went hand in hand, but with the return of the Heraclidæ, the latter went out of fashion, though the former still lingered long, but in a modified form. In Rome, on the other hand, as we shall presently see, the worship of the Serpent was a later introduction, but as it strengthened, so did the prevalence of human sacrifices; and till Christianity put a stop to them they certainly were considered an important means of appeasing the wrath or propitiating the favour of the gods. It may, in Rome, have been to some extent derived from Etruria, or encouraged by the example of Carthage, where human sacrifices certainly prevailed till the destruction of the city, and wherever Moloch—"horrid king"—was worshipped; and in all these instances the practice seems to have risen and fallen with Serpent Worship.

In Mexico and Dahomey, where in modern times human sacrifices have been practised to an extent not known elsewhere, there too Serpent Worship was and is the typical and most important form of propitiation; while in India, there can be little doubt but that the two existed together from the earliest time. The sacrifice of men could not, however, stand before the intellectual acumen of the Aryan, and was utterly antagonistic to the mild doctrines of the Buddhist. It consequently was abolished wherever it was possible to do so; but the more innocent worship of the Serpent cropped up again and again wherever neglected, and remained in many places long after the sister form had practically lost its meaning. Both still exist in India at the present day, but not apparently practised together or by the same tribes. It is not, however, by any means clear whether the dissociation is real, or whether we merely assume it is so in consequence of our ignorance of the subject. Human sacrifices, especially among the Khonds, have attracted the attention both of governments and of individuals. No one has turned his attention to the modern forms of Serpent Worship.

Notwithstanding all these coincidences—and they might easily be extended—it must not be overlooked that nowhere can we trace any direct connexion between the two forms of faith. No human sacrifice was anywhere made to propitiate the serpent, nor was it ever pretended that any human victim was ever devoured by the snake god. In all instances the serpent is the Agathodæmon, the bringer of health or good fortune, the protector of men or of treasure, and nowhere was it sought to propitiate him by sacrifice of life beyond what was necessary for food, or to appease him by blood offerings.

When the subject has been more thoroughly investigated than has hitherto been the case, it may be possible to trace a more direct connexion between the two forms of faith than we are now able to do. At all events we shall then be in a position to say whether it was a real partnership or only an accidental juxtaposition. In the meanwhile, all that is required in this place is to draw attention to the subject, and to point out a coincidence which is so remarkable that when investigated it may hereafter lead to the most important results.

Egypt

In an attempt to investigate any form of ancient mythology from an historical point of view, we naturally turn first to Egypt; for not only was Egypt the earliest civilized of all the countries of the ancient world, in so far at least as we at present know, but she was pre-eminently the parent of all idolatries. With the Egyptians all knowledge was considered as divine, and whatever they saw, they worshipped. Their gods had been kings; their kings were gods; and all the animal kingdom was considered worthy of worship in a greater or less degree. From bulls to beetles, or from crocodiles to cats, it made little difference; all came alike to a people so essentially religious as the Egyptians seem to have been. It is little wonder, therefore, that Serpents, and it may be Trees, should be included in their multifarious Pantheon, and it is easy to detect numerous instances of the honours bestowed on both. Still it would be straining the argument beyond its legitimate issue to describe the Egyptians as in any sense an essentially Tree or Serpent worshipping people. The serpent was worshipped on the banks of the Nile among other animals, perhaps in some instances with a certain degree of pre-eminence; but on the whole the accounts are hardly sufficient to enable us to say that the serpent was more honoured than his associated animal gods. At the same time it must be admitted that the serpent very frequently appears in the sculptures of the Temple walls, and frequently in a place of honour, as on the brow of the king, or as a prominent ornament of his dress, but hardly ever there with that pre-eminence he attained in other countries.

The relative position of Tree Worship among the Egyptians seems to be almost the same. It is true that the important part which the Tamarisk plays in the legend of Isis and Osiris, as told by Plutarch, might tend to a somewhat different conclusion, and the prominence given to the other tree, which marked and shaded the tomb of Osiris in the same legend, might lead to the conclusion that a form of Tree Worship prevailed in Egypt before the multifarious Theban pantheon was elaborated. The authority, however, for these facts is not such as can be relied upon, and the sculptures again do not favour the belief that Trees were considered as divine on the banks of the Nile, though they may justify the belief that the sycamore was sacred to the goddess Netpe, and the persea to Athor.

The great test of such a subject in Egypt are the sculptures which cover the walls of the Temples. These are the Bible of the Egyptians, in so far at least as we know it. Any one studying these with that object might easily pick out fifty or a hundred examples which would tend to show that the Egyptians were both Tree and Serpent worshippers; but, on a fair review of the whole subject, these would probably be found to be only a fractional part of the nature worship of the Egyptians, and neither the most prominent nor the most important. In spite, therefore, of the passages in classical authors which may be quoted against this view, it would probably be incorrect to include the ancient Egyptians among the votaries either of the Serpent or of Trees.

The earliest distinct allusion which we have to those mysterious properties which the ancients attributed to certain Trees, is to be found in the second and third chapters of Genesis. The planting of the Trees of Life and Knowledge in the Garden of Eden is there described in minute detail, and judging from subsequent forms of the story, their custody seems to have been intrusted to the serpent. Taken by itself, this narrative has always appeared one of the least intelligible parts of the Pentateuch, and numberless theories have been formed to account for what seemed so completely outside the range of ordinary human experience. With the knowledge we now possess, it does not seem so difficult to understand what was meant by the curse on the serpent, or the prohibition to eat the fruit of the trees. When the writers of the Pentateuch set themselves to introduce the purer and loftier worship of the Elohim, or of Jehovah, it was first necessary to get rid of that earlier form of faith which the primitive inhabitants of the earth had fashioned for themselves. The serpent, as the principal deity of that early religion, was cursed "above all cattle, and above every beast of the field"; and in future there was to be for ever enmity between the serpent and "man of woman born." The confusion of ideas on this subject seems to have arisen from the assumption that the curse was directed at the reptile as such, and not rather at a form of worship which the writers of the Pentateuch must have regarded with horror, and which they thought it necessary to denounce in the strongest terms and in the form they believed would be most intelligible by those to whom it was addressed. The tree it was not necessary should be cursed; the fruit of the tree of knowledge had been eaten, and no further result could be obtained by access to it, while the tree of life was guarded by a cherub with a flaming sword, and all approach prevented. Its fruits could not then be obtained, nor have they to the present day.

The two chapters which refer to this, however,—as indeed the whole of the first eight of Genesis,—are now generally admitted by scholars to be made up of fragments of earlier books or earlier traditions belonging, properly speaking, to Mesopotamian rather than to Jewish history, the exact meaning of which the writers of the Pentateuch seem hardly to have appreciated when they transcribed them in the form in which they are now found. The history of the Jews and of the Jewish religion commences with the call of Abraham, and from that time forward the worship of Serpents and Trees took an infinitely less important position, though still occasionally cropping up, often when least expected, but apparently not as a religion of the Jews, but as a backsliding towards the feelings of the pre-existing races among whom they were located.

There is apparently no mention of serpents, either in the Bible or in any of the traditions in connexion with Abraham or his immediate descendants; but that Patriarch "planted a grove at the well of the covenant (Beersheba), and called there "on the name of the Lord"—a circumstance the more worthy of note, as it is the earliest mention of a form of worship to which continual allusions are afterwards made in Jewish history. The oak, or rather the terebinth tree, under which Abraham is said to have entertained the angels at Mamre, became an object of extreme veneration to his descendants, and, if we may trust Eusebius, was worshipped down to the time of Constantine. The pious zeal of that emperor led him to desecrate its altars, and apparently to cut down the sacred tree to make way for a Christian church which he erected on the spot, and which was then or afterwards dedicated to St. George.

With the time of Moses the indications became more distinct and palpable. We gather from the context in the Bible, and still more from the narrative of Josephus, that the tree or bush on Horeb, from which the Lord appeared to Moses as a flame, had been considered sacred before that event. It was, indeed, apparently in consequence of its sanctity that it was chosen for the delivery of the oracle, while the conversion on that occasion of Moses' rod into a serpent brings these two names into the juxtaposition in which they are so frequently found. This miracle on Horeb would, however, be more impressive and more to the point were it not that it was repeated by Aaron before Pharaoh, and copied by the Egyptians; but at the burning bush it stands alone, and without any apparent motive for its exhibition there, except the appropriateness of the combination.

With the Brazen Serpent in the Wilderness we tread on surer ground; it is the first record we have of actual worship being performed to the Serpent, and it is also remarkable, as the cause of this adoration is said to have been its healing powers. From the readiness with which this explanation was adopted by the Jews, it would seem as if that characteristic had been ascribed to the Serpent before that time. We now, however, learn it for the first time, though we afterwards become so familiar with it in Greek mythology, where the Serpent himself represents Æsculapius, and is the indispensable concomitant of Hygieia.

From this time we lose sight of the worship of the Serpent from the narrative of the Bible, till it somewhat unexpectedly reappears in the time of Hezekiah. We then learn that the brazen image that Moses had set up, had for more than five centuries been preserved in the Temple, and that "unto those days the children of Israel did burn incense to it." It was only then, after six centuries of toleration, that it was resolved to put an end to this idolatry, together with the kindred worship of the Groves. In the intermediate period there is hardly any expression that countenances the belief that the worship of Serpents generally prevailed among the Jews, unless it be one in the Wisdom of Solomon, where it is said, "They worshipped serpents void of reason," in strange contrast with the New Testament expression, "Be ye wise as serpents."

Neither in the Bible, however, nor in the Talmud, is there anything that would justify the assertion that Serpent Worship, even in the most modified form, prevailed among the Jews after its abolition by Hezekiah. It cropped up again, in the Christian sect of Ophites, but probably in this instance the superstition was derived from Persia.

The case is different with the worship of Trees or Groves. The first form of this appears to have arisen from the veneration paid to natural groves, and the worship offered therein to Baal and other foreign gods, but the Grove or Asherah is also frequently an image, no doubt like that emblem so often represented on the Assyrian sculptures. This is an artificial tree, such as might have been placed alongside of the Brazen Serpent within the Temple at Jerusalem.

It hardly admits of doubt but that this worship of the Asherah or of Groves was a true and essential form of Tree Worship, but it seems to have been local, and entirely opposed to the spirit of the Jewish religion. As a rule it is reprobated by their chroniclers and prophets, and eventually disappears. Had it ever been really adopted by the Jewish legislators, we might perhaps be able to ascertain more correctly its origin and affiliations. Possibly we may do so when the Assyrian antiquities are more completely investigated than they now are. For the present we must rest content with the knowledge that both Trees and Serpents were worshipped in Judea, and hope that some new light may some day be thrown on the subject.

Even, however, if in abeyance, we can hardly suppose that Serpent Worship was extinguished in Judea, inasmuch as immediately after the Christian era we found it bursting forth again with wonderful exuberance in the sects of the Nicolaitans, the Gnostics, and more especially that called the Ophites. Of the latter, Tertullian tells us, "they even prefer the Serpent to Christ, because the former brought the knowledge of good and evil into the world. They point also to his majesty and power, inasmuch as when Moses raised the Brazen Serpent in the Wilderness, whoever looked on it was healed; and they even quote the Gospels to prove that Christ was an imitation of the serpent, because it is said, 'As Moses lifted up the serpent in the wilderness, so must the Son of Man be lifted up.'" Epiphanius describes these ceremonies in the following terms: "They keep a living serpent in a chest, and at the time of the mysteries entice him out by placing bread before him. The door being opened he issues forth, and having ascended the table folds himself above the bread. This they call a perfect sacrifice. They not only break and distribute this among the votaries, but whosoever wishes it may kiss the serpent. This the wretched people call the Eucharist. They conclude the ceremonies by singing a hymn through him to the Supreme Father."

There are other paragraphs to the same effect, and the representations of serpents and Serpent Worship in the so-called Gnostic form are too numerous and too familiar to require further notice here.

We have no means of knowing how long this worship of the Serpent continued to prevail in Syria—most probably down to the seventh century, when the Mahomedan invasion swept away a large mass of the parasitic superstitions which had fastened themselves on Christianity; but the literature of that age is so mixed up with fables and misrepresentations, that it is very difficult to write confidently about anything it describes.

Except the instance above alluded to, of the Terebinth at Mamre, I am not aware of any authentic instance of direct Tree Worship in Syria after the Christian era, but there may be, though, as they have not hitherto been looked for, they may still remain unknown.

America

There are few things in connexion with the ancient mythology of America more certain than that there existed in that country before its discovery by Columbus extreme veneration for the serpent. Whether or not this should be designated "worship" is not so clear. The total absence of any native literature renders it extremely difficult to realise the exact interpretation to be put on any observed phenomena, and we gather very little trustworthy information from the early Christian missionaries or historians. They were either too ignorant or too prejudiced to take a dispassionate view of what they saw, and were too much inclined to see the serpent of Eve, or the deluge of Noah, in the vague traditions of the natives; though, to account for these, they were obliged to make St. Thomas missionary to Mexico—before it was founded—as well as first Bishop of Madras. The consequence is, that we are dependent either on a very imperfect examination of the Sculptures, or on very vague oral traditions, for our knowledge of the subject; and it need hardly be added, that with only such data it is extremely difficult to arrive at any satisfactory conclusion. At the same time, however, it must be admitted that if a systematic examination of such data as exist were undertaken, with special reference to Tree and Serpent Worship, a great deal might yet be effected; but as no one has yet attempted the investigation, the subject must for the present be left in its original obscurity.

The principal deity of the Aztec Pantheon seems Tezcatlipoca, or Tonacatlecoatl, literally, the Sun Serpent. According to Sahagun, in his character of God of Hosts, he was addressed by the Mexican high priest: "We entreat that those who die in war may be received by thee, our father the sun, and our brother the earth, for thou alone reignest."

The name of the primitive goddess, the wife of Tezcatlipoca, was Cihuacohuatl, or Tonacacihua, the female serpent or the female sun. She, according to the Mexicans, gave to the light at a single birth two children, one male the other female, to whom they refer the origin of mankind.

A still more remarkable myth is that of Quetzalcoatl, literally the feathered serpent. He is by some represented as born of a pure virgin in the province of Tollan; by others as a stranger coming from a "far countrie," some time between the sixth and ninth century of our era. Be this as it may, he was the great lawgiver and civilizer of the inhabitants of Anahuac. He taught them religion, gave them laws, instructed them in agriculture and the use of metals, and the various arts of life. He is generally represented as an old man, with a white flowing beard and venerable aspect. He was, in fact, the Lycurgus and the Bacchus of Central America, and having finished his mission he withdrew, like the former, it is said, by sea, promising to return. So implicitly was this believed by his subjects, that when the Spaniards appeared on the coast they were joyfully hailed as the returning god and his companions. Alas! they came only to destroy them and their institutions.

If all the evidences bearing on this legend were thoroughly sifted by some one competent to the task, I feel confident they would result in an historical residuum; and if so, it would throw great light on one of the most perplexing problems connected with the civilization of the New World.

Serpent Worship was the faith of a great and prosperous kingdom in Cambodia at the time just indicated as the age of the Mexican prophet; and it is more than probable that the worship prevailed in China and the islands to the eastward at that time. Is it possible that it may have crossed the Pacific, and landed on the western coast of America, and, finally, bloomed in Anahuac? If such a solution were possible, it would explain many similarities between the religion and arts of the Old World and the New, which are now extremely puzzling for want of some such evidence of intercommunication.

On the other hand, if we may trust the antiquaries of the United States, there are great serpent mounds formed of earth, 1,000 feet long and more, which would seem to prove that before the present race of Red Indians inhabited the states Ohio and Iowa, a race of Serpent Worshippers occupied their places, and they have been the ancestors of the Toltecs. When, however, we remember with what curious credulity Stukeley manufactured a Dracontium out of Avebury, and Bathurst Deane saw a serpent seven miles long in the groups of Menhirs at Carnac, we must pause before we feel sure that these American mounds do really represent serpents at all. This point cannot be settled without much more accurate surveys and more cautious observers than have yet turned their attention to the subject.

If it should turn out that these are really representations of the great serpent, and that this worship is indigenous in the New World, we are thrown back on the doctrine that human nature is alike everywhere, and that man in like circumstances and with like degree of civilization does always the same things, and elaborates the same beliefs. It may be so, but I confess it appears to me that at present the evidence preponderates the other way. It should be mentioned, however, that in America the snake that is worshipped is always the indigenous rattlesnake. Whether as separate images or as adorning the walls of the temples of Yucatan, this characteristic seems invariable, and in so far would favour the local origin of the faith. The greatest difficulty of the investigation arises from almost absolute destruction of all the monuments of the capital by its barbarous conquerors, and the consequent paucity of real reliable data on which to found our conclusions.

It seems, however, impossible to read the numerous evidences which Müller has collected together with so much industry not to feel convinced that Serpent Worship did prevail all over the continent. In Peru apparently with qualities similar to those of the Serpents in the Old World. But in Mexico, and among the North American Indians, occasionally with attributes of terror which were never ascribed to him on this side of the Atlantic. Quetzalcoatl is always an exception to this inference; and on the whole it seems more reasonable to suppose that these characteristics are to be ascribed more to the horror of the Christian narrators than to the feelings of the worshippers. We have no native accounts, and depend consequently wholly on those who looked on the worship from an outside and antagonistic point of view.

If, however, we may trust Bernal Diaz, he tells us that living rattlesnakes were kept in the great temple at Mexico as sacred and petted objects. They were kept in a cabin of diversified form, in which a quantity of feathers had been strewed, and there they laid their eggs and nursed their snakelings. They were fed with the bodies of the sacrificed, and with dogs' meat. The same author tells us that on Cortes' march to Mexico they arrived at a place called Terraguca, which the Spaniards called the Town of Serpents, on account of the enormous figures of these reptiles which they found in the temples, and which the natives worshipped as gods. But though it is impossible to read any of the narratives of the conquerors without being struck with the frequency with which sacred Serpents and Serpent Worship are spoken of, it is always as a thing accursed, and to be avoided; never as an object worthy of attention, or to be inquired into, and their narratives consequently throw very little light on the subject. The Sculptures would do more; but it will require a long and patient investigation by some one competent person on the spot before their evidence can be considered as available; at present we know very little of what they may contain.

It need hardly be remarked that human sacrifices were found accompanying Serpent Worship in America almost to as great an extent as in Dahomey. Even here, however, it is probable we must make a distinction which may be of some importance. In Africa the sacrificial rites seem to be purely ancestral. In America they were made to propitiate gods, not apparently the ancestors of the reigning family, nor nearer to them in time than Quetzalcoatl. The principal object seems always to have been augury to obtain from the gods an indication of their will, which does not seem to have been the case in Dahomey. It was also no doubt considered that the sacrifice itself was agreeable to the deity, and it was expected that the oracle, which was the declaration of his will, would be favourable in proportion to the number of the victims.

It is by no means improbable that when looked for, Tree Worship will also be found to have prevailed extensively in the New World. Mr. Tylor mentions two instances that came under his notice. The first was a venerable deciduous cypress, with a stem sixty feet in circumference near its root, and with a fountain gushing up within the hollow of the trunk itself. It was hung all over with votive offerings, besides hundreds of locks of hair, teeth, and bits of ribbon. The other was treated in the same manner, and had the valuable property for whoever touched it, that all feeling of weariness left him. Müller also finds traces of Tree Worship all over the continent of America, and generally in juxtaposition, if not in actual connexion, with that of the Serpent.

ESSAYS

The Antipathy of the Elephant and the Serpent

by PLINY, THE ELDER

AFRICA PRODUCES ELEPHANTS, BEYOND THE DESERTS OF the Syrtes, and in Mauritania; they are found also in the countries of the Aethiopians and the Troglodytae. But it is India that produces the largest, as well as the serpent, which is perpetually at war with the elephant, and is itself of so enormous a size, as easily to envelope the elephants with its folds, and encircle them in its coils. The contest is equally fatal to both; the elephant, vanquished, falls to the earth, and by its weight, crushes the serpent which is entwined around it.

The sagacity which every animal exhibits in its own behalf is wonderful, but in these it is remarkably so. The serpent has little difficulty in climbing up to so great a height, and therefore, watching the road, which bears marks of their footsteps when going to feed, it darts down upon them from a lofty tree. The elephant knows that it is quite unable to struggle against the folds of the serpent, and so seeks for trees or rocks against which to rub itself. The serpent is on its guard against this, and tries to prevent it, by first of all confining the legs of the elephant with the folds of its tail; while the elephant, on the other hand, endeavours to disengage itself with its trunk. The serpent, however, thrusts its head into its nostrils, and thus, at the same moment, stops the breath and wounds the most tender parts. When it is met unexpectedly, the serpent raises itself up, faces its opponent, and flies more especially at the eyes; this is the reason why elephants are so often found blind, and worn to a skeleton with hunger and misery. What other course can one assign for such mighty strifes as these, except that Nature is desirous, as it were, to make an exhibition for herself, in pitting such opponents against each other?

The Bruised Serpent

by W. H. HUDSON

SOME HOLD THAT OUR ABHORRENCE OF THE SERPENT tribe, the undiscriminating feeling which involves the innocent with the harmful, is instinctive in man. Many primitive, purely animal promptings and impulses survive in us, of which, they argue, this may be one. It is common knowledge that the sight of a serpent affects many persons, especially Europeans, in a sudden violent manner, with a tremor and tingling of the nerves, like a million messages of startling import flying from the centre of intelligence to all outlying parts of the bodily kingdom; and these sensations of alarm, horror, and disgust are, in most cases, accompanied or instantly followed by an access of fury, a powerful impulse to crush the offensive reptile to death. The commonness of the feeling and its violence, so utterly out of proportion to the danger to be apprehended, do certainly give it the appearance of a true instinctive impulse; nevertheless, such appearance may be deceptive. Fear, however it may originate, is of all emotions the least rational; and the actions of a person greatly excited by it will most nearly resemble those of the lower animals.

Darwin, on the slightest evidence, affirms that monkeys display an instinctive or inherited fear of snakes. There are many who would think any further inquiry into the matter superfluous; for, they would argue, if monkeys fear snakes in that way, then assuredly we, developed monkeys, must regard them with a feeling identical in character and origin. To be able thus to skim with the swallow's grace and celerity over dark and possibly unfathomable questions is a very engaging accomplishment, and apparently a very popular one. What is done with ease will always be done with pleasure; and what can be easier or more agreeable than to argue in this fashion: "Fear of snakes is merely another example of historical memory, recalling a time when man, like his earliest ancestors, the anthropoid apes, was sylvan and solitary; a mighty climber of trees whose fingers were frequently bitten by bird-nesting colubers, and who was occasionally swallowed entire by colossal serpents of arboreal habits."

The instinctive fear of enemies, although plainly traceable in insects, with some other creatures low in the organic scale, is exceedingly rare among the higher vertebrates; so rare indeed as to incline any one who has made a real study of their actions to doubt its existence. It is certain that zoological writers are in the habit of confusing instinctive or inherited

74

with traditional fear, the last being the fear of an enemy which the young learn from their parents or other adults they associate with. Fear is contagious; the alarm of the adults communicates itself to the young, with the result that the object that excited it remains thereafter one of terror. Not only in this matter of snakes and monkeys, but with regard to other creatures, Darwin lays it down that in the higher vertebrates the habit of fear of any particular enemy quickly becomes instinctive; and this false inference has been accepted without question by Herbert Spencer, who was obliged to study animal habits in books, and was consequently to some extent at the mercy of those who wrote them.

It is frequently stated in narratives of travel in the less settled portions of North America that all domestic animals excepting the pig, have an instinctive dread of the rattlesnake; that they know its whirring sound, and are also able to smell it at some distance, and instantly come to a dead halt, trembling with agitation. The fear is a fact; but why *instinctive?* Some time ago, while reading over again a very delightful book of travels, I came to a passage descriptive of the acute sense of smell and sagacity of the native horse; and the writer, as an instance in point, related that frequently, when riding at a swift pace across country on a dark night, over ground made dangerous by numerous concealed burrows, his beast had swerved aside suddenly, *as if he had trod on a snake.* His sense of smell had warned him in time of some grass-covered kennel in the way. But that image of the snake, introduced to give a more vivid idea of the animal's action in swerving aside, was false; and because of its falseness and the want of observation it betrayed, the charm of the passage was sensibly diminished. For not once or twice, but many scores of times it has happened to me, in that very country so graphically described in the book, while traveling at a swinging gallop in the bright daylight, that my horse has trodden on a basking serpent and has swerved not at all, nor appeared conscious of a living, fleshy thing that yielded to his unshod hoof. Passing on, I have thrown back a glance to see my victim writhing on the ground, and hoped that it was bruised only, not broken or fatally injured, like the serpent of the Roman poet's simile, over which the brazen chariot wheel has passed. Yet if the rider saw it—saw it, I mean, before the accident, although too late for any merciful action—the horse must have seen it. The reason he did not swerve was because serpents are very abundant in that country, in the proportion of about thirty harmless individuals to one that is venomous; consequently it is a rare thing for a horse to be bitten; and the serpentine form is familiar to and excites no fear in him. He saw the reptile lying just in his way, motionless in the sunlight, "lit with colour like a rock with flowers," and it caused no emotion, and was no more to him than the yellow and purple blossoms he trampled upon at every yard.

It is not the same in the western prairies of North America. Venomous serpents are relatively more abundant there, and grow larger, and their bite is more dangerous. The horse learns to fear them, especially the rattlesnake, on account of its greater power, its sluggish habits and warning faculties. The sound of the rattle calls up the familiar ophidian image to his mind; and when the rattle has failed to sound, the smell will often serve as a warning; which is not strange when we consider that even man, with his feeble olfactory sense, is sometimes able to discover the presence of a rattlesnake, even at a distance of several feet, by means of its powerful musky effluvium. The snake-eating savages of Queensland track their game by the slight scent it leaves on the ground in travelling, which is quite imperceptible to Europeans. In the same way the horse is said to smell wolves, and to exhibit instinctive terror when they are still at a distance and invisible. The terror is not instinctive. The horses of the white settlers on some frontier lands, exposed to frequent attacks from savages, smell the coming enemy, and fly in panic before he makes his appearance; yet when horses are taken from the savages and used by the whites, these too after a time learn to show terror at the smell of their former masters. Their terror is derived from the horses of the whites. The hunter Selous, as a result of ten years of observation while engaged in the pursuit of big game in the heart of Africa, affirms that the horse has no instinctive fear of the lion; if he has never been mauled or attacked by them, nor associated with horses that have learnt from experience or tradition to dread them, he exhibits no more fear of lions than of zebras and camelopards. The fact is the horse fears in different regions the lion, wolf, puma, redskin, and rattlesnake, just as the burnt child dreads the fire.

But here is an incident, say the believers in Darwin's notion, which proves that the fear of certain animals is instinctive in the horse. A certain big-game hunter brought home a lion's hide, rolled up before it was properly dried and wrapped up in canvas. It was opened in the stable where there were several horses, and the covering was no sooner removed and the hide peeled open than the horses were thrown into a panic. The true explanation is that horses are terrified at any strange *animal* smell, and a powerful smell from the hide of any animal unknown to them would have had the same effect. That fear of a strange animal smell is probably an instinct, but it may not be. In a state of nature the horse learns from experience that certain smells indicate danger, and in Patagonia and on the pampas, when he flies in terror from the scent of a puma which is imperceptible to a man, he pays not the slightest attention to the two most powerful mammalian stenches in the world—that of the skunk, and that of the pampas male deer, *Cervus campestris*. Experience has taught him—or it has come down to him as a tradition—that these most violent odours emanate from animals that cannot harm him.

So much for this view. On the other hand, our enmity to the serpent, which often exists together with a mythic and anthropomorphic belief in the serpent's enmity to us, might be regarded as purely traditional, having its origin in the Scriptural narrative of man's disobedience and expulsion from Paradise. Whether we believe with theologians that our great spiritual enemy was the real tempter, who merely made use of the serpent's form as a convenient disguise in which to approach the woman, or take without gloss the simple story as it stands in Genesis, which only says that the serpent was the most subtle of all things made and the sole cause of our undoing, the result for the creature is equally disastrous. A mark is set upon him: "Because thou hast done this thing thou art cursed above all cattle, and above every beast of the field; upon thy belly shalt thou go, and dust shalt thou eat all the days of thy life: and I will place enmity between thy seed and her seed; and it shall bruise thy head, and thou shalt bruise its heel." This prophecy, so far as it tells against the creature, has been literally fulfilled.

The Satanic theory concerning snakes—that "destructive delusion," which Sir Thomas Browne shrewdly remarks, "hath much enlarged the opinion of their mischief"—makes it necessary for the theologian to believe not only that the serpent of Paradise before its degradation walked erect on two legs, as the Fathers taught—some going so far as to give it a beautiful head as well as a ready tongue—but also that after the devil had cast aside the temporary coil something of his demoniac spirit remained thereafter in it, to be transmitted by inheritance, like a variation in structure or a new instinct, to its remotest descendants. There is the further objection, although not an important one, that it would be unjust to afflict the serpent so grievously for a crime of which it had only been made the involuntary agent.

Believers in an instinct in man inimical to the serpent might still argue that the Scriptural curse only goes to show that this reptile was already held in general abhorrence—that, in fact, the feeling suggested the fable. That the fable had some such origin is probable, but we are just as far from an instinct as ever. The general feeling of mankind, or, at any rate, of the leading men during the earliest civilised periods of which we have any knowledge, was one of veneration, even of love, for the serpent. The Jews alone were placed by their monotheistic doctrine in direct antagonism to all nature-worship and idolatry. In their leaders—prophets and priests—the hatred of the heathen and of heathen modes of thought was kept alive, and constantly fanned into a fierce flame by the prevalent tendency in the common people to revert to the surrounding older and lower forms of religion, which were more in harmony with their mental conditions. The proudest boast of their highest intellects was that they had never bowed in reverence or kissed their hand to anything in nature. In such circumstances it was unavoidable that the specific object—rock, or tree, or animal—singled out for worship, or for superstitious veneration, should to some extent become involved in the feeling first excited against the worshipper. If the Jews hated the serpent with a peculiarly bitter hatred, it was doubtless because all others looked on it as a sacred animal, an incarnation of the Deity. The chosen people had also been its worshippers at an earlier period, as the Bible shows, and while hating it, they still retained the old belief, intimately connected with serpent-worship everywhere, in the creature's preternatural subtlety and wisdom. The priests of other Eastern nations introduced it into their sacred rites and mysteries; the Jewish priests introduced it historically into the Garden of Eden to account for man's transgression and fall. "Be ye wise as serpents," was a saying of the deepest significance. In Europe men were anciently taught by the Druids to venerate the adder; the Jews—or Jewish books—taught them to abhor it. To my way of thinking, neither blessing nor banning came by instinct.

Veneration of the serpent still survives in a great part of the world, as in Hindustan and other parts of Asia. It is strong in Madagascar, and flourishes more or less throughout Africa. It lingers in North America, and is strong in some places where the serpents, used in religious serpent dances, unlike those of Madagascar, are venomous, and it has not yet wholly died out in Europe. The Finns have a great regard for the adder.

It may be added here that there are many authenticated instances of children becoming attached to snakes and making pets of them. The solution of a question of this kind is sometimes to be found in the child-mind. My experience is that when young children see this creature, its strange appearance and manner of progression, so unlike those of other animals known to them, affect them with amazement and a sense of mystery, and that they fear it just as they would fear any other strange thing. Monkeys are doubtless affected in much the same way, although, in a state of nature, where they inhabit forests abounding with the larger constrictors and venomous tree-snakes, it is highly probable that they also possess a traditional fear of the serpent form. It would be strange if they did not. The experiment of presenting a caged monkey with a serpent carefully wrapped up in paper and watching his behaviour when he gravely opens the parcel, expecting to find nothing more wonderful than the familiar sponge-cake or succulent banana—well, such an experiment has been recorded in half a hundred important scientific works, and out of respect to one's masters one should endeavour not to smile when reading it.

A third view might be taken, which would account for our feeling towards the serpent without either instinct or tradition. Extreme fear of all ophidians may simply result from a vague knowledge of the fact that some kinds are venomous, that in some rare cases death follows swiftly on their bite, and that, not being sufficiently intelligent to distinguish the noxious from the innocuous—at all events while under the domination of a sudden violent emotion—we destroy them all alike, thus adopting Herod's rough-and-ready method of ridding his city of one inconvenient babe by a general massacre of innocents.

It might be objected that in Europe, where animosity to the serpent is greatest, death from snake-bite is hardly to be feared, that Fontana's six thousand experiments with the viper, showing how small is the amount of venom possessed by this species, how rarely it has the power to destroy human life, have been before the world for a century. And although it must be admitted that Fontana's work is not in the hand of every peasant, the fact remains that death from snake-bite is a rare thing in Europe, probably not more than one person losing his life from this cause for every two hundred and fifty who perish by hydrophobia, of all forms of death the most terrible. Yet while the sight of a snake excites in a majority of persons the most violent emotions, dogs are universal favourites, and we have them always with us and make pets of them, in spite of the knowledge that they may at any time become rabid and inflict that unspeakable dreadful suffering and destruction on us. This leads to the following question: Is it not at least probable that our excessive fear of the serpent, so unworthy of us as rational beings and the cause of so much unnecessary cruelty, is, partly at all events, a result of our superstitious fear of sudden death? For there exists, we know, an exceedingly widespread delusion that the bite of a venomous serpent must kill, and kill quickly. Compared with such ophidian monarchs as the bush-master, fer-de-lance, hamadryad, and ticpolonga, the viper of Europe—the poor viper of many experiments and much, not too readable, literature—may be regarded as almost harmless, at all events not much more harmful than the hornet. Nevertheless, in this cold northern world, even as in other worlds where nature elaborates more potent juices, the delusion prevails, and may be taken in account here, although its origin cannot now be discussed.

Against sudden death we are taught to pray from infancy, and those who believe that their chances of a happy immortality are enormously increased when death comes slowly, approaching them, as it were, visibly, so that the soul has ample time to make its peace with an incensed Deity, have not far to look for the cause of the feeling. It is true that death from hydrophobia is very horrible, and, comparatively, of frequent occurrence, but it does not find its victim wholly unprepared. After being bitten he has had time to reflect on the possible, even probable, consequence, and to make due preparation for the end; and even at the last, although tortured to frenzy at intervals by strange unhuman agonies, however clouded with apprehensions his intellect may be, it is not altogether darkened and unconscious of approaching dissolution. We know that men in other times have had no such fear of sudden death, that among the most advanced of the ancients some even regarded death from lightning-stroke as a signal mark of Heaven's favour. We, on the contrary, greatly fear the lightning, seldom as it hurts; and the serpent and the lightning are objects of terror to us in about the same degree, and perhaps for the same reason.

Thus any view which we may take of this widespread and irrational feeling is at once found to be so complicated with other feelings and matters affecting us that no convincing solution seems possible. Perhaps it would be as well to regard it as a compound of various elements: traditional feeling having its origin in the Hebrew narrative of man's fall from innocency and happiness; our ignorance concerning serpents and the amount of injury they are able to do us; and, lastly, our superstitious dread of swift and unexpected death. Sticklers for the simple—and to my mind erroneous—theory that a primitive instinct is under it all, may throw in something of that element if they like—a small residuum existing in races that emerged in comparatively recent times from barbarism, but which has been eliminated from a long-civilised people like the Hindoos.

For my own part I am inclined to believe that we regard serpents with a destructive hatred purely and simply because we are so taught from childhood. A tradition may be handed down without writing, or even articulate speech. We have not altogether ceased to be "lower animals" ourselves. Show a child by your gestures and actions that a thing is fearful to you, and he will fear it; that you hate it, and he will catch your hatred. So far back as memory carries me I find the snake, in its unwarrantable intrusion on the scene, ever associated with loud exclamations of astonishment and rage, with a hurried search for those primitive weapons always lying ready to hand, sticks and stones, then the onset and triumphant crushing of that wonderfully fashioned vertebra in its scaly varicoloured mantle, coiling and writhing for a few moments under the cruel rain of blows, appealing not with voice but with agonised yet ever graceful action for mercy to the merciless; and finally, the paean of victory from the slayer, lifting his face still aglow with righteous wrath, a little St. George in his own estimation; for has he not rid the earth of another monster, one of that demoniac brood that was cursed of old, and this without injury to his sacred heel?

On the Movement of Snakes

by ARISTOTLE

THE REASON WHY SNAKES ARE FOOTLESS IS, FIRST, THAT nature creates nothing without a purpose but always with a view to what is best for each thing within the bounds of possibility, preserving the particular essence and purpose of each; and secondly, as we have already said, because no red-blooded animal can move by means of more than four points. It is clear from all this that all red-blooded animals whose length is out of proportion to the rest of their bodily construction, like the snakes, can none of them have feet; for they cannot have more than four feet (for if they had, they would be bloodless), whereas, if they had two or four feet, they would be practically incapable of any movement at all, so slow and useless would their movement necessarily be.

Secondary Sexual Characters of Snakes

by CHARLES DARWIN

I HAVE LITTLE TO SAY ABOUT SNAKES. DR. GÜNTHER IN-forms me that the males are always smaller than the females, and generally have longer and slenderer tails; but he knows of no other difference in external structure. In regard to color, Dr. Günther can almost always distinguish the male from the female by his more strongly-pronounced tints; thus the black zigzag band on the back of the male English viper is more distinctly defined than in the female. The difference is much plainer in the Rattlesnakes of North America, the male of which, as the keeper in the Zoological Gardens showed me, can instantly be distinguished from the female by having more lurid yellow about its whole body. In South Africa the *Bucephalus capensis* presents an analogous difference, for the female "is never so fully variegated with yellow on the sides, as the male." The male of the Indian *Dipsas cynodon,* on the other hand, is blackish-brown, with the belly partly black, while the female is reddish or yellow-ish-olive with the belly either uniform yellowish or marbled with black. In the *Tragops dispar* of the same country, the male is bright green, and the female bronze-colored. No doubt the colors of some snakes serve as a protection, as the green tints of tree-snakes and the various mottled shades of the species which live in sandy places; but it is doubtful whether the colors of many kinds, for instance of the common English snake or viper, serve to conceal them; and this is still more doubtful with the many foreign species which are colored with extreme elegance.

During the breeding-season their anal scent-glands are in active func-tion; and so it is with the same glands in lizards, and as we have seen with the submaxillary glands of crocodiles. As the males of most animals search for the females, these odoriferous glands probably serve to excite or charm the female, rather than to guide her to the spot where the male may be found. Male snakes, though appearing so sluggish, are amorous; for many have been observed crowding round the same female, and even round the dead body of a female. They are not known to fight together from rivalry. Their intellectual powers are higher than might have been anticipated. An excellent observer in Ceylon, Mr. E. Layard, saw a Cobra thrust its head through a narrow hole and swallow a toad. "With this encumbrance he could not withdraw himself; finding this, he reluctantly disgorged the precious morsel, which began to move off; this was too much for snake philosophy to bear, and the toad was again seized, and again was the snake, after violent efforts to escape, compelled to part with its prey. This time, however, a lesson had been learned, and the toad was seized by one leg, withdrawn, and then swallowed in triumph."

It does not, however, follow because snakes have some reasoning power and strong passions, that they should likewise be endowed with sufficient taste to admire brilliant colors in their partners, so as to lead to the adornment of the species through sexual selection. Nevertheless, it is difficult to account in any other manner for the extreme beauty of certain species; for instance, of the coral-snakes of South America, which are of a rich red with black and yellow transverse bands. I well remember how much surprise I felt at the beauty of the first coral-snake which I saw gliding across a path in Brazil. Snakes colored in this peculiar manner, as Mr. Wallace states on the authority of Dr. Günther, are found nowhere else in the world except in South America, and here no less than four genera occur. One of these, Elaps, is venomous; a second and widely-distinct genus is doubtfully venomous, and the two others are quite harmless. The species belonging to these distinct genera inhabit the same districts, and are so like each other, that no one "but a naturalist would distinguish the harmless from the poisonous kinds." Hence, as Mr. Wallace believes, the innocuous kinds have probably acquired their colors as a protection, on the principle of imitation; for they would naturally be thought dangerous by their enemies. The cause, however, of the bright colors of the venomous Elaps remains to be explained, and this may perhaps be sexual selection.

A Serpent in Motion

by JOHN RUSKIN

YOU SEE THAT ONE-HALF OF IT CAN MOVE ANYWHERE without stirring the other; and accordingly you may see a foot or two of a large snake's body moving one way, and another foot or two moving the other way, and a bit between not moving at all; which I, altogether, think we may specifically call "Parliamentary" motion.

* * * *

That rivulet of smooth silver—how does it flow, think you? It literally rows on the earth, with every scale for an oar; it bites the dust with the ridges of its body. Watch it when it moves slowly; a wave, but, without wind! a current, but with no fall! all the body moving at the same instant, yet some of it to one side, some to another, and some forward, and the rest of the coil backwards; but all with the same calm will and equal way —no contraction, no extension; one soundless, causeless march of sequent rings, a spectral procession of spotted dust, with dissolution in its fangs, dislocation in its coils. Startle it: the winding stream will become a twisted arrow; the wave of poisoned life will lash through the grass like a cast lance.

The Serpent's Tongue

by W. H. HUDSON

"BUT NOW," SAYS RUSKIN, "HERE'S THE FIRST THING, IT seems to me, we've got to ask the scientific people what use a serpent has for its tongue, since it neither works it to talk with, or taste with, or hiss with, nor, as far as I know, to lick with, and, least of all, to sting with— and yet, for people who do not know the creature, the little vibrating

forked thread, flicked out of its mouth and back again, as quick as lightning, is the most striking part of the beast; but what is the use of it?
Nearly every creature but a snake can do some sort of mischief with its
tongue. A woman worries with it, a chameleon catches flies with it, a cat
steals milk with it, a pholas digs holes in the rock with it, and a gnat digs
holes in *us* with it; but the poor snake cannot do any manner of harm
with it whatsoever; and what is *his* tongue forked for?"

The writer's manner in this paragraph, and the unexpectedness of the
mocking question that leaps out at the end, suggests the idea that there
are, in man, two sorts of forked tongues, and that one sort is not worked
for mischief. Certainly few of these "vibrating forked threads" in literature have flickered more startlingly, like forked lightning, and to the purpose, than Ruskin's own. The passage is admirable, both in form and
essence; it shines even in that brilliant lecture on *Living Waves* from
which it is taken, and where there are very many fine things, along with
others indifferent, and a few that are bad. But there is this fault to be
found with it: after putting his question to the "scientific people," the
questioner assumes that no answer is possible; that the stinging and hissing and licking theories have been discarded, the serpent's tongue can
do no manner of mischief, and is quite useless. A most improbable conclusion, since the fact stares us in the face that the serpent does use its
tongue; for instance, it exserts and makes it vibrate rapidly, but why it
does so remains to be known. It is true that in the long life of a species an
organ does sometimes lose its use without dwindling away, but persists
as a mere idle appendage: it is, however, very unlikely that this has happened in the case of the serpent's tongue; the excitability and extreme
activity at times of that organ rather incline one to the opinion that it has
only changed its original use for a new one, as has happened in the case
of some of the creatures mentioned in the passage quoted above.

"A chameleon," says Ruskin, "catches flies with its tongue," inferring
that the snake has no such accomplishment. Yet the contrary has been
often maintained. "The principal use of the tongue," says Lacepede in his
Natural History of Serpents, "is to catch insects, which it catches by
means of its double tongue." This notion about the use of the double
tongue is quite common among the older ophiologists, and, along with it,
the belief that snakes prey chiefly on insects. And here I cannot resist the
temptation to quote a few more words touching on this point from Lacepede—a very perfect example of the teleological spirit in science which
flourished a century ago, and made things easy for the naturalist. "We are
not," he says, "to be amazed at the vast number of serpents, both species
and individuals, which inhabit the intertropical countries. There they
find the degree of warmth which seems congenial to their natures, and
the smaller species find abundance of insects to serve them for food. In
those torrid regions, where Nature has produced an infinite multitude of
insects and worms, she has likewise produced the greatest number of

serpents to destroy the worms and insects; which otherwise would multiply so exceedingly as to destroy all vegetable productions, and to reduce the most fertile regions of the earth into barren deserts, inaccessible to man and animals; nay, even these noxious and troublesome insects would be finally obliged to destroy each other, and nothing would remain but their mangled limbs."

Here the French naturalist pauses, aghast at the frightful picture of desolation he has himself conjured up.

When enumerating the uses to which a serpent does *not* put its tongue, Ruskin might very well have said that it is not used as a tactile organ. That it is a tactile organ is a very modern supposition—a small hypothesis about a small matter, but with a curious and rather amusing history. It was in the first place given out merely as a conjecture, but no sooner given than accepted as an irrefragable fact by some of the greatest authorities among us. Thus Dr. Günther, in his article on snakes in the *Encyclopædia Britannica,* ninth edition, says, "The tongue is exserted for the purpose of feeling some object, and sometimes under the influence of anger or fear."

Doubtless those who invented this use for the organ were misled by observing snakes in captivity, in the glass cases or cages in which it is usual to keep them; observing them in such conditions, it was easy to fall into the mistake, since the serpent, when moving, is frequently seen to thrust his tongue against the obstructing glass. It should be remembered that glass *is* glass, a substance that does not exist in nature; that a long and sometimes painful experience is necessary before even the most intelligent among the lower animals are brought to understand its character; and, finally, that the delicate, sensitive tongue comes against it for the same reason that the fly buzzes and the confined wild bird dashes itself against it in their efforts to escape. In a state of nature when the snake is approached, whether by its prey or by some large animal, the tongue is obtruded; again, when it is cautiously progressing through the herbage, even when unalarmed, the tongue is exserted at frequent intervals; but I can say, after long experience of snakes, that the exserted organ never touches earth, or rock, or leaf, or anything whatsoever, consequently that it is not a tactile organ.

Another suggestion, less improbable on the face of it than the one just cited, is that the tongue, without touching anything, may, in some way not yet known to us, serve as an organ of intelligence. The serpent's senses are defective; now when, in the presence of a strange object or animal, the creature protrudes its long slender tongue—not to *feel* the object, as has been shown—does it not do so to *test* the air, to catch an emanation from the object which might in some unknown way convey to the brain its character, whether animate or inanimate, cold or warm blooded, bird, beast, or reptile, also its size, etc.? The structure of the organ itself does not give support to this supposition; it could not *taste* an emanation without some such organs as are found in the wonderfully formed antennae of insects, and with these it is not provided.

Only by means of a sensitiveness to air waves and vibrations from other living bodies near it, in degree infinitely more delicate than that of the bat's wing—the so-called sixth sense of that animal—could the serpent's tongue serve as an organ of intelligence. Here, again, the structure of the tongue is against such an hypothesis; and if the structure were different it would only remain to be said that the instrument performs its work very badly.

Another explanation which has been put forward by two well-known writers on serpent life, Dr. Stradling and Miss Hopley, remains to be noticed. These observers came independently to the conclusion that the snake makes use of his tongue as a decoy to attract its prey.

In the case of one of these writers, the idea was suggested by an incident in our Zoological Gardens. A fowl was placed in a boa's cage to be eaten, and immediately began hunting about for food on the floor of the cage; the serpent—apparently seen merely as an inanimate object—protruded its tongue, whereupon the fowl rushed and pecked at it, mistaking it for a wriggling worm. Such a thing could not well happen in a state of nature. The tongue may resemble a wriggling worm, or, when vibrated very quickly, a fluttering moth; but we cannot assume that the serpent, however motionless it may lie, however in its colour and pattern it may assimilate to its surroundings, is not recognised as a separate and living thing by a bird or any other wild animal.

From the foregoing it will be seen that so far from being silent on this subject, as Ruskin imagined, the "scientific people" have found out or invented a variety of uses for the serpent's tongue. By turns it has been spoken of as an insect-catching organ, a decoy, a tactile organ, and, in some mysterious way, an organ of intelligence. And, after all, it is none of these things, and the way is still open for fresh speculation.

I have on numberless occasions observed the common pit-viper of southern South America, which is of a sluggish disposition, lying in the sun on a bed of sand or dry grass, coiled or extended at full length. Invariably, on approaching a snake of this kind, I have seen the tongue exserted; that nimble, glistening organ was the first, and for some time the only sign of life or wakefulness in the motionless creature. If I stood still at a distance of some yards to watch it, the tongue would be exserted again at intervals; if I moved nearer, or lifted my arms, or made any movement, the intervals would be shorter and the vibrations more rapid, and still the creature would not move. Only when I drew very near would other signs of excitement follow. At such times the tongue has scarcely seemed to me the "mute forked flash" that Ruskin calls it, but a tongue that said something, which although not audible, was clearly understood and easy to translate into words. What it said or appeared to say was: "I am not dead nor sleeping, and I do not wish to be disturbed, much less

trodden upon; keep your distance, for your own good as well as for mine."
In other words, the tongue was obtruded and vibrated with a *warning*
purpose.

Doubtless every venomous serpent of sluggish habits has more ways
than one of making itself conspicuous to and warning off any large heavy
animal that might injure by passing over and treading on it; and I think
that in ophidians of this temper the tongue has become, incidentally, a
warning organ. Small as it is, its obtrusion is the first of a series of warning motions, and may therefore be considered advantageous to the animal; and, in spite of its smallness, I believe that in very many instances
it accomplishes its purpose without the aid of those larger and violent
movements and actions resorted to when the danger becomes pressing.

All large animals, including man, when walking on an open space, see
the ground before them, with every object on it, even when the head is
raised and when the animal's attention is principally directed to something in the distance. The motions of the legs, the exact measurement of
every slight obstruction and object in the way—hillocks, depressions in
the soil, stones, pebbles, sticks, etc.—are almost automatic; the puma
may have nothing but his far-seen quarry in his mind, and the philosopher be thinking only of the stars, as they move, both quite unconscious
of what their feet are doing; but the ground must be seen all the same,
otherwise they could not go smoothly even over a comparatively smooth
surface.

When the man or other animal progressing in this ordinary way comes
to where a serpent, with a protective or assimilative colour and appearance, lies motionless in the path, he certainly sees it, but without distin-
guishing it as a serpent. The vari-coloured surface it rests on and with
which it is in harmony is motionless, consequently without animal life
and safe to tread on—a rough flooring composed of mould, pebbles and
sand, dead and green herbage, withered leaves, twisted vines, and sticks
warped by the sun, brown and grey and mottled. But if the smallest
thing moves on that still surface, if a blade trembles, or a minute insect
flutters or flies up, the vision is instantly attracted to the spot and concentrated on a small area, and as by a flash every object on it is clearly
seen, and its character recognised. Those who have been accustomed to
walk much in dry, open places, in districts where snakes are abundant,
have often marvelled at the instantaneous manner in which something
that had been previously seen as a mere strip or patch of dull colour on
the mottled earth, as a part of its indeterminate pattern, has taken the
serpent form. And when once it has been recognised as a serpent it is
seen so vividly and in such sharp contrast to its surroundings as to appear
the most conspicuous and unmistakable object in nature. Why, in such
cases, they ask in astonishment, did they not recognise its character
sooner? I believe that in such cases it is the suddenly exserted, glistening,

vibrating tongue that first attracts the eye to the dangerous spot and reveals the serpent to the mind.

This warning character is, I believe, as has already been intimated, an incidental use of the tongue, probably confined, or at all events most advantageous to the vipers and to other venomous serpents of lethargic habits. In the case of the extremely active, non-venomous snake, that glides away into hiding on the slightest alarm, the tongue would be of little use or no value as a warning organ. Between a snake of this kind and the slumberous pit-viper the difference in habit is extreme. But at bottom, all ground snakes are alike in disposition—all hate to be disturbed, and move only when necessity drives; and we can imagine that when the tremendous weapon of a lethal tooth had been acquired, when experience began to teach the larger mammalians to view the serpentine form with suspicion and to avoid it, the use of the tongue as a warning would react on the serpent, making it more and more lethargic in habit—as inactive, in fact, as every snake loves to be.

There is, I imagine, another and more important use of the tongue, older than its warning use, although this may date back in time to the Miocene period, when the viperine form existed—a use of the tongue common to all ophidians that possess the habit of exserting and vibrating that organ when excited. The subject is somewhat complicated, for we have not only to consider the tongue, but the whole creature of which the tongue is so small a part; its singularity and anomalous position in nature, and the many and diverse ways in which the animals it preys on are affected by its appearance. Furthermore, I have now in my mind two separate functions, the first of which occasionally, perhaps often, passes into and becomes one with the other.

When the common or ring snake pursues a frog, the chase would in most cases prove a very vain one but for that fatal weakness in the hunted animal, which quickly brings its superior activity to naught. The snake need not even be seen for the effect to be produced, as any one can prove for himself by pushing his walking-stick, snake-wise, through the grass and causing it to follow up the frog's motions, whereupon, after some futile efforts to escape, the creature collapses, and stretching out its forefeet like arms that implore mercy, emits a series of piteous, wailing screams. Thus, all that is necessary for this end to be reached is that the frog should be conscious of something, no matter what, pushing after it through the grass. There is here, apart from the question in animal psychology, a little mystery involved; for how comes it that in the course of the countless generations during which the snake has preyed on the frog, this peculiar weakness has not been eliminated by means of the continual destruction of the individuals most subject to it, and, on the other hand, the preservation of all those possessing it in a less degree, or not at all? It is hard for a good Darwinian to believe that the frog is excessively prolific for the snake's advantage rather than for its own. But this question need not detain us; there are vulnerable spots and weak joints in the defensive armour of all animals. What I wish to draw attention to is the fact that, speaking metaphorically, the serpent, of all creatures that kill their own meat, is the most *unsportsmanlike* in its methods, that is has found out and subtly taken advantage of the most secret and unsuspected weaknesses of the animals on which it preys.

We have seen how the common snake catches the frog; but frogs are found only in wet places, and snakes abound everywhere, and the sedentary snake of the dry uplands must feed on the nimble rodent, volatile bird, and elusive lizard. How does he manage to catch them? For considering how alert and quick-sighted these small hunted creatures are, it must, I think, be assumed that the snake cannot, except in rare instances, approach them unseen and take them unawares. I believe that in many cases the snake succeeds by approaching its intended victim while appearing to be stationary. This stratagem is not confined to the ophidians: in a somewhat different form it is found in a great variety of animals. Perhaps the most familiar example is afforded by the widely distributed hunting-spider. The plan followed by this spider, on a smooth surface where it cannot hide its form, is to advance boldly towards its prey, and when the fly, who has been suspiciously watching its approach, is about to dart away, to become motionless. This appears to excite the fly's curiosity, and he does not take flight; but very soon his restive spirit returns, he moves about this way and that, to see all round him, and each time he turns his bright eyes away the spider rapidly moves a little nearer; but when the fly looks again, appears motionless as before. In this way, little by little, the space is lessened, and yet the fly, still turning at intervals to regard the suspicious-looking object, does not make his escape, simply because he does not know that the space has been lessened. Seeing the spider always motionless the illusion is produced that it has not moved: the dividing distance has been accurately measured once for all, and no second act of judgement is required; the fly, knowing his own quickness and volatile powers, feels himself perfectly safe; and this goes on until by chance he detects the motion and instantly flies away, or else fails to detect it and is caught. Cats often succeed in capturing birds by a similar stratagem.

The snake, unlike the spider and cat, cannot make the final spring and rush, but must glide up to within striking distance: this he is able to do by means of the faculty he possesses of progressing so gradually and evenly as to appear almost motionless; the tongue which he exserts and rapidly vibrates at intervals when approaching his victim helps in producing the deception.

Long observation has convinced me that a snake on the ground, moving or resting, is not a sight that violently excites birds, as they are excited by the appearance of a fox, cat, weasel, hawk, or any other creature whose enmity is well known to them. I have frequently seen little birds running

about and feeding on the ground within a few feet of a snake lying conspicuously in their sight; furthermore, I have been convinced on such
occasions that the birds knew the snake was there, having observed them
raise their heads at intervals, regard the reptile for a few moments attentively, then go on seeking food. This shows that birds do sometimes
come near snakes and see them with little or no fear, but probably with
some slight suspicion and a great deal of curiosity, on account of the
singularity of their appearance, their resemblance to vegetable rather
than to animal forms of life, and, above all, to their strange manner of
progression. Now the bird, or lizard, or small mammal, thus brought by
chance near to a hungry, watchful snake, once it begins to regard the
snake curiously, is in imminent danger of destruction in one of two ways,
or by a combination of both: in the first case it may be deluded as to the
distance of the suspicious-looking object and in the end seized, just as the
fly is seized by the salticus spider, before it can make its escape; secondly,
it may, while regarding its singular enemy, be thrown into a trance or
convulsive fit and so rendered powerless to escape, or it may even be
moved to cast itself into the open jaws of the snake. In either case, the
serpent's tongue would, I believe, play a very important part. In a case
of the first kind the snake would approach its intended victim so slowly
and continuously as almost to appear not to be moving; still, in most
cases the movement probably would be detected but for the tongue, which
attracts the eye by its eccentric motions, its sudden successive appearances and disappearances; watching the tongue, the long, sinuous body
slowly gliding over the intervening space would not be observed; only the
statuesque raised head and neck would be visible, and these would appear not to move. The snake's action in such a case would resemble the
photographer's trick to make a restive child sit still while its picture is
being taken by directing its attention to some curious object, or by causing a pocket-handkerchief to flutter above the camera.

Snakes have been observed to steal upon their victims in this quiet,
subtle manner; the victim, bird or lizard, has been observed to continue
motionless in a watchful attitude, as if ready to dart away, but still attentively regarding the gradually approaching head and flickering tongue;
and in the end, by a sudden, quick-darting motion on the part of the snake,
the capture has been effected. Cases of this description are usually set
down to "fascination," which I think is a mistake.

Fascination is a fine old word, which has done good service and has
had a long day and happily outlived its evil repute: but it had its faults at
the best of times; it originally expressed things purely human, and therefore did not exactly fit things serpentine, and was, to some extent, mis-
leading. What its future history—in science—will be cannot be guessed.
In France it has been used to describe a mild form of hypnotism induced
by the contemplation of a bright spot, and no doubt there would be a
certain propriety in applying the word to the soothing somnolent effect

produced on the human subject by the revolving mirror invented by Dr. Luys. But this is not the form we are concerned with. Fascination in serpent life is something very different; in the present state of knowledge on the subject the old word cannot be discarded. We are now in possession of a very large number of well-authenticated cases of undoubted fascination in which the victims are seen to act in a variety of ways, but all alike exhibit very keen distress. The animal that falls under the spell appears to be conscious of his loss of power, as in the case of the frog pursued by the ring-snake. He is thrown into violent convulsions, or trembles, or screams, or struggles to escape, and sometimes rushes in terror away only to return again, perhaps in the end to jump into the serpent's jaws. A brother of mine once observed a pipit running with flutterings round and round a coiled snake, uttering distressed chirps and cries; the snake, vibrating its tongue, moved its head round to follow the motions of the bird. This is a common form—the desire and vain striving to escape. But when an animal is seen to remain motionless, showing no signs of distress or fear, attentively regarding the gradually approaching snake, such a case cannot, I think, be safely set down to fascination, nor to anything more out of the common than curiosity, and, as in the case of the volatile, sprightly fly and terrestrial spider, to the illusion produced in the victim's mind that the suspicious-looking object is stationary.

Concerning the use, here suggested, of the tongue in fascination, I can scarcely expect that those whose knowledge of the snake is derived from books, from specimens in museums, and from seeing the animal alive in confinement, will regard it as anything more than an improbable supposition, unsupported by facts. But to those who have attentively observed the creature in a state of nature, and have been drawn to it by, and wondered at, its strangeness, the explanation, I venture to think, will not seem improbable. To weigh, count, measure, and dissect for purposes of identification, classification, and what not, and to search in bones and tissues for hidden affinities, it is necessary to see closely; but this close seeing would be out of place and a hindrance in other lines of inquiry. To know the creature, undivested of life or liberty or of anything belonging to it, it must be seen with an atmosphere, in the midst of the nature in which it harmoniously moves and has its being, and the image it casts on the observer's retina and mind must be identical with its image in the eye and mind of the other wild creatures that share the earth with it. It is not here maintained that the tongue is everything, nor that it is the principal agent in fascination, but only that it is a necessary part of the creature, and of the creature's strangeness, which is able to produce so great and wonderful an effect. The long, limbless body, lithely and mysteriously gliding on the surface; the glittering scales and curious mottlings, bright or lurid; the statuesque, arrowy head, sharp-cut and immovable; the round lidless eyes, fixed and brilliant; and the long, bifurcated tongue, shining black or crimson, with its fantastic flickering play before the close-shut, lipless mouth—that is the serpent, and probably no single detail in the fateful creature's appearance could be omitted and the effect of its presence on other animals be the same.

The Serpent's World

by RAYMOND L. DITMARS

A LITHE BLACK FORM IS STRETCHED UPON THE TOP OF an old stone wall. The long and slender body lies in slightly suggested undulations. It appears tense and yet again soft and pliant as its outline follows the slightly uneven surface of the stones. Its hue is really blue-black and it glows with the luster of a new gun-barrel. The effect upon the average observer is three-fold. The thing is startling, it is decorative, and it is wholly incongruous—this vivid form so bold in contrast to its surroundings. The head quivers slightly. If the observer's eyes are keen this is seen to be caused by the rapid darting of a forked tongue. Then the black object appears to flow over the opposite side of the wall. There is a rustling murmur among dried leaves—a hissing-scrape—the sound so characteristic of a rapidly moving snake, and the thing is gone.

Thus we meet the blacksnake, an inoffensive type and a useful one, but startling, nevertheless, unless one has some knowledge of serpent life.

The supposition may be that such creatures are aimless wanderers, to be thus encountered now and then; that they crawl into some hole to pass the winter and emerge the coming year to prowl again and bob up in un-expected places.

Summing up the life history of the average blacksnake produces an interesting picture. It gives an idea of snakes generally. The serpent is lifted from the thought of a mere gliding thing in the grass and assumes individuality among the legions of animal life.

To begin with, the blacksnake is hatched from an egg. Some snakes are viviparous and produce living young and others are oviparous; that is, they lay eggs. The egg-laying kinds exceed the others in number, but not by a great majority. But to return to the origin of the blacksnake.

A female blacksnake has been steadily searching for a suitable hollow under a large flat stone. She is seeking a stone thick enough to absorb the sun's rays and retain considerable of this heat during the night. The stone must also be thick enough not to pass too great an amount of heat directly through it to the ground. The hollow beneath must be in ground or debris soft enough to be readily shoved about with her body in forming a nest for her eggs. The ground must be moderately damp. The rock should be on a hillside. While moderate dampness is sought the ground should be well drained. A part of the necessary moisture needed to develop the eggs will come from condensation beneath the rock during the night. With these requirements to be met the search for a suitable place will take a number of days. The time is invariably during the very early summer.

Finding the proper place the female serpent crawls beneath the rock and from the center shoves the earth outward with folds of her body. A circular or ovoid area is hollowed, with protective, sharply sloping sides and within this the eggs are laid to the number of one to two dozen. They are creamy white with a pliable, but tough covering. In form and size they are not unlike the eggs of the smaller birds. They are a bit more cylindrical perhaps, but this does not hold good with all snake eggs. Their chief difference is the pliable shell, like very thin leather.

The female blacksnake takes no further interest in her eggs, and has no further thought of her future young. She goes her way.

The eggs actually grow. They absorb moisture and from the threadlike embryos the infant serpents within them increase in size until they are tightly packed within the eggs which have increased a third in diameter and may become lumpy and irregular in outline. A sharp point upon each infant's snout has developed—the "egg tooth"—this used to slit the shell and escape. The period of incubation has covered about eight weeks.

Emerging from the eggs the little serpents stay close by their nest for a day or so. They are quite unlike the parent, being gray, with large brown blotches. Within a week they are eating insect larvae, possibly young grasshoppers. This is very different food from that which they will seek when they have grown a few inches, but that is the way with all very young snakes, the early feeding habits of many of which remain a mystery.

Growth is rapid. They increase to twice their size by Autumn, but remain quite unlike the parent in retaining their gray coat, although the brownish blotches are becoming darker. With the tang of chilling nights the inclination is to seek a deep fissure among the rocks and once it is found not to wander far away from it during the day. This is to be the winter shelter. The young serpent has already explored it—gone deeply into it. Whether or not that force called instinct prompts the reptile to realize that the fissure is deep enough to shelter it from penetration from frost, is a question. Certain it is that its investigation leads it to shelter safe from that curious point on the thermometer we call "thirty-two" if the scale be Fahrenheit, or "zero" at Centigrade. That is a fateful point in the decrease of temperature for most snakes. They can endure, while benumbed and motionless in hibernation, a temperature of close to freezing, but at or below that point where water freezes they are likely to be killed.

Well before the first slight frosts the little serpents of the brood are safely stowed away. Possibly a few have found the same crevice. They are sleek and fat and as during the winter sleep animation is practically suspended, they will emerge in much the same condition with the spring. Their next year's hibernation will be under quite different conditions. Not far from where they are lies the parent's den and they will find it. A few of them may have already found it.

From this point we will select the story of an individual. Possibly the story of the snake noted on the stone wall. Spring has warmed the ledgy bank and a young serpent issues from the hibernating crevice. It lurks near the sheltering fissure during the fickle weather of late April and early May then starts afield possibly reconnoitering along the borders of a marsh—for last year's frogs, developing during the summer from tadpoles, form ideal food for a snake of this size. There is a brief rest, hiding in a pile of loose stones as the serpent's lidless eyes are becoming dim with the thickening of the old skin. The eyes become white, like bubbles filled with smoke. Then they clear as an oily secretion forms under the old epidermis loosening it over the entire body.

The snake pushes the loose skin back over the upper jaw and lower jaw by rubbing among the rocks, then crawling forth catches the moist, tissue-like garment in the stubble and slowly crawls out of it, turning it wrongside out the entire length of the body clear to the tip of the tail. Right at the point where the skin is being turned backward there is a slight writhing of the scaly sides of the body—a contracting to the rear, where the old epidermis is still encased and a muscular expanding forward of this. The skin slips backward and delicate as it is there is not a tear. It is an exquisite job, skillfully and slowly performed. It may take a full half hour. But there is a snake-skin in the grass! The whole garment is inverted. The integument that has covered the jaws gapes open and on the head-parts are the coverings of the lidless eyes like miniature, strongly concave lenses.

This early summer shedding is an event. The slim young creature glistens like new satin. It is a darker gray. The spots are fainter and will be gone after the next shedding. Wild mice are to be hunted in the nests, very young examples that are easily swallowed. With the assimilation of such prey growth is speeded. By late summer the young reptile is over two feet long and close to matching the lustrous blue-black of the parent. Only the abdominal parts are lighter—a pale, slaty gray.

A chill is again descending upon the woods at night. This is particularly apparent when the nights are still—when no breeze is stirring. On such nights there is a very heavy dew bringing into sharp evidence the webs of spiders which spin in the grass. At the very beginning of this period the blacksnake has turned its nose "homeward." But what is home? This means the parent's den. And here the snake is guided by an influence as remarkable and inexorably systematic as the autumnal migration of birds.

It may be two miles from the den when the seasons start to turn. Separating it from its goal may be marshes, undulating brooks, labyrinths of stone and tangles of vegetation. The force which appears to guide it is sense of direction. What else could there be? The topography of the ground produces hills and canyons. The vegetation is the equivalent to sightless jungle. The rocks present mazes of passages, but the serpent steadily works toward the den where its parents have hibernated for years, where their ancestors have hibernated, and their ancestors back for hundreds, and possibly much longer periods of years. The den of the adults is a specific spot—a ledge on a wild hillside, usually facing south. The whole side of the hill or mountain may be ledgy, but in that expanse of rock there is some spot where a fissure, or series of fissures lead a great distance inward and downward. The snakes found it ages ago. I have wandered over a whole mountainside and seldom found more than one den. The serpents that prowl the area for a mile or more know that spot and return to it each fall for shelter from *cold*. That word signifies the turning point in a snake's existence. Activity is influenced by the temperature of environmental air. The serpent's normal blood temperature is usually one degree lower than that of the air. A temperature of seventy to ninety is best conducive to its vivacity. Below seventy it slows down. At fifty it is nearly helpless. At forty it shows bare signs of life. Above ninety it seeks cooler shelter, undergrowth or damp ground where evaporation produces a lower temperature at the immediate surface. Even the serpents of the tropics avoid open places in the full glare of sun and desert types are averse to venturing abroad during the day unless scattered patches of vegetation offer close-lying oases of shelter from the heat.

So guided from the plight of exposure to cold the serpent starts for the den with the Autumn. It may linger at times through areas which I call "transient rocks."

These are large masses of stone retaining considerable heat from the sun as the night comes on. In such places, which are usually good feeding grounds, the snake may hesitate during a period of "Indian Summer," but moves on again after a shock or two from cool nights, warning it of frosts not far away.

A typical den is on the southerly slope of a hill or mountain of ledgy character. There may be a precipitous face of rock and at the bottom a jumbled mass of great fragments weighing tons. The spot denotes cataclysmic forces in action in dim ages past. Such forces have shattered the face of the cliff and among these shattered portions is a crevice at the bottom, or there may be several adjacent crevices. These form the den. The area is secluded and tangled. Wild grape writhes its way among the rocks. Numerous struggling trees have sought root wherever they could. "The crevice," however, is usually adjacent to a platform of broken stones or open patch, or patches, where in the spring the serpents emerge and in clusters lie intoxicated with the return of the life-giving sun with its temperature so necessary for their activity.

The blacksnake finds the hibernating lair of its parents and ancestors, ascending the slope past the first hibernating crevice of its early youth, where now with its stouter body it could barely squeeze in. It glides through the tangle of grape and woodbine to find other members of its kind, and still others of the serpent clan very different from itself. There are copperheads and rattlers on the shelf of the ledge, coiled tightly in precise circular fashion as is the way of these fanged species, each with a symmetrical, and lateral loop of the neck laid flat upon its coils ready for a lunge of the head. The blacksnake may glide directly over some of these forms, but there is never a move on the part of the poisonous members, seldom as much as a tongue flash. The serpent clan is particularly tolerant or passive about the changing of position, arrival or departure of other members unless such are of the attacking or cannibal types and in the northerly areas of the blacksnake's range there are no such disturbing enemies. The blacksnake is alleged to attack the rattler, but he does nothing of the kind. He may eat an occasional young garter or ribbon snake, but he never battles with the rattler. He has no means of fighting such a powerful snake. Despite the scientific name constrictor, the black-snake is not a constrictor. The title was applied to him years past by Linnaeus, in times when the respective habits of serpents were but vaguely noted.

So the rattlers, copperheads, and blacksnakes go into the den together in fine fraternity. I have seen bevies of heads of the three kinds peering from the crevices in spring when they had been lured by the warming ground to peek out, but were not inclined to venture forth as yet.

Such is the typical mountain den. Other kinds of serpents are not so keen about the higher ledges. The big mountain blacksnake, a slower and much heavier serpent than the racer occasionally takes advantage of such dens, but prefers sheltering deep in some disintegrating hollow of a big tree where the rotting debris is safe from freezing temperature. The striped snake and water snake prefer crevices in shaly banks close to streams.

During May the ledge-dens are populous with the emerged members— on certain days. These are times when the air is still and shade temperature along the ledge is close to seventy. As the ledge usually faces south and is in a great sheltered pocket of the mountain—for we have noted how par-ticular the serpents are in selecting this spot—the ledge area is warmer than the outside open country.

May is the breeding season. It is the only breeding period throughout the warm months. During this time of the year occasional blacksnakes, of either sex may deliberately attack a human intruder upon the ledge. I have had them follow me twenty-five feet or more and make long sweeping strikes as high as my knees. Possibly one in twenty individuals will do this. The others skim over the rocks in flight with a grace and speed that invariably causes me to ponder just how they do it. I have never noted a rattler or copperhead indicate any hint of actually attacking a human, as does the harmless member of the ledge clan.

There is no thought of eating among any of the serpents on the ledge until the mating period is over. By the end of May the exodus into surrounding woods and meadows where food is numerous is well under way. There is an outward stop at the transient rocks, then the clan radiates out in all directions. A favorite path of exploration is, oddly enough, provided by their greatest enemy—man. This is the old stone wall with its sheltering labyrinth of passageways and offering good hunting for the smaller rodents.

By mid-June, if the season is normally warm the average den is deserted. Selected as it is to get every benefit of the Spring sun the rocks are too hot for the snakes. On mountains running to a flat top and with numerous shelving rocks sun-sheltered by brush, some of the rattlers may remain not far from the den if hunting is good and water is available. Around the greater number of dens, however, one may look for days during the summer and see not the sign of a snake. The clan is scouting far afield and some may be as much as two miles away.

In a way, such habits apply to all serpents. They are not aimless wanderers. They live in little worlds of their own. Even in the mild winters of southern Florida, where hibernation is short and there may be practically no frost, I have noted that the great diamond rattler, found singly, here and there the greater part of the year, has its favorite spots to congregate in moderate numbers during the cool season. There are no extensive dens, but every rattler has its homing spot and six or eight may gather here each fall. The favorite sheltering place is under the roots of a great pine, which, standing well out of the soil at the base of the tree, offer cave-like shelters beneath, these extensively hollowed out by some burrowing mammal, or possibly a big gopher tortoise. The tropical serpents have similar places. And with them the shelter may be utilized in avoiding undue heat instead of the benumbing touch of lowering temperature avoided by their northern allies. The roots of sage brush or fissured rocks form dens for the desert kinds. But all of them have specific places to which they regularly return, which places are the mating grounds. Summer wanderings are directly guided by two necessities—food and water.

The Snake in the Stomach

by HENRY D. THOREAU

AH, THE VERY BROOKS SEEM FULLER OF REFLECTIONS than they were! Ah, such provoking sibylline sentences they are! The shallowest is all at once unfathomable. How can that depth be fathomed where a man may see himself reflected? The rill I stopped to drink at I drink in more than I expected. I satisfy and still provoke the thirst of thirsts. Nut Meadow Brook where it crosses the road beyond Jenny Dugan's that was. I do not drink in vain. I mark that brook as if I had swallowed a water snake that would live in my stomach. I have swallowed something worth the while. The day is not what it was before I stooped to drink. Ah, I shall hear from that draught! It is not in vain that I have drunk. I have drunk an arrowhead. It flows from where all fountains rise.

How many ova have I swallowed? Who knows what will be hatched within me? There were some seeds of thought, methinks, floating in that water, which are expanding in me. The man must not drink of the running streams, the living waters, who is not prepared to have all nature reborn in him,—to suckle monsters. The snake in my stomach lifts his head to my mouth at the sound of running water. When was it that I swallowed a snake? I have got rid of the snake in my stomach. I drank of stagnant waters once. That accounts for it. I caught him by the throat and drew him out, and had a well day after all. Is there not such a thing as getting rid of the snake which you have swallowed when young, when thoughtless you stooped and drank at stagnant waters, which has worried you in your waking hours and in your sleep ever since, and appropriated the life that was yours? Will he not ascend into your mouth at the sound of running water? Then catch him boldly by the head and draw him out, though you may think his tail be curled about your vitals.

(Aug. 17, 1851)

Snake Myths Smashed by Science

by C. B. PERKINS

SOME SNAKES WILL CHASE HUMAN BEINGS. ALL REPTILES that have eyes with elliptically shaped pupils are poisonous. Certain snakes can milk cows, swallow their young, roll along the ground like barrel loops, or even outdistance a race horse.

At one time or another, every one has heard one or more of these statements made. Some persons say with all sincerity that they have actually seen one of these reptilian phenomena occur—"with my own eyes." Constant repetition has led many to accept these snake stories as established fact.

But are any of them actually true, or are they all mere legends and misconceptions?

To provide a straightforward, and fully reliable reply to this query, the editors of POPULAR SCIENCE MONTHLY put the most widespread of these snake stories up to C. B. Perkins, curator of reptiles at the San Diego, Calif., zoo. For more than thirty years he has been a close student of the habits of snakes of all species, from diamond-back rattlers and giant boa constrictors to tiny six-inch worm snakes. Here are his answers.

Do snakes sometimes swallow their young to protect them from attack?

A hungry king snake might eat the young of another snake, but for breakfast, not for the little ones' protection. If you happened along at about that time and observed the process, the evidence "before your very eyes" might convince you that the snake was swallowing its offspring for fear that you would attack them. Or if you met a female rattlesnake and beat it to death with a club, fearing that it was about to strike, you might force out some unborn young. In the excitement, you might conclude that the youngsters emerged from the rattler's stomach. You'd be wrong. Snakes do not swallow their young to protect them.

Is it a stinger that a snake thrusts out of its mouth and waves around? Can any snake sting or poison its prey with its pointed tail?

That forked ribbon which emerges from a snake's mouth, sometimes with rapier-like thrusts, is nothing more nor less than a tongue. It is not an instrument of either aggression or defense. It carries no poison, and its touch is so delicate that you cannot feel it against the palm of your hand, although you might feel it against the back, since the hairs there are more sensitive than your bare palm. Snakes inject poison with their fangs, not their tongues. A rattlesnake will, when angry, project its tongue perhaps two inches, waving it excitedly up and down. In fact, a rattler may betray nervousness and excitement by waving its tongue some time before it begins to sound its better-known and more ominous warning. No, snake tongues are harmless, and so are snake tails. The tails of more than one species do end in a conical scale, coming to a point that closely resembles a "stinger." The bull snake is one example. Hunters have reported squeezing the tails of reptiles killed along the trail until "a stinger like that of the velvet ant or a bee appeared." Their observation was correct, but their conclusion faulty. They saw a conical scale, not a stinger.

Are there any nonpoisonous snakes in this country that are dangerous because of their great size?

No. The largest varieties are the bull snake, also known by many other names, and the indigo, a mild-tempered serpent found in the Southeast. If any of these fellows is near enough to you and ready to bite, you may as well stand and take it, for he'll probably get you anyway. The bite is like several pin scratches. A little iodine over the spot will prevent any infection.

Do racers sometimes use their bodies to whip persons who catch them?

This yarn probably started with some one who once caught a whip snake, or racer. While he held it, the snake undoubtedly twisted and writhed, throwing itself into a frenzy of movement, and its tail struck against the captor's legs or body. But not severely. Were I literally to whip you with a snake, the snake would die. Racers are not in the habit of thus committing suicide. You may be sure that when a snake whips a man, it hurts the snake more than it does the human victim.

Is there any rule for telling whether a particular snake is deadly?
It has often been said that all snakes born alive are poisonous, and all snakes hatched from eggs are nonpoisonous.

Well, the garter snake is born alive and is completely harmless. And the coral snake hatches from an egg and he's poisonous. You can't be sure even from the appearance of a snake whether it is poisonous or not. Small neck and large head do not necessarily connote poison, as some people believe. Some snakes having eyes with elliptically shaped pupils are only mildly poisonous, such as the lyre snake found in Texas, Utah, Nevada, Arizona, and California. Pit vipers—moccasins, rattlers, and copperheads—have elliptical pupils and are very poisonous. The coral snake has round pupils and is poisonous, but the round-pupiled boa is not. Ordinarily, the whirring rattle identifies the rattler, but the sound might come from some harmless snake moving among dry leaves. Again, a rattler may have lost its rattles by accident, and therefore make no warning sound. This loss, however, makes it no less dangerous. No, the best advice I can give is to study the poisonous reptiles inhabiting your locality by observing them in a zoo.

Do snakes ever chase human beings, or attack them without provocation?

Unless cornered, no snake in this country is aggressive, and all will attempt to escape. Even the rattlesnake strikes only in self-defense. Once I happened on a blow snake, heard it hissing, and because it was the mating season, I advanced slowly, hoping to observe a pair mating in the wild. Several times, as I moved forward, the snake started toward me, but when I retreated the reptile halted. Not once did it advance after I had moved away to what the reptile apparently considered a safe distance. An inexperienced observer might consider this snake's actions an attack, but it was only a vigorous defense.

What about "hoop snakes" that take their tails in their mouths and roll rapidly along the ground? Are they fact or fiction?

Fiction, although reports of the appearance of hoop snakes have some slight background of fact. In the southeastern United States there are two kinds of burrowing mud snakes. They are seldom seen, but occasionally freshets wash them out of mud banks into near-by meadows. The reptiles tend to form circles as they lie there in the shallow water. Barring their color, they then resemble the inner tube of a bicycle tire. Here fact ends and fiction begins. Some fanciful soul spots the coiled snake, and his fertile imagination has it rolling overland in no time at all. After the yarn has been repeated a few times, the snakes are rolling as easily as the facile tongues of the story tellers.

Will snakes eat vegetables or fruit?

Snakes eat animal food only. In most zoos, rats predominate on the reptilian menu, followed by mice, rabbits, frogs, chickens, fish, insects, and earthworms.

Is there really any kind of a snake that can milk a cow?

This story crops up from time to time, generally when a farmer or dairy hand has seen a snake near the milk shed just before he discovers one of his cows dry. Having heard the story about snakes milking cows, he puts two and two together, and gets five. Snake was present, cow was found dry, therefore snake milked cow. To milk a cow dry, the snake would not only have to hang onto the cow with its teeth—an indignity that no self-respecting bovine would permit—but it would have to extract quarts of milk and retain the fluid while it crawled away toward its hiding place like an inflated sausage balloon. Once I poured two ounces of milk down the throat of a snake. When I placed it on the ground, the milk ran out of its mouth, for the snake, although able to expand its body to accommodate the liquid, was unable to retain it. A cow-milking snake seen by a farmer is generally a king snake on the hunt for mice. Why, then, is the farmer's cow dry? I haven't the slightest idea. This is one of the most fantastic of all the yarns that have gathered around the subject of snakes. Why people should pick on the reptiles as the heroes or villains of their tallest tales is a mystery, but it has been going on ever since Eve pulled the one about the talking serpent. Even hunters and woodsmen, who ought to know better, add to the list.

Do bull snakes always kill and eat rattlesnakes on sight?

The bull is not a snake eater either by inclination or by habit. Other snakes do not form a part of its diet. The king snake and some racers may devour other snakes under certain conditions, but bulls and rattlers are not naturally unfriendly. In January, 1937, I placed a red rattler, a Pacific rattler, and a bull snake in the same cage. They have grown up together, they still share the same quarters, and I've seen no sign of trouble to indicate enmity, jealousy, or murderous intent among any of them.

Do rattlesnakes anchor themselves before striking, by forcing their rattles down into the earth?

I wish this one were true, even of only one or two individual specimens. I could reap a fortune with them in a side show. But unfortunately, the statement is pure legend, wholly without foundation. No man of science has ever seen and reported a rattler anchoring itself. Isn't it curious that people actually believe so-called eyewitnesses who retail stories like this, or describe in detail a water moccasin or copperhead three feet longer than any ever reported by trained collectors?

Can some snakes crawl faster than a race horse can run?

On a collecting trip into Oklahoma several years ago, I spotted a snake known as a prairie coach whip, a racer that legend declares possesses the speed of a thoroughbred horse. It was lying near the top of a mud cliff, perhaps seventy feet away, and seemed to be watching my movements intently. As I turned and walked away, the snake followed me for about 100 feet. When I stopped, it stopped. When I turned and started toward it, the coach whip reversed itself and slithered away, and although its departure seemed swift, I gained on it easily until it disappeared into a hole. That snake followed me, I believe, not because of an aggressive spirit but merely out of curiosity, and his subsequent flight certainly broke no speed records. I don't know what his exact speed was, but I do know that time trials with electrical recording equipment have shown that racers have a top speed of about three and a half miles an hour. No, I seriously doubt that any snake could provide satisfactory competition for a Man o' War, a Seabiscuit, or even a junkman's plug.

Are there any snakes that have a poisonous breath?

Well, not so long ago an aged farmer came upon a hognose snake, or spreading adder, near his corn crib. "That varmint stood on its tail and blew his breath in my face," he reported to me with the utmost sincerity. After this incident, the farmer said he had to take to his bed, where he stayed several days, cold sweats breaking out on his body each day at sundown. Now the hognose is a very interesting snake. It can flatten its head like a cobra, and to the accompaniment of loud hisses, make lightning stabs at its adversary. If it fails with this bluff, it may turn on its back, mouth open and tongue hanging out, playing possum. Sometimes a hognose will remain inert in this position until its mouth fills with dust. Probably this particular hognose had been scared by the farmer's sudden approach, and undoubtedly it hissed and stabbed with a will. But the reptile certainly never stood up on its tail, and with equal certainty, I believe it was fear and nervous shock, not a "poisonous breath" that put the farmer between the sheets. Nothing I can tell him, however, will make him change his original version of the incident.

Is a snake in striking position when it is coiled?

When a snake is coiled up it is either sleeping or resting. In a defensive striking position, part of its body is more or less coiled on the ground, but head and neck are raised, generally in an S loop. Incidentally, the distance that a snake can cover when striking is much less than is popularly believed. A rattlesnake can strike accurately only as far as it can straighten out the raised loop mentioned above, or approximately one third to one half of its total length. If you hear a snake rattle stand perfectly still, for a rattler will seldom strike a motionless object.

Are all rattlers vicious?

By no means. The red diamond rattler often permits itself to be captured and put into a sack without even sounding its rattle. In captivity, it becomes quite tame.

Are there many deadly snakes that are extremely small?

No. Among the supposed examples of tiny poisoners is the desert worm snake. In reality, this reptile is quite defenseless. Most deadly snakes are large.

SHORT STORIES

Dust and the Serpent

by LEO CRANE

"And dust shall be the serpent's meat."

Isaiah, 65:25

ANY ONE WHO HAS HEARD CHARLIE NIXON BELLOW FROM a little stand just outside the entrance to the Consolidated's side show, and who has listened long enough to understand just what Charlie Nixon bellows about, half believes that all the great wonders of the world are there congregated. The big reverberating bass voice intones the song of the ballyhoo man in all sincerity. That, however, means nothing, for Charlie Nixon is paid for it, and the chief object of his song is to trap the unwary into paying. His boast that all the queer things of the earth and the marvels thereof are within the tented space is a mistake. Charlie Nixon would admit this himself, were he safe in doing so. He would say that there is no longer such a snake-charmer as Kundoo, who came from upper India, and who could pipe a cobra almost into fidelity, which is a rare accomplishment even for a brown man of caste; and perhaps Charlie Nixon might mention that there are no longer with the Consolidated the two Moquis, Chua and his wife. This would seem to be a matter of no importance, for a Moqui is merely a Moqui, and one might be tempted to say that his wife doesn't count.

It is not to be expected that a plain ballyhoo man can make the light shine on all dark places, even when honest and sincere; but the truth of the matter is that Kundoo, the snake-charmer of the East, and Chua, the Moqui snake man of the West, had a little affair in common.

Chua was not his real name. He was a Moqui and came from the Chua people, or from the "people of the snake." His real name was Tokochi, the "wildcat," and this should be kept in mind. He was getting old, and he was with the Consolidated outfit, together with his wife Buliso, so that the enlightened people of the East might look at a real Moqui snake-dancer. Buliso was not old, for a Moqui Indian woman, and she was not ill-favored. This, when one knows that her name means "the Evening Primrose," has quite a little bearing on the story. In fact, Buliso, the woman, may be looked to as the beginning of this matter. Chua, the "snake," was very proud of her; Kundoo, the Eastern, offered her insult. Thus there was a feud between these two.

105

Chua was not a vicious man, but he was faithful to his racial traditions. He was of reddish-brown color, with high cheek-bones and a straight broad nose. His eyes—and they were the slanting eyes of the true Moqui—could be gentle when Buliso engaged them. His black hair, coarse and straight, was done up in a queue in the back, and, according to the Moqui style, hung over his forehead in a bang. There was an earnestness in his face, backed by the half-religious, half-fanatical character of one who had performed the snake-dance, and who could therefore be termed no coward.

Kundoo came from those crafty, subtle folk of the upper hills, where they learn many things besides the charming of cobras. He would sit on a little platform, surrounded by a half-shield of plate-glass and gauze netting, and would play weird tunes on a flutelike pipe, and curious snakes would sway their bodies in time with his variations. It was a chilling exhibition, unless one knew that Kundoo did not endanger himself with venomous serpents at every performance. A snake is a snake and deadly, to the ignorant open-mouth beyond the netting, who has paid his coin and does not wish to be disillusioned. Now at the right-hand corner of the platform was a green-painted box, and sometimes, when the lassitude of the day lay heavy on Kundoo, so that he pined for serious amusement, he would open this box and play an older, a most weird strain, as Eastern as the sunrise. Then would come forth Rama, the cobra.

Rama, the cobra, was not the sort of snake to gyrate for the marvelling public. He was rather sluggish, and he would sway his yellow-brown body until a peculiar run on the flute would irritate, and then Rama would expand that terrible cobra's hood, which is a strangely fascinating sight, but which one does not hunger to see. Kundoo would only smile, a pale emotionless smile, such as he could have used on seeing an enemy die. They were the best of friends, Rama and Kundoo, the one sometimes nestling in the bosom of the other, though any one, even considering friendship, is a brave man when sitting quietly within five feet of a swaying cobra.

Thus he played one day when Chua, the snake man, stood outside the partition of glass. Chua grunted and stared. He had never seen a snake like that. Kundoo, glancing stealthily out of the corner of his eye, observed the Moqui, and remembering their grievances, smiled coldly. Otwell, the manager, stood by, watching too.

"Great snake, Harris," he said to the press-agent.

"Great!" echoed that worthy man.

"It would be worth your life to do that."

"Quicker than lightning they are," admitted the press-agent.

"Well, I guess. Say, how long do you suppose that gingersnap Kundoo would linger if Rama took it into his devil's head to strike?"

"Oh, about twelve minutes, maybe;— not more than twenty."

The Moqui smiled. He could understand their talk; and they spoke of a consummation which, had he not been of the Hopitu people, which means the peaceful ones, he could have longed to hurry.

Some day, he thought, gritting his teeth, that saffron cur in the snake's box would understand that it was no light matter to give offence to a true Moqui, who never forgets. But Chua, the snake-dancer, made no sign of interest. He stood still, listening.

"Tell the truth, boss," said Harris, "I believe Kundoo would rather die himself than lose that snake."

"I believe it too," added the manager.

Chua gave a little start, and smiled again, though one could hardly have guessed from the pose of him that he understood.

"I don't like cobras, but they are some valuable," commented the manager. "As for Kundoo, he's a jewel; we don't want to lose either of 'em."

"No," said Harris, casually, and they strolled away together.

Chua remained, watching. His eyes scarcely left the snake cage until Kundoo had piped the sinuous living death back into its green-painted box and Rama was no more to be seen. All this while the Moqui thought of many things. He smiled at times, a cold, calculating smile. When it happened that Kundoo turned and looked at him, a long stare passed between them. The stolid Moqui quivered not an eyelash, and the thin classic face of the Eastern was like a death mask. Nevertheless, Chua did not feel altogether comfortable. There was a steely glitter in those Eastern eyes, a cruelty of power, which his cruder Western nature could not understand, and therefore somewhat feared.

Turning from the place, Chua faced Harris, the press-agent, who had returned from his stroll about. It was a relief, after that awful stare, to speak with some one he knew to be kindly. Chua and Harris had been more than friendly, for Harris had passed through the pueblo country, and knew the sunlight, the stretches, and the desert of it. Chua was impelled to boast mildly when with friends.

"You think he great man with snake?"

"Wonderful, Chua," said Harris, nodding gravely.

"Ugh-h-h!" grunted Moqui.

Harris knew enough to keep quiet.

"Much bad snake?" questioned Chua a minute later.

"Much," said Harris.

"Ugh-h-h!" and there was another silence.

"How much bad snake?"

"Like lightning," described Harris. "Kill—half hour—no medicine."

"Ugh!" sighed the Indian, crossing his arms before him. "Me snake man. Me catch snake, no music, with hand—So . . ."

Harris took him by the arm warningly and said:

"Don't you fool with that snake, Chua! I know you great snake man, but—this no pueblo snake. Kill! You sabbe!"

The Moqui smiled disdainfully.

"You ever see snake like this? . . ." and he made a peculiar noise with his tongue and lips. It was a noise, a nervous vibration, and yet a treble note, thin and not hissing, unlike the sound of the cricket, different from the hollow clatter of pips in a gourd. Harris gave a little involuntary start, and then laughed.

"Rattler, eh?"

Chua nodded gravely.

"That much bad snake," he said, and stalked away.

Charlie Nixon (it was during the forenoon and he was resting his immense voice) said quietly, at Harris's elbow.

"What did the mutt say, ol' man?"

"Why, he was meaning a rattlesnake. Say! you ought to see 'em— they're snakes! They haven't any of this cobra delicacy and sinuous terror, but they mean business just the same. I don't want to hear any rattlers 'round here. That noise he made—why, it gave me a jolt. An' you ought to see the snake-dances in his country. I've been down there, and they'd show this Kundoo fellow some points. Go right after 'em with their bare hands! You bet! But a rattler's a square, honest sort of snake, though; he gives warning. That cobra, ugh! it makes a fellow faint to look at it. Just like the people, too; I wouldn't trust that chap Kundoo any farther than I could toss a bull by the tail. But the Moquis, they're all right."

Chua knew how to keep his own counsel. He wanted no word trouble with Kundoo, though that devil had insulted him and his traditions. Were they out in the desert country, there would be little to relate of this matter, save the finding of a bone or two in the washes of the mesa. But Chua knew that such an argument would not prevail in the white man's territory. He smiled when he thought of snakes. What did that saffron reed know of snakes! He—he, a snake man—could show him more than a mere piping on a flute. Let him wait!

And as he thought of these things, he looked over to where Buliso, his wife, sat weaving a crude basket of the Moqui pattern. Her hair was arranged in the long pendants of the Hopi married one. She worked industriously. In her ears were the wooden disks ornamented with turquoise mosaic which he had gotten for her long ago. Then he thought of that saffron-hued devil from the marshes of the East, and Chua, the serpent, vowed vengeance.

The next afternoon, when the tents were quiet, Chua wandered about in an aimless way until he came to a high glass case. In this case there were many compartments, and in these compartments snakes. Sometimes active in the relentless pursuit of a luckless mouse, for the most part the reptiles lay as if dozing in a stupid torpor. Chua examined this case and shook his head. There were too many snakes; he wanted one. Then it was that he turned to a huge glass box, where, coiled like a thick mat, was resting a diamond-woven thing, its spade-shaped head lying as a deadly dart upon the topmost fold. The tail resembled a bunch of disks tightly strung together. Chua looked down through the glass, into the eyes of the snake, and smiled.

This was a real snake, one from his own country. It was a vicious-looking thing, a bottle of labelled poison, quiet, dozing, carrying with it the lives of many men. And this was the sort of snake he had handled fearlessly when in the religious fervor of the dances. As if conscious of its vitriolic powers, the snake lay passive, save when the two little pools of hatred which it had for eyes twinkled in the beams of the sunlight.

Chua could remember searching for such snakes with the priests, fairly digging them out of their holes in the sands and bringing them to the kivas, sometimes tied in a shirt sleeve, to be transferred to the snake bags amid ceremonies; and he could hear the hissing of them in the kivas when they were sprinkled with meal; and the invocations and the chants of the tribal doctors Chua seemed to hear as faint dreaming sounds. He recalled the ceremony of snake-washing, and he wondered if that saffron reed would care to wash such a snake as this. Chua grunted and smiled again. At some performance of the afternoon, when the cobra would be brought forth, Chua meant to humiliate them, master and pet together. It would be a grand stroke, this revenge of his planning, and he would not stand without glory in the affair. He went away to busy himself in the manufacture of a peculiar wand, a stick from which drooped two long feathers. It was a snake whip of the Moqui priests.

But a whole week passed before Chua had his opportunity. This came one hot summer's day. The afternoon performance was on, and the thousands packed in the great exhibition tent, where are the arenas and the race-course, knew nothing of this little drama of the cages. Those few loungers in the outer tent were treated to a sight seldom, perhaps never before, witnessed in even so marvellous a gathering of sights as a circus.

Kundoo had found the long humid afternoon irksome, and he piped Rama out from the green box. Those loungers who had found more interest in the caged beasts than in the aerial performances of acrobats strolled to this half glass, half netted enclosure and looked on. The cobra's little eyes glittered as evil beads. Weird was the music Kundoo played for its swaying, and the snake of the East bent gracefully to the rhythmic strains.

Then it was that a crash of glass sounded from the other side of the tent, and there was immediately a stirring of the straw, as Chua, waving his feathered wand and shouting, pursued something gliding before him.

"Look out!" called one of the showmen, warning the knot of people aside. "There's a snake loose in the straw. Stand away, you folks. We'll have him in a minute."

The circus hand made no pretence of capturing the snake himself, however, and they saw it coil on a little cleared patch of earth. As if angry that it had been given liberty in so tumultuous a fashion, the snake writhed itself into a position and attitude of defence.

Kundoo dared not cease the piping of his weird music. This momentary confusion and noise had so animated the cobra that its wicked little head beat out of time, and all the attention of the player had to be kept riveted on the thing before him. The eyes of the charmer and the charmed both glistened in a momentary emotion of hostility and excitement. Kundoo played as though for his very life. The beads of sweat stood out on his forehead. Gradually the piping soothed the cobra back into the graceful languor.

Chua had advanced to the rattler. He cast his blue blanket before the snake, and immediately there had been a strike into the thick folds of it. Now was the straightened reptile prevented from coiling for another blow. The feathered wand stroked it with the confidence of a practised hand. A minute of this and the rattler was confused. Unable to coil, it was partially defenceless, and a sudden pressure of the wand behind its head allowed the swift hand of Chua to grasp its neck. He stood upright, saluting with his feathered wand in a spirit of triumph, his face smiling; and then, with a fling as quick as his grasping of the snake, Chua slung the rattler over into the enclosure where sat Kundoo piping his tremulous song to the cobra. The flopping of the rattlesnake's length on the floor caused Kundoo to break his music in sheer consternation. The cobra dropped its head to the floor, as if exhausted and limp, on the strains ceasing. And in that moment Kundoo leaped in spasmodic fear over the top of the netting, falling into the straw outside. He lay panting, his eyes showing the terror that possessed him. Chua grunted disdainfully. The saffron reed of the East had been introduced to a real snake, a snake of the West.

Now the two ribbons of death eyed each other in the enclosure. Enchantment and the weird music of it had fled. The sinuous lengths stirred with quick writhings, as if measuring each its venom. At one end, the Western poison coiled in a thick heap, its blunt head swaying angrily, its fangs playing through its lips in a half-fanciful wickedness. The East, at first startled and trembling from the spell of the charm, was now enraged. In the cobra's eyes gleamed a deadly fire. Its head, balanced on one-third of its erect length, swayed from side to side in a quivering arc of wrath, and the hood distended until it was a horrible puff, bloated and ugly.

Kundoo, pale and distressed, trembled at the side of the glass box. Chua, stolidly intent, stared from the other side. Now would they see a snake in action, not piped into dreaming idleness by the quaverings of a faking magician. Now would they see the great snake of the Painted Desert defend its title against this pitiful adder of the foreigner. Chua thrilled with silent exultation.

There swayed the thong of yellowish-brown—hooded, malignant,

erect; the rattler had coiled, a tense spring, the blunt head of it rigid as
an evil dart, poisoned and vicious. Only a yard of sanded floor separated
them now. Only half minute of suspense intervened. The rattler sounded
its terrible slogan of battle, and the cobra answered this with a thin treble
note. The rattler's head shot forward, a rigid thing, pulsating with rage.
So quick was this propulsion that the spectators started forward, their
noses touching the close meshes of the netting. The cobra met this attack
with a lightning stroke. The rattler was struck while in the air. As the
snakes dropped to the floor of the enclosure, the cobra whipped away
from the squirming foe, and sounding its high-pitched note again, was
almost instantly ready for a second attack at the far end of the cage.

Kundoo's eyes lighted with an eager glint on seeing this. The rattler
coiled and sprang again, but this time wildly, and there seemed not so
much of evil in its effort. Again was he met by the terrible dart of the
cobra, and again the rattler tried to coil. But this time there was a weak-
ening and the movement betrayed an exhaustion. The two snakes faced
each other now without stirring. The head of the rattlesnake played in
and out with a slowly diminshing motion, as the stopping pendulum of
an old clock. Pitifully the half-coiled length began to relax. The head
sank lower and lower. Still eyeing its foe of the farther East, the rattler
gave a convulsive shudder, and the rattles of it sounded a last hollow
defiance.

Chua, the Indian, stared like a wild-eyed thing at the side of the enclosure. As the snake's head drooped lower and lower, he looked up to
meet the mocking smile his enemy bestowed on him. The rattlesnake lay
as an old glove. The blunt head ceased to move, was still. Chua, the Moqui,
walked away muttering, and Kundoo, picking up his pipe, began to play
the cobra into gentleness.

The East had triumphed. Chua marvelled when he ceased trembling.
What powers had this devil that he could not prevail against them? His
champion, his very god, had been defeated in the struggle. And who knew
but that one of his very ancestors lived in the body of the vanquished
snake, tortured by that poison of the Eastern mires, a polluted thing.
Chua was shamed. He would kill that cobra. What did he fear of a snake!
He had carried them in his mouth, and he cared not a whit more for
one than the other. He would kill that vile, puff-throated thing himself
this very night.

When the tents were still, and only the noise of an elephant rustling
the hay, or the stamping of a restless horse in the near-by stable, could
be heard, Chua, the Indian, slipped down toward the house of the cobra.
Silently he went along, using every art of the swift-moving Indian. In his
hand he carried one of the boomerangs of his people. It was a piece of
seasoned wood, hard and polished. Once the snake was out—dumped
from its retreat in the green-painted box—what chance would it have
against that swiftly whirling thing which he had killed running rabbits?

Chua balanced the curved weapon in his hand and rejoiced that his ancestors of the Chua people would not go unavenged.

But hardly had he stooped close to the side of the netted enclosure, when, in the dim light, a figure came slowly toward him. There was a single oil-lamp burning to the left, and not until Kundoo had advanced within its pale circle did the Moqui see him.

No word was spoken. But it seemed that a silent accusation passed from the thin ascetic-looking one to his cruder brother of the desert. All the colors of the two worlds met in these two beings—behind the one, generations of a cultivation, an art, a religion, and an occult mysticism that had long ago reached the pinnacle of perfection and had begun to decline; with the other lived the purer virility of a desert people, the courage of fanaticism, the strength imparted by a rigorous life in a barren, arid country. In this moment of meeting, looking into each other's eyes as if from across the deep chasm separating them, the subtle intelligence again proved its power. The Moqui became rigid. His eyes stared into those of the Eastern as if into a vast enchanted pit. Never before had the Moqui felt that he was prisoner to a pair of darkly glowing eyes. In the first instant, before the power held him, Chua had trembled to see that from the loose neck of the other's tunic the slender head of the cobra played out, and he knew that the snake he sought lay safe against the brown skin of its master. Then all this disappeared, faded, was lost in the wonderful captivity he played to those fascinating eyes. The robe's sharp outline, the contour of the Hindoo's head, the bright circle of the light, all blurred slowly into a vague half-clouded atmosphere, and that other one which he had called a saffron reed swayed gracefully, became a yellowish tinged thing, a hideous malignant thing, with glittering eyes and a long, slender, evil head—a thing that resembled . . . was a swaying snake! . . .

Weakness overcame the Moqui. He fancied the thing at his throat.

Then the spell was lifted, and weak as his own champion had been after the terrific struggle with the cobra, Chua sank down into the straw and watched the robed figure of the other fade into the dark recesses of the dim tent. He could hear the sandals scraping over the earth and rustling in the thin layers of straw.

A moment of deep labored breathing, almost gasping, and the Moqui started for the outer air. He wanted to rid himself of the horrid atmosphere and to stand under the stars. It was very dark on the circus lot. He hurried away among the wagons into the black. In his hand he still carried the boomerang, but he had forgotten it, save that it was something into which he tried to press his nails.

Then Chua heard the scraping sandals again. He trembled, he shook as a leaf in the wind. Was the devil following him? He stepped into the deep shadow of a big canvas-covered wagon and waited, fear in his heart, quivering. A few minutes he waited. The deep inhalations of the night air seemed to fill him with a sterner purpose, a courage more nearly like that he had carried through the lonely arid stretches of the deserts.

About fifty feet away glimmered the faint circle of a light. The lamp itself was hung from a wagon end, and only the halo of its beam could be seen straight fifty feet before the crouching Indian. The shuffling sandals came on, on, and then a vague figure, robed, gliding, he could see advancing in the pale light. The figure came slowly into the clearer circle, and a glint at the throat of the Eastern showed where the head of the cobra nestled, one evil power kissing the brown skin of the other.

Chua, the Moqui, scarcely dared to breathe. What chance had he against this evil pair? They had vanquished his very gods. Then something like that old fanaticism of the dance impelled him to swift action. Those eyes were not fastened on his, as when in the tent he had been enchanted. But whenever they again ensnared him, Chua felt the polished surface of the boomerang and balanced the wooden weight in his hand. Could he—dared he—the man was in the full circle now, under the masked light, and the one tiny bead showed plainly at his throat.

Suddenly, as a panther would prepare to spring, the sinews of the Moqui grew tense and hard. The boomerang swept in a wide circle. It went hurling through the air. It struck the other, Kundoo, fairly in the breast.

Chua, the Moqui, leaped upright, and stood a quivering savage. He threw upward his arms in an invocation.

"Now, god of snakes! . . ." he said.

And when Kundoo was found next day, it was said that the cobra had turned in spite against him. It lay, a broken coil, in his tunic, the fangs in his throat.

Egotism; or, the Bosom Serpent

by NATHANIEL HAWTHORNE

"HERE HE COMES!" SHOUTED THE BOYS ALONG THE street. "Here comes the man with a snake in his bosom!"

This outcry, saluting Herkimer's ears as he was about to enter the iron gate of the Elliston mansion, made him pause. It was not without a shudder that he found himself on the point of meeting his former acquaintance, whom he had known in the glory of youth, and whom now after an interval of five years, he was to find the victim either of a diseased fancy or a horrible physical misfortune.

"A snake in his bosom!" repeated the young sculptor to himself. "It must be he. No second man on earth has such a bosom friend. And now, my poor Rosina, Heaven grant me wisdom to discharge my errand aright! Woman's faith must be strong indeed since thine has not yet failed."

Thus musing, he took his stand at the entrance of the gate and waited until the personage so singularly announced should make his appearance. After an instant or two he beheld the figure of a lean man, of unwholesome look, with glittering eyes and long black hair, who seemed to imitate the motion of a snake; for, instead of walking straight forward with open front, he undulated along the pavement in a curved line. It may be too fanciful to say that something, either in his moral or material aspect, suggested the idea that a miracle had been wrought by transforming a serpent into a man, but so imperfectly that the snaky nature was yet hidden, and scarcely hidden, under the mere outward guise of humanity. Herkimer remarked that his complexion had a greenish tinge over its sickly white, reminding him of a species of marble out of which he had once wrought a head of Envy, with her snaky locks.

The wretched being approached the gate, but, instead of entering, stopped short and fixed the glitter of his eye full upon the compassionate yet steady countenance of the sculptor.

"It gnaws me! It gnaws me!" he exclaimed.

And then there was an audible hiss, but whether it came from the apparent lunatic's own lips, or was the real hiss of a serpent, might admit of a discussion. At all events, it made Herkimer shudder to his heart's core.

"Do you know me, George Herkimer?" asked the snake-possessed.

Herkimer did know him; but it demanded all the intimate and practical acquaintance with the human face, acquired by modelling actual likenesses in clay, to recognize the features of Roderick Elliston in the visage that now met the sculptor's gaze. Yet it was he. It added nothing to the wonder to reflect that the once brilliant young man had undergone this odious and fearful change during the no more than five brief years of Herkimer's abode at Florence. The possibility of such a transformation being granted, it was as easy to conceive it effected in a moment as in an age. Inexpressibly shocked and startled, it was still the keenest pang when Herkimer remembered that the fate of his cousin Rosina, the ideal of gentle womanhood, was indissolubly interwoven with that of a being whom Providence seemed to have unhumanized.

"Elliston! Roderick!" cried he, "I had heard of this; but my conception came far short of the truth. What has befallen you? Why do I find you thus?"

"Oh, 'tis a mere nothing! A snake! A snake! The commonest thing in the world. A snake in the boson—that's all," answered Roderick Elliston. "But how is your own breast?" continued he, looking the sculptor in the eye with the most acute and penetrating glance that it had ever been his fortune to encounter. "All pure and wholesome? No reptile there? By my faith and conscience, and by the devil within me, here is a wonder! A man without a serpent in his bosom!"

"Be calm, Elliston," whispered George Herkimer, laying his hand upon the shoulder of the snake-possessed. "I have crossed the ocean to meet you. Listen! Let us be private. I bring a message from Rosina—from your wife!"

"It gnaws me! It gnaws me!" muttered Roderick.

With this exclamation, the most frequent in his mouth, the unfortunate man clutched both hands upon his breast as if an intolerable sting or torture impelled him to rend it open and let out the living mischief, even should it be intertwined with his own life. He then freed himself from Herkimer's grasp by a subtle motion, and, gliding through the gate, took refuge in his antiquated family residence. The sculptor did not pursue him. He saw that no available intercourse could be expected at such a moment, and was desirous, before another meeting, to inquire closely into the nature of Roderick's disease and the circumstances that had reduced him to so lamentable a condition. He succeeded in obtaining the necessary information from an eminent medical gentleman.

Shortly after Elliston's separation from his wife—now nearly four years ago—his associates had observed a singular gloom spreading over his daily life, like those chill, gray mists that sometimes steal away the sunshine from a summer's morning. The symptoms caused them endless perplexity. They knew not whether ill health were robbing his spirits of elasticity, or whether a canker of the mind was gradually eating, as such cankers do, from his moral system into the physical frame, which is but the shadow of the former. They looked for the root of this trouble in his shattered schemes of domestic bliss,—wilfully shattered by himself,—but could not be satisfied of its existence there. Some thought that their once brilliant friend was in an incipient stage of insanity, of which his passionate impulses had perhaps been the forerunners; others prognosticated a general blight and gradual decline. From Roderick's own lips they could learn nothing. More than once, it is true, he had been heard to say, clutching his hands convulsively upon his breast,—"It gnaws me! It gnaws me!"—but, by different auditors, a great diversity of explanation was assigned to this ominous expression. What could it be that gnawed the breast of Roderick Elliston? Was it sorrow? Was it merely the tooth of physical disease? Or, in his reckless course, often verging upon profligacy, if not plunging into its depths, had he been guilty of some deed which made his bosom a prey to the deadlier fangs of remorse? There was plausible ground for each of these conjectures; but it must not be concealed that more than one elderly gentleman, the victim of good cheer and slothful habits, magisterially pronounced the secret of the whole matter to be Dyspepsia!

Meanwhile, Roderick seemed aware how generally he had become the subject of curiosity and conjecture, and, with a morbid repugnance to such notice, or to any notice whatsoever, estranged himself from all companionship. Not merely the eye of man was a horror to him; not merely the light of a friend's countenance; but even the blessed sunshine, likewise, which in its universal beneficence typifies the radiance of the Creator's face, expressing his love for all the creatures of his hand. The dusky twilight was now too transparent for Roderick Elliston; the blackest midnight was his chosen hour to steal abroad; and if ever he were seen, it was when the watchman's lantern gleamed upon his figure, gliding along the street, with his hands clutched upon his bosom, still muttering, "It gnaws me! It gnaws me!" What could it be that gnawed him?

After a time, it became known that Elliston was in the habit of resorting to all the noted quacks that infested the city, or whom money would tempt to journey thither from a distance. By one of these persons, in the exultation of a supposed cure, it was proclaimed far and wide, by dint of handbills and little pamphlets on dingy paper, that a distinguished gentleman, Roderick Elliston, Esq., had been relieved of a SNAKE in his stomach! So here was the monstrous secret, ejected from its lurking place into public view, in all its horrible deformity. The mystery was out; but not so the bosom serpent. He, if it were anything but a delusion, still lay coiled in his living den. The empiric's cure had been a sham, the effect, it was supposed, of some stupefying drug which more nearly caused the death of the patient than of the odious reptile that possessed him. When Roderick Elliston regained entire sensibility, it was to find his misfortune the town talk—the more than nine days' wonder and horror—while, at his bosom, he felt the sickening motion of a thing alive, and the gnawing of that restless fang which seemed to gratify at once a physical appetite and a fiendish spite.

He summoned the old black servant, who had been bred up in his father's house, and was a middle-aged man while Roderick lay in his cradle.

"Scipio!" he began; and then paused, with his arms folded over his heart. "What do people say of me, Scipio."

"Sir! my poor master! that you had a serpent in your bosom," answered the servant with hesitation.

"And what else?" asked Roderick, with a ghastly look at the man.

"Nothing else, dear master," replied Scipio, "only that the doctor gave you a powder, and that the snake leaped out upon the floor."

"No, no!" muttered Roderick to himself, as he shook his head, and pressed his hands with a more convulsive force upon his breast, "I feel him still. It gnaws me! It gnaws me!"

From this time the miserable sufferer ceased to shun the world, but rather solicited and forced himself upon the notice of acquaintances and strangers. It was partly the result of desperation on finding that the cavern of his own bosom had not proved deep and dark enough to hide the secret, even while it was so secure a fortress for the loathsome fiend that had crept into it. But still more, this craving for notoriety was a symptom of the intense morbidness which now pervaded his nature. All persons chronically diseased are egoists, whether the disease be of the mind or body; whether it be sin, sorrow, or merely the more tolerable calamity of some endless pain, or mischief among the cords of mortal life. Such individuals are made acutely conscious of a self, by the torture in which it dwells. Self, therefore, grows to be so prominent an object with them that they cannot but present it to the face of every casual passer-by. There is a pleasure—perhaps the greatest of which the sufferer is susceptible—in displaying the wasted or ulcerated limb, or the cancer in the breast; and the fouler the crime, with so much the more difficulty does the perpetrator prevent it from thrusting up its snake-like head to frighten the world; for it is that cancer, or that crime, which constitutes their respective individuality. Roderick Elliston, who, a little while before, had held himself scornfully above the common lot of men, now paid full allegiance to this humiliating law. The snake in his bosom seemed the symbol of a monstrous egotism to which everything was referred, and which he pampered, night and day, with a continual and exclusive sacrifice of devil worship.

He soon exhibited what most people considered indubitable tokens of insanity. In some of his moods, strange to say, he prided and gloried himself on being marked out from the ordinary experience of mankind, by the possession of a double nature, and a life within life. He appeared to imagine that the snake was a divinity,—not celestial, it is true, but darkly infernal,—and that he thence derived an eminence and a sanctity, horrid, indeed, yet more desirable than whatever ambition aims at. Thus he drew his misery around him like a regal mantle, and looked down triumphantly upon those whose vitals nourished no deadly monster. Oftener, however, his human nature asserted its empire over him in the shape of a yearning for fellowship. It grew to be his custom to spend the whole day in wandering about the streets, aimlessly, unless it might be called an aim to establish a species of brotherhood between himself and the world. With cankered ingenuity, he sought out his own disease in every breast. Whether insane or not, he showed so keen a perception of frailty, error, and vice, that many persons gave him credit for being possessed not merely with a serpent, but with an actual fiend, who imparted this evil faculty of recognizing whatever was ugliest in man's heart.

For instance, he met an individual, who, for thirty years, had cherished a hatred against his own brother. Roderick, amidst the throng of the street, laid his hand on this man's chest, and looking full into his forbidding face,—

"How is the snake to-day?" he inquired, with a mock expression of sympathy.

"The snake!" exclaimed the brother hater—"what do you mean?"

"The snake! The snake! Does he gnaw you?" persisted Roderick. "Did you take counsel with him this morning when you should have been saying your prayers? Did he sting, when you thought of your brother's health, wealth, and good repute? Did he caper for joy, when you remembered the profligacy of his only son? And whether he stung, or whether he frolicked, did you feel his poison throughout your body and soul, converting everything to sourness and bitterness? That is the way of such serpents. I have learned the whole nature of them from my own!"

"Where is the police?" roared the object of Roderick's persecution, at the same time giving an instinctive clutch to his breast. "Why is this lunatic allowed to go at large?"

"Ha, ha!" chuckled Roderick, releasing his grasp of the man. "His bosom serpent has stung him then!"

Often it pleased the unfortunate young man to vex people with a lighter satire, yet still characterized by somewhat of snakelike virulence. One day he encountered an ambitious statesman, and gravely inquired after the welfare of his boa constrictor; for of that species, Roderick affirmed, this gentleman's serpent must needs be, since its appetite was enormous enough to devour the whole country and constitution. At another time, he stopped a close-fisted old fellow, of great wealth, but who skulked about the city in the guise of a scarecrow, with a patched blue surtout, brown hat, and mouldy boots, scraping pence together, and picking up rusty nails. Pretending to look earnestly at this respectable person's stomach, Roderick assured him that his snake was a copperhead, and had been generated by the immense quantities of that base metal, with which he daily defiled his fingers. Again, he assaulted a man of rubicund visage, and told him that few bosom serpents had more of the devil in them than those that breed in the vats of a distillery. The next whom Roderick honored with his attention was a distinguished clergyman, who happened just then to be engaged in a theological controversy, where human wrath was more perceptible than divine inspiration.

"You have swallowed a snake in a cup of sacramental wine," quoth he.

"Profane wretch!" exclaimed the divine; but, nevertheless, his hand stole to his breast.

He met a person of sickly sensibility, who, on some early disappointment, had retired from the world, and thereafter held no intercourse with his fellow-men, but brooded sullenly or passionately over the irrevocable past. This man's very heart, if Roderick might be believed, had been changed into a serpent, which would finally torment both him and itself to death. Observing a married couple, whose domestic troubles were matter of notoriety, he condoled with both on having mutually taken a house adder to their bosoms. To an envious author, who depreciated works which he could never equal, he said that his snake was the slimiest and filthiest of all the reptile tribe, but was fortunately without sting.

A man of impure life, and a brazen face, asking Roderick if there were any serpent in his breast, he told him that there was, and of the same species that once tortured Din Rodrigo, the Goth. He took a fair young girl by the hand, and gazing sadly into her eyes, warned her that she cherished a serpent of the deadliest kind within her gentle breast; and the world found the truth of those ominous words, when, a few months afterwards, the poor girl died of love and shame. Two ladies, rivals in fashionable life, who tormented one another with a thousand little stings of womanish spite, were given to understand that each of their hearts was a nest of diminutive snakes, which did quite as much mischief as one great one.

But nothing seemed to please Roderick better than to lay hold of a person infected with jealousy, which he represented as an enormous green reptile, with an ice-cold length of body, and the sharpest sting of any snake save one.

"And what one is that?" asked a by-stander, over-hearing him.

It was a dark-browed man who put the question; he had an evasive eye, which in the course of a dozen years had looked no mortal directly in the face. There was an ambiguity about this person's character,—a stain upon his reputation,—yet none could tell precisely of what nature, although the city gossips, male and female, whispered the most atrocious surmises. Until a recent period he had followed the sea, and was, in fact, the very shipmaster whom George Herkimer had encountered, under such singular circumstances, in the Grecian Archipelago.

"What bosom serpent has the sharpest sting?" repeated this man; but he put the question as if by a reluctant necessity, and grew pale while he was uttering it.

"Why need you ask?" replied Roderick, with a look of dark intelligence. "Look into your own breast. Hark! my serpent bestirs himself! He acknowledges the presence of a master fiend!"

And then, as the by-standers afterwards affirmed. a hissing sound was heard, apparently in Roderick Elliston's breast. It was said, too, that an answering hiss came from the vitals of the shipmaster, as if a snake were actually lurking there and had been aroused by the call of its brother reptile. If there were in fact any such sound, it might have been caused by a malicious exercise of ventriloquism on the part of Roderick.

Thus making his own actual serpent—if a serpent there actually was in his bosom—the type of each man's fatal error, or hoarded sin, or unquiet conscience, and striking his sting so unremorsefully into the sorest spot, we may well imagine that Roderick became the pest of the city. Nobody could elude him—none could withstand him. He grappled with the ugliest truth that he could lay his hand on, and compelled his adversary to do the same. Strange spectacle in human life where it is the instinctive effort of one and all to hide those sad realities, and leave them undisturbed beneath a heap of superficial topics which constitute the materials of intercourse between man and man! It was to be tolerated that Roderick Elliston should break through the tacit compact by which the world has done its best to secure repose without relinquishing evil. The victims of his malicious remarks, it is true, had brothers enough to keep them in countenance; for, by Roderick's theory, every mortal bosom harboured either a brood of small serpents or one overgrown monster that had devoured all the rest. Still the city could not bear this new apostle. It was demanded by nearly all, and particularly by the most respectable inhabitants, that Roderick should no longer be permitted to violate the received rules of decorum by obtruding his own bosom serpent to the public gaze, and dragging those of decent people from their lurking places.

Accordingly, his relatives interfered and placed him in a private asylum for the insane. When the news was noised abroad, it was observed that many persons walked the streets with freer countenances and covered their breasts less carefully with their hands.

His confinement, however, although it contributed not a little to the peace of the town, operated unfavourably upon Roderick himself. In solitude his melancholy grew more black and sullen. He spent whole days—indeed, it was his sole occupation—in communing with the serpent. A conversation was sustained, in which, as it seemed, the hidden monster bore a part, though unintelligibly to the listeners, and inaudible except in a hiss. Singular as it may appear, the sufferer had now contracted a sort of affection for his tormentor, mingled, however, with the intensest loathing and horror. Nor were such discordant emotions incompatible. Each, on the contrary, imparted strength and poignancy to its opposite. Horrible love—horrible antipathy—embracing one another in his bosom, and both concentrating themselves upon a being that had crept into his vitals or been engendered there, and which was nourished with his food, and lived upon his life, and was as intimate with him as his own heart, and yet was the foulest of all created things! But not the less was it the true type of a morbid nature.

Sometimes, in his moments of rage and bitter hatred against the snake and himself, Roderick determined to be the death of him, even at the expense of his own life. Once he attempted it by starvation; but, while the wretched man was on the point of famishing, the monster seemed to feed upon his heart, and to thrive and wax gamesome, as if it were his sweetest and most congenial diet. Then he privily took a dose of active poison, imagining that it would not fail to kill either himself or the devil that possessed him, or both together. Another mistake; for if Roderick had not yet been destroyed by his own poisoned heart nor the snake by gnawing it, they had little to fear from arsenic or corrosive sublimate. Indeed, the venomous pest appeared to operate as an antidote against all other poisons. The physicians tried to suffocate the fiend with tobacco smoke. He breathed it as freely as if it were his native atmosphere. Again, they drugged their patient with opium and drenched him with intoxicating liquors, hoping that the snake might thus be reduced to stupor and perhaps be ejected from the stomach. They succeeded in rendering Roderick insensible; but, placing their hands upon his breast, they were inexpressibly horror stricken to feel the monster wriggling, twining, and darting to and fro within his narrow limits, evidently enlivened by the opium or alcohol, and incited to unusual feats of activity. Thenceforth they gave up all attempts at cure or palliation. The doomed sufferer submitted to his fate, resumed his former loathsome affection for the bosom fiend, and spent whole miserable days before a looking-glass, with his mouth wide open, watching, in hope and horror, to catch a glimpse of the snake's head far down within his throat. It is supposed that he succeeded; for the attendants once heard a frenzied shout, and, rushing into the room, found Roderick lifeless upon the floor.

He was kept but little longer under restraint. After minute investigation, the medical directors of the asylum decided that his mental disease did not amount to insanity, nor would warrant his confinement, especially as its influence upon his spirits was unfavorable, and might produce the evil which it was meant to remedy. His eccentricities were doubtless great; he had habitually violated many of the customs and prejudices of society; but the world was not, without surer ground, entitled to treat him as a madman. On this decision of such competent authority Roderick was released, and had returned to his native city the very day before his encounter with George Herkimer.

As soon as possible after learning these particulars the sculptor, together with a sad and tremulous companion, sought Elliston at his own house. It was a large, sombre edifice of wood, with pilasters and a balcony, and was divided from one of the principal streets by a terrace of three elevations, which was ascended by successive flights of stone steps. Some immense old elms almost concealed the front of the mansion. This spacious and once magnificent family residence was built by a grandee of the race early in the past century, at which epoch, land being of small comparative value, the garden and other grounds had formed quite an extensive domain. Although a portion of the ancestral heritage had been alienated, there was still a shadowy enclosure in the rear of the mansion where a student, or a dreamer, or a man of stricken heart might lie all day upon the grass, amid the solitude of murmuring boughs, and forget that a city had grown up around him.

Into this retirement the sculptor and his companion were ushered by Scipio, the old black servant, whose wrinkled visage grew almost sunny with intelligence and joy as he paid his humble greetings to one of the two visitors.

"Remain in the arbor," whispered the sculptor to the figure that leaned upon his arm. "You will know whether, and when, to make your appearance."

"God will teach me," was the reply. "May He support me too!"

Roderick was reclining on the margin of a fountain which gushed into the fleckered sunshine with the same clear sparkle and the same voice of airy quietude as when trees of primeval growth flung their shadows across its bosom. How strange is the life of a fountain!—born at every moment, yet of an age coeval with the rocks, and far surpassing the venerable antiquity of a forest.

"You have come! I have expected you," said Elliston, when he became aware of the sculptor's presence.

His manner was very different from that of the preceding day—quiet, courteous, and, as Herkimer thought, watchful both over his guest and himself. This unnatural restraint was almost the only trait that betokened anything amiss. He had just thrown a book upon the grass, where it lay half opened, thus disclosing itself to be a natural history of the serpent tribe, illustrated by lifelike plates. Near it lay that bulky volume, the Ductor Dubitantium of Jeremy Taylor, full of cases of conscience, and in which most men, possessed of a conscience, may find something applicable to their purpose.

"You see," observed Elliston, pointing to the book of serpents, while a smile gleamed upon his lips, "I am making an effort to become better acquainted with my bosom friend; but I find nothing satisfactory in this volume. If I mistake not, he will prove to be *sui generis,* and akin to no other reptile in creation."

"Whence came this strange calamity?" inquired the sculptor.

"My sable friend Scipio has a story," replied Roderick, "of a snake that had lurked in this fountain— pure and innocent as it looks—ever since it was known to the first settlers. This insinuating personage once crept into the vitals of my grandfather and dwelt there many years, tormenting the old gentleman beyond mortal endurance. In short it is a family peculiarity. But, to tell you the truth, I have no faith in this idea of the snake's being an heirloom. He is my own snake, and no man's else."

"But what was his origin?" demanded Herkimer.

"Oh, there is poisonous stuff in any man's heart sufficient to generate a brood of serpents," said Elliston with a hollow laugh. "You should have heard my homilies to the good town's-people. Positively, I deem myself fortunate in having bred but a single serpent. You, however, have none in your bosom, and therefore cannot sympathize with the rest of the world. It gnaws me! It gnaws me!"

With this exclamation Roderick lost his self-control and threw himself upon the grass, testifying his agony by intricate writhings, in which Herkimer could not but fancy a resemblance to the motions of a snake. Then, likewise, was heard that frightful hiss, which often ran through the sufferer's speech, and crept between the words and syllables without interrupting their succession.

"This is awful indeed!" exclaimed the sculptor—"an awful infliction, whether it be actual or imaginary. Tell me, Roderick Elliston, is there any remedy for this loathsome evil?"

"Yes, but an impossible one," muttered Roderick, as he lay wallowing with his face in the grass. "Could I for one instant forget myself, the serpent might not abide within me. It is my diseased self-contemplation that has engendered and nourished him."

"Then forget yourself, my husband," said a gentle voice above him; "forget yourself in the idea of another!"

Rosina had emerged from the arbor, and was bending over him with the shadow of his anguish reflected in her countenance, yet so mingled with hope and unselfish love that all anguish seemed but an earthly shadow and a dream. She touched Roderick with her hand. A tremor shivered through his frame. At that moment, if report be trustworthy, the sculptor beheld a waving motion through the grass, and heard a tinkling sound, as if something had plunged into the fountain. Be the truth as it might, it is certain that Roderick Elliston sat up like a man renewed, restored to his right mind, and rescued from the fiend which had so miserably overcome him in the battle-field of his own breast.

"Rosina!" cried he, in broken and passionate tones, but with nothing of the wild wail that had haunted his voice for so long, "forgive! forgive!"

Her happy tears bedewed his face.

"The punishment has been severe," observed the sculptor. "Even Justice might now forgive; how much more a woman's tenderness! Roderick Elliston, whether the serpent was a physical reptile, or whether the morbidness of your nature suggested that symbol to your fancy, the moral of the story is not the less true and strong. A tremendous Egotism, manifesting itself in your case in the form of jealousy, is as fearful a fiend as ever stole into the human heart. Can a breast, where it has dwelt so long, be purified?"

"Oh yes," said Rosina with a heavenly smile. "The serpent was but a dark fantasy, and what it typified was as shadowy as itself. The past, dismal as it seems, shall fling no gloom upon the future. To give it its due importance we must think of it but as an anecdote in our Eternity."

The Man and the Snake

by AMBROSE BIERCE

It is of veritabyll report, and attested of so many that there be nowe of wyse and learned none to gaynsaye it, that ye serpent hys eye hath a magnetick propertie that whosoe falleth into its svasion is drawn forwards in despyte of his wille, and perisheth miserabyll by ye creature hys bythe.

STRETCHED AT EASE UPON A SOFA, IN GOWN AND SLIPpers, Harker Brayton smiled as he read the foregoing sentence in old Morryster's *Marvells of Science.* "The only marvel in the matter," he said to himself, "is that the wise and learned in Morryster's day should have believed such nonsense as is rejected by most of even the ignorant in ours."

A train of reflection followed—for Brayton was a man of thought—and he unconsciously lowered his book without altering the direction of his eyes. As soon as the volume had gone below the line of sight, something in an obscure corner of the room recalled his attention to his surroundings. What he saw, in the shadow under his bed, was two small points of light, apparently about an inch apart. They might have been reflections of the gas jet above him, in metal nail heads; he gave them but little thought and resumed his reading. A moment later something—some impulse which it did not occur to him to analyze—impelled him to lower the book again and seek for what he saw before. The points of light were still there. They seemed to have become brighter than before, shining with a greenish lustre that he had not at first observed. He thought, too, that they might have moved a trifle—were somewhat nearer. They were still too much in shadow, however, to reveal their nature and origin to an indolent attention, and again he resumed his reading. Suddenly something in the text suggested a thought that made him start and drop the book for the third time to the side of the sofa, whence, escaping from his hand, it fell sprawling to the floor, back upward. Brayton, half-risen, was staring intently into the obscurity beneath the bed, where the points of light shone with, it seemed to him, an added fire. His attention was now fully aroused, his gaze eager and imperative. It disclosed, almost directly under the foot-rail of the bed, the coils of a large serpent—the points of light were its eyes! Its horrible head, thrust flatly forth from the innermost coil and resting upon the outermost, was directed straight

124

toward him, the definition of the wide, brutal jaw and the idiot-like fore-head serving to show the direction of its malevolent gaze. The eyes were no longer merely luminous points; they looked into his own with a meaning, a malign significance.

II

A snake in a bedroom of a modern city dwelling of the better sort is, happily, not so common a phenomenon as to make explanation alto-gether needless. Harker Brayton, a bachelor of thirty-five, a scholar, idler and something of an athlete, rich, popular and of sound health, had re-turned to San Francisco from all manner of remote and unfamiliar coun-tries. His tastes, always a trifle luxurious, had taken on an added exuber-ance from long privation; and the resources of even the Castle Hotel being inadequate to their perfect gratification, he had gladly accepted the hos-pitality of his friend, Dr. Druring, the distinguished scientist. Dr. Druring's house, a large, old-fashioned one in what is now an obscure quarter of the city, had an outer and visible aspect of proud reserve. It plainly would not associate with the contiguous elements of its altered environment, and appeared to have developed some of the eccentricities which come of isolation. One of these was a "wing," conspicuously irrelevant in point of architecture, and no less rebellious in matter of purpose; for it was a com-bination of laboratory, menagerie and museum. It was here that the doctor indulged the scientific side of his nature in the study of such forms of animal life as engaged his interest and comforted his taste—which, it must be confessed, ran rather to the lower types. For one of the higher nimbly and sweetly to recommend itself unto his gentle senses it had at least to retain certain rudimentary characteristics allying it to such "drag-ons of the prime" as toads and snakes. His scientific sympathies were distinctly reptilian; he loved nature's vulgarians and described himself as the Zola of zoölogy. His wife and daughters not having the advantage to share his enlightened curiosity regarding the works and ways of our ill-starred fellow-creatures, were with needless austerity excluded from what he called the Snakery and doomed to companionship with their own kind, though to soften the rigors of their lot he had permitted them out of his great wealth to outdo the reptiles in the gorgeousness of their sur-roundings and to shine with a superior splendor.

Architecturally and in point of "furnishing" the Snakery had a severe simplicity befitting the humble circumstances of its occupants, many of whom, indeed, could not safely have been intrusted with the liberty that is necessary to the full enjoyment of luxury, for they had the trouble-some peculiarity of being alive. In their own apartments, however, they were under as little personal restraint as was compatible with their pro-tection from the baneful habit of swallowing one another; and, as Bray-ton had thoughtfully been apprised, it was more than tradition that some of them had at divers times been found in parts of the premises where it would have embarrassed them to explain their presence. Despite the Snakery and its uncanny associations—to which, indeed, he gave little attention—Brayton found life at the Druring mansion very much to his mind.

III

Beyond a smart shock of surprise and a shudder of mere loathing Mr. Brayton was not greatly affected. His first thought was to ring the call bell and bring a servant; but although the bell cord dangled within easy reach he made no movement toward it; it had occurred to his mind that the act might subject him to the suspicion of fear, which he certainly did not feel. He was more keenly conscious of the incongruous nature of the situation than affected by its perils; it was revolting, but absurd.

The reptile was of a species with which Brayton was unfamiliar. Its length he could only conjecture; the body at the largest visible part seemed about as thick as his forearm. In what way was it dangerous, if in any way? Was it venomous? Was it a constrictor? His knowledge of nature's danger signals did not enable him to say; he had never deciphered the code.

If not dangerous the creature was at least offensive. It was *de trop*— "matter out of place"—an impertinence. The gem was unworthy of the setting. Even the barbarous taste of our time and country, which had loaded the walls of the room with pictures, the floor with furniture and the furniture with bric-a-brac, had not quite fitted the place for this bit of the savage life of the jungle. Besides—insupportable thought!—the exhalations of its breath mingled with the atmosphere which he himself was breathing.

These thoughts shaped themselves with greater or less definition in Brayton's mind and begot action. The process is what we call consideration and decision. It is thus that we are wise and unwise. It is thus that the withered leaf in an autumn breeze shows greater or less intelligence than its fellows, falling upon the land or upon the lake. The secret of human action is an open one: something contracts our muscles. Does it matter if we give to the preparatory molecular changes the name of will?

Brayton rose to his feet and prepared to back softly away from the snake, without disturbing it if possible, and through the door. Men retire so from the presence of the great, for greatness is power and power is menace. He knew that he could walk backward without error. Should the monster follow, the taste which had plastered the walls with paintings had consistently supplied a rack of murderous Oriental weapons from which he could snatch one to suit the occasion. In the mean time the snake's eyes burned with a more pitiless malevolence than before.

Brayton lifted his right foot free of the floor to step backward. That moment he felt a strong aversion to doing so.

"I am accounted brave," he thought; "is bravery, then, no more than pride? Because there are none to witness the shame shall I retreat?"

He was steadying himself with his right hand upon the back of a chair, his foot suspended.

"Nonsense!" he said aloud; "I am not so great a coward as to fear to seem to myself afraid.''

He lifted the foot a little higher by slightly bending the knee and thrust it sharply to the floor—an inch in front of the other! He could not think how that occurred. A trial with the left foot had the same result; it was again in advance of the right. The hand upon the chair back was grasping it; the arm was straight, reaching somewhat backward. One might have said that he was reluctant to lose his hold. The snake's malignant head was still thrust forth from the inner coil as before, the neck level. It had not moved, but its eyes were now electric sparks, radiating an infinity of luminous needles.

The man had an ashy pallor. Again he took a step forward, and another, partly dragging the chair, which when finally released fell upon the floor with a crash. The man groaned; the snake made neither sound nor motion, but its eyes were two dazzling suns. The reptile itself was wholly concealed by them. They gave off enlarging rings of rich and vivid colors, which at their greatest expansion successively vanished like soap-bubbles; they seemed to approach his very face, and anon were an immeasurable distance away. He heard, somewhere, the continuous throbbing of a great drum, with desultory bursts of far music, inconceivably sweet, like the tones of an æolian harp. He knew it for the sunrise melody of Memnon's statue, and thought he stood in the Nileside reeds hearing with exalted sense that immortal anthem through the silence of the centuries.

The music ceased; rather, it became by insensible degrees the distant roll of a retreating thunder-storm. A landscape, glittering with sun and rain, stretched before him, arched with a vivid rainbow framing in its giant curve a hundred visible cities. In the middle distance a vast serpent, wearing a crown, reared its head out of its voluminous convolutions and looked at him with his dead mother's eyes. Suddenly this enchanting landscape seemed to rise swiftly upward like the drop scene at a theatre, and vanished in a blank. Something struck him a hard blow upon the face and breast. He had fallen to the floor; the blood ran from his broken nose and his bruised lips. For a time he was dazed and stunned, and lay with closed eyes, his face against the floor. In a few moments he had recovered, and then knew that this fall, by withdrawing his eyes, had broken the spell that held him. He felt that now, by keeping his gaze averted, he would be able to retreat. But the thought of the serpent within a few feet of his head, yet unseen—perhaps in the very act of springing upon him and throwing its coils about his throat—was too horrible! He lifted his head, stared again into those baleful eyes and was again in bondage.

The snake had not moved and appeared somewhat to have lost its power upon the imagination; the gorgeous illusions of a few moments before were not repeated. Beneath that flat and brainless brow its black, beady eyes simply glittered as at first with an expression unspeakably malignant. It was as if the creature, assured of its triumph, had determined to practise no more alluring wiles.

Now ensued a fearful scene. The man, prone upon the floor, within a yard of his enemy, raised the upper part of his body upon his elbows, his head thrown back, his legs extended to their full length. His face was white between its stains of blood; his eyes were strained open to their uttermost expansion. There was froth upon his lips; it dropped off in flakes. Strong convulsions ran through his body, making almost serpentile undulations. He bent himself at the waist, shifting his legs from side to side. And every movement left him a little nearer to the snake. He thrust his hands forward to brace himself back, yet constantly advanced upon his elbows.

IV

Dr. Druring and his wife sat in the library. The scientist was in rare good humor.

"I have just obtained by exchange with another collector," he said, "a splendid specimen of the *ophiophagus*."

"And what may that be?" the lady inquired with a somewhat languid interest.

"Why, bless my soul, what profound ignorance! My dear, a man who ascertains after marriage that his wife does not know Greek is entitled to a divorce. The *ophiophagus* is a snake that eats other snakes."

"I hope it will eat all yours," she said, absently shifting the lamp. "But how does it get the other snakes? By charming them, I suppose."

"That is just like you, dear," said the doctor, with an affectation of petulance. "You know how irritating to me is any allusion to that vulgar superstition about a snake's power of fascination."

The conversation was interrupted by a mighty cry, which rang through the silent house like the voice of a demon shouting in a tomb! Again and yet again it sounded, with terrible distinctness. They sprang to their feet, the man confused, the lady pale and speechless with fright. Almost before the echoes of the last cry had died away the doctor was out of the room, springing up the stairs two steps at a time. In the corridor in front of Brayton's chamber he met some servants who had come from the upper floor. Together they rushed at the door without knocking. It was unfastened and gave away. Brayton lay upon his stomach on the floor, dead. His head and arms were partly concealed under the foot rail of the bed. They pulled the body away, turning it upon the back. The face was daubed with blood and froth, the eyes were wide open, staring—a dreadful sight!

"Died in a fit," said the scientist, bending his knee and placing his hand upon the heart. While in that position, he chanced to look under the bed. "Good God!" he added, "how did this thing get in here?"

He reached under the bed, pulled out the snake and flung it, still coiled, to the center of the room, whence with a harsh, shuffling sound it slid across the polished floor till stopped by the wall, where it lay without motion. It was a stuffed snake; its eyes were two shoe buttons.

Old Rattler and the King Snake

by DAVID STARR JORDAN

"I only know thee humble, bold,
Haughty, with miseries untold,
And the old curse that left thee cold,
And drove thee ever to the sun
On blistering rocks. . . .
        Thou whose fame
Searchest the grass with tongue of flame,
Making all creatures seem thy game,
When the whole woods before thee run,
Asked but—when all is said and done—
To lie, untrodden, in the sun!"—BRET HARTE.

OLD RATTLER WAS A SNAKE, OF COURSE, AND HE LIVED in the King's River Cañon, high up and down deep in the mountains of California.

He had a hole behind and below a large, flat granite rock, not far from the river, and he called it his home; for in it he slept all night and all winter, but when the sun came back in the spring and took the frost out of the air and the rocks, then he crawled out to lie until he got warm. The stream was clear and swift in the cañon, the waterfalls sang in the side gulch of Roaring River, the wind rustled in the long needles of the yellow pines, and the birds called to their mates in the branches. But Old Rattler did not care for such things. He was just a snake, you know, and his neighbors did not think him a good snake at that, for he was surly and silent, and his big, three-cornered, "coffin-shaped" head, set on a slim, flat neck, was very ugly to see. But when he opened his mouth he was uglier still, for in his upper jaw he had two long fangs, and each one was filled with deadly poison. His vicious old head was covered with gray and wrinkled scales, and his black, beadlike eyes snapped when he opened his mouth to find out whether his fangs were both in working order.

Old Rattler was pretty stiff when he first came from his hole on the morning of this story. He had lain all night coiled up like a rope among the rocks, and his tail felt very cold. But the glad sun warmed the cockles of his heart, and in an hour or two he became limber, and this made him happy in his snaky fashion. But, being warm, he began to be hungry, for it had been a whole month since he had eaten anything. When the first new moon of August came, his skin loosened everywhere and slipped down over his eyes like a veil, so that he could see nothing about him, and could not hunt for frogs by the river nor for chipmunks among the trees. But with the new moon of September all this was over. The rusty brown old coat was changed for a new suit of gray and black, and the diamond shaped checkers all over it were clean and shiny as a set of new clothes ought to be.

There was a little striped chipmunk running up and down the sugar-pine tree over his head, pursing his little mouth and throwing himself into pretty attitudes, as though he were the center of an admiring audience, and Old Rattler kept a steady eye on him. But he was in no hurry about it all. He must first get the kinks out of his neck, and the cold cramps from his tail. There was an old curse on his family, so the other beasts had heard, that kept him always cold, and his tail was the coldest part of all. So he shook it a little, just to show that it was growing limber, and the bone clappers on the end rustled with a sharp, angry noise. Fifteen rattles he had in all—fifteen and a button—and to have so many showed that he was no common member of his hated family. Then he shook his tail again, and more sharply. This was to show all the world that he, Old Rattler, was wide awake, and whoever stepped on him would better look out. Then all the big beasts and little beasts who heard the noise fled away just as fast as ever they could; and to run away was the best thing they could do, for when Old Rattler struck one of them with his fangs all was over with him. So there were many in the cañon, beasts and birds and snakes too, who hated Old Rattler, but only a few dared face him. And one of these was Glittershield, whom men call the King of Snakes, and in a minute I shall tell you why.

And when Old Rattler was doing all that I have said, the King Snake lay low on a bed of pine needles, behind a bunch of fern, and watched with keen, sharp eye. The angry buzz of Rattler's tail, which scared the chipmunks and the bullfrogs and all the rest of the beast folk, was music for Glittershield. He was a snake too, and snakes understand some things better than any of the rest of us.

Glittershield was slim and wiry in his body, as long as Old Rattler himself, but was not so large around. His coat was smooth and glossy, not rough and wrinkly like Old Rattler's, and his up-raised head was small and pretty—for a snake. He was the best dressed of all his kind, and he looked his finest as he faced Old Rattler. His head was shiny black, his throat and neck as white as milk, while all down his body to the end of his tail he was painted with rings, first white, then black, then crimson, and every ring was bright as if it had just been freshly polished that very day.

So the King Snake passed the sheltering fern and came right up to Old Rattler. Rattler opened his sleepy eyes, threw himself on guard with a snap and a buzz, and shook his bony clappers savagely. But the King of Snakes was not afraid. Every snake has a weak spot somewhere, and that is the place to strike him. If he hadn't a weak spot no one else could live about him, and then perhaps he would starve to death at last. If he had not some strong points, where no one could harm him, he couldn't live himself.

As the black crest rose, Old Rattler's tail grew cold, his head dropped, his mouth closed, he straightened out his coil, and staggered helplessly toward his hole.

This was the chance for Glittershield. With a dash so swift that all the rings on his body—red, white, and black—melted into one purple flash, he seized Old Rattler by his throat. He carried no weapons, to be sure. He had neither fangs nor venom. He won his victories by force and dash, not by mean advantage. He was quick and strong, and his little hooked teeth held like the claws of a hawk. Old Rattler closed his mouth because he couldn't help it, and the fangs he could not use were folded back against the roof of his jaw.

The King Snake leaped forward, wound his body in a "love-knot" around Old Rattler's neck, took a "half-hitch" with his tail about the stomach, while the rest of his body lay in a curve like the letter S between the two knots. Then all he had to do was to stiffen up his muscles, and Old Rattler's backbone was snapped off at the neck.

All that remained to Glittershield was to swallow his enemy. First he rubbed his lips all over the body, from the head to the tail, till it was slippery with slime. Then he opened his mouth very wide, with a huge snaky yawn, and face to face he began on Old Rattler. The ugly head was hard to manage, but, after much straining, he clasped his jaws around it, and the venom trickled down his throat like some fiery sauce. Slowly head and neck and body disappeared, and the tail wriggled despairingly, for the tail of the snake folk can not die till sundown, and when it went at last the fifteen rattles and the button were keeping up an angry buzz. And all night long the King of Snakes, twice as big as he ought to be, lay gorged and motionless upon Old Rattler's rock.

And in the morning the little chipmunk ran out on a limb above him, pursed up his lips, and made all kinds of faces, as much as to say, "I did all this, and the whole world was watching while I did it."

"Rikki-Tikki-Tavi"

by RUDYARD KIPLING

THIS IS THE STORY OF THE GREAT WAR THAT RIKKI-TIKKI-tavi fought single-handed, through the bath-rooms of the big bungalow in Segowlee cantonment. Darzee, the tailor-bird, helped him, and Chuchundra, the muskrat, who never comes out into the middle of the floor, but always creeps round by the wall, gave him advice; but Rikki-tikki did the real fighting.

He was a mongoose, rather like a little cat in his fur and his tail, but quite like a weasel in his head and his habits. His eyes and the end of his restless nose were pink; he could scratch himself anywhere he pleased, with any leg, front or back, that he chose to use; he could fluff up his tail till it looked like a bottle-brush, and his war-cry as he scuttled through the long grass, was: "*Rikk-tikk-tikki-tikki-tchk!*"

One day, a high summer flood washed him out of the burrow where he lived with his father and mother, and carried him, kicking and clucking, down a roadside ditch. He found a little wisp of grass floating there, and clung to it till he lost his senses. When he revived, he was lying in the hot sun on the middle of a garden path, very draggled indeed, and a small boy was saying: "Here's a dead mongoose. Let's have a funeral."

"No," said his mother; "let's take him in and dry him. Perhaps he isn't really dead."

They took him into the house, and a big man picked him up between his finger and thumb and said he was not dead but half choked; so they wrapped him in cotton-wool, and warmed him, and he opened his eyes and sneezed.

"Now," said the big man (he was an Englishman who had just moved into the bungalow); "don't frighten him, and we'll see what he'll do."

It is the hardest thing in the world to frighten a mongoose, because he is eaten up from nose to tail with curiosity. The motto of all the mongoose family is, "Run and find out"; and Rikki-tikki was a true mongoose. He looked at the cotton-wool, decided that it was not good to eat, ran all round the table, sat up and put his fur in order, scratched himself, and jumped on the small boy's shoulder.

"Don't be frightened, Teddy," said his father. "That's his way of making friends."

"Ouch! He's tickling under my chin," said Teddy.

132

Rikki-tikki looked down between the boy's collar and neck, snuffed at his ear, and climbed down to the floor, where he sat rubbing his nose.

"Good gracious," said Teddy's mother, "and that's a wild creature! I suppose he's so tame because we've been kind to him."

"All mongooses are like that," said her husband. "If Teddy doesn't pick him up by the tail, or try to put him in a cage, he'll run in and out of the house all day long. Let's give him something to eat."

They gave him a little piece of raw meat. Rikki-tikki liked it immensely, and when it was finished he went out into the veranda and sat in the sunshine and fluffed up his fur to make it dry to the roots. Then he felt better.

"There are more things to find out about in this house," he said to himself, "than all my family could find out in all their lives. I shall certainly stay and find out."

He spent all that day roaming over the house. He nearly drowned himself in the bath-tubs, put his nose into the ink on a writing-table, and burned it on the end of the big man's cigar, for he climbed up in the big man's lap to see how writing was done. At nightfall he ran into Teddy's nursery to watch how kerosene lamps were lighted, and when Teddy went to bed Rikki-tikki climbed up too; but he was a restless companion, because he had to get up and attend to every noise all through the night, and find out what made it. Teddy's mother and father came in, the last thing, to look at their boy, and Rikki-tikki was awake on the pillow. "I don't like that," said Teddy's mother; "he may bite the child." "He'll do no such thing," said the father. "Teddy's safer with that little beast than if he had a bloodhound to watch him. If a snake came into the nursery now—"

But Teddy's mother wouldn't think of anything so awful.

Early in the morning Rikki-tikki came to early breakfast in the veranda riding on Teddy's shoulder, and they gave him banana and some boiled egg; and he sat on all their laps one after the other, because every well-brought-up mongoose always hopes to be a house-mongoose some day and have rooms to run about in, and Rikki-tikki's mother (she used to live in the General's house at Segowlee) had carefully told Rikki what to do if he ever came across white men.

Then Rikki-tikki went out into the garden to see what was to be seen. It was a large garden, only half cultivated, with bushes as big as summer houses of Marshal Niel roses, lime and orange trees, clumps of bamboos, and thickets of high grass. Rikki-tikki licked his lips. "This is a splendid hunting-ground," he said, and his tail grew bottle-brushy at the thought of it, and he scuttled up and down the garden, snuffing here and there till he heard very sorrowful voices in a thorn-bush.

It was Darzee, the tailor-bird, and his wife. They had made a beautiful nest by pulling two big leaves together and stitching them up the edges with fibers, and had filled the hollow with cotton and downy fluff. The nest swayed to and fro, as they sat on the rim and cried.

"What is the matter?" asked Rikki-tikki.

"We are very miserable," said Darzee. "One of our babies fell out of the nest yesterday and Nag ate him."

"H'm!" said Rikki-tikki, "that is very sad—but I am a stranger here. Who is Nag?"

Darzee and his wife only cowered down in the nest without answering, for from the thick grass at the foot of the bush there came a low hiss—a horrid cold sound that made Rikki-tikki jump back two clear feet. Then inch by inch out of the grass rose up the head and spread hood of Nag, the big black cobra, and he was five feet long from tongue to tail. When he had lifted one-third of himself clear of the ground, he stayed balancing to and fro exactly as a dandelion-tuft balances in the wind, and he looked at Rikki-tikki with the wicked snake's eyes that never change their expression, whatever the snake may be thinking of.

"Who is Nag?" he said "*I* am Nag. The great God Brahm put his mark upon all our people when the first cobra spread his hood to keep the sun off Brahm as he slept. Look, and be afraid!"

He spread out his hood more than ever, and Rikki-tikki saw the spectacle-mark on the back of it that looks exactly like the eye part of a hook-and-eye fastening. He was afraid for the minute; but it is impossible for a mongoose to stay frightened for any length of time, and though Rikki-tikki had never met a live cobra before, his mother had fed him on dead ones, and he knew that all a grown mongoose's business in life was to fight and eat snakes. Nag knew that too, and at the bottom of his cold heart he was afraid.

"Well," said Rikki-tikki, and his tail began to fluff up again, "marks or no marks, do you think it is right for you to eat fledglings out of a nest?"

Nag was thinking to himself, and watching the least little movement in the grass behind Rikki-tikki. He knew that mongooses in the garden meant death sooner or later for him and his family; but he wanted to get Rikki-tikki off his guard. So he dropped his head a little, and put it on one side.

"Let us talk," he said. "You eat eggs. Why should not I eat birds?"

"Behind you! Look behind you!" sang Darzee.

Rikki-tikki knew better than to waste time in staring. He jumped up in the air as high as he could go, and just under him whizzed by the head of Nagaina, Nag's wicked wife. She had crept up behind him as he was talking, to make an end of him; and he heard her savage hiss as the stroke missed. He came down almost across her back, and if he had been an old mongoose he would have known that then was the time to break her back with one bite; but he was afraid of the terrible lashing return-stroke of the cobra. He bit, indeed, but did not bite long enough, and he jumped clear of the whisking tail, leaving Nagaina torn and angry.

"Wicked, wicked Darzee!" said Nag, lashing up as high as he could reach toward the nest in the thorn-bush; but Darzee had built it out of reach of snakes, and it only swayed to and fro.

Rikki-tikki felt his eyes growing red and hot (when a mongoose's eyes grow red, he is angry), and he sat back on his tail and hind legs like a little kangaroo, and looked all around him, and chattered with rage. But Nag and Nagaina had disappeared into the grass. When a snake misses its stroke, it never says anything or gives any sign of what it means to do next. Rikki-tikki did not care to follow them, for he did not feel sure that he could manage two snakes at once. So he trotted off to the gravel path near the house, and sat down to think. It was a serious matter for him.

If you read the old books of natural history, you will find they say that when the mongoose fights the snake and happens to get bitten, he runs off and eats some herb that cures him. That is not true. The victory is only a matter of quickness of eye and quickness of foot,—snake's blow against mongoose's jump,—and as no eye can follow the motion of a snake's head when it strikes, that makes things much more wonderful than any magic herb. Rikki-tikki knew he was a young mongoose, and it made him all the more pleased to think that he had managed to escape a blow from behind. It gave him confidence in himself, and when Teddy came running down the path, Rikki-tikki was ready to be petted.

But just as Teddy was stooping, something flinched a little in the dust, and a tiny voice said: "Be careful. I am death!" It was Karait, the dusty brown snakeling that lies for choice on the dusty earth; and his bite is as dangerous as the cobra's. But he is so small that nobody thinks of him, and so he does the more harm to people.

Rikki-tikki's eyes grew red again, and he danced up to Karait with the peculiar rocking, swaying motion that he had inherited from his family. It looks very funny, but it is so perfectly balanced a gait that you can fly off from it at any angle you please; and in dealing with snakes this is an advantage. If Rikki-tikki had only known, he was doing a much more dangerous thing than fighting Nag, for Karait is so small, and can turn so quickly, that unless Rikki bit him close to the back of the head, he would get the return-stroke in his eye or lip. But Rikki did not know: his eyes were all red, and he rocked back and forth, looking for a good place to hold. Karait struck out. Rikki jumped sideways and tried to run in, but the wicked little dusty gray head lashed within a fraction of his shoulder, and he had to jump over the body, and the head followed his heels close.

Teddy shouted to the house: "Oh, look here! Our mongoose is killing a snake"; and Rikki-tikki heard a scream from Teddy's mother. His father ran out with a stick, but by the time he came up, Karait had lunged out once too far, and Rikki-tikki had sprung, jumped on the snake's back, dropped his head far between his fore legs, bitten as high up the back as he could get hold, and rolled away. That bite paralyzed Karait, and Rikki-tikki was just going to eat him up from the tail, after the custom of his family at dinner, when he remembered that a full meal makes a slow mongoose, and if he wanted all his strength and quickness ready, he must keep himself thin.

He went away for a dust-bath under the castor-oil bushes, while Teddy's father beat the dead Karait. "What is the use of that?" thought Rikki-tikki. "I have settled it all"; and then Teddy's mother picked him up from the dust and hugged him, crying that he had saved Teddy from death, and Teddy's father said that he was a providence, and Teddy looked on with big scared eyes. Rikki-tikki was rather amused at all the fuss, which, of course, he did not understand. Teddy's mother might just as well have petted Teddy for playing in the dust. Rikki was thoroughly enjoying himself.

That night, at dinner, walking to and fro among the wine-glasses on the table, he could have stuffed himself three times over with nice things; but he remembered Nag and Nagaina, and though it was very pleasant to be patted and petted by Teddy's mother, and to sit on Teddy's shoulder, his eyes would get red from time to time, and he would go off into his long war-cry of "*Rikk-tikk-tikki-tikki-tchk!*"

Teddy carried him off to bed, and insisted on Rikki-tikki sleeping under his chin. Rikki-tikki was too well bred to bite or scratch, but as soon as Teddy was asleep he went off for his nightly walk round the house, and in the dark he ran up against Chuchundra, the muskrat, creeping round by the wall. Chuchundra is a broken-hearted little beast. He whimpers and cheeps all the night, trying to make up his mind to run into the middle of the room, but he never gets there.

"Don't kill me," said Chuchundra, almost weeping. "Rikki-tikki, don't kill me."

"Do you think a snake-killer kills muskrats?" said Rikki-tikki scornfully.

"Those who kill snakes get killed by snakes," said Chuchundra, more sorrowfully than ever.

"And how am I to be sure that Nag won't mistake me for you some dark night?"

"There's not the least danger," said Rikki-tikki; "but Nag is in the garden, and I know you don't go there."

"My cousin Chua, the rat, told me—" said Chuchundra, and then he stopped.

"Told you what?"

"H'sh! Nag is everywhere, Rikki-tikki. You should have talked to Chua in the garden."

"I didn't—so you must tell me. Quick, Chuchundra, or I'll bite you!"

Chuchundra sat down and cried till the tears rolled off his whiskers. "I am a very poor man," he sobbed. "I never had spirit enough to run out into the middle of the room. H'sh! I mustn't tell you anything. Can't you *hear*, Rikki-tikki?"

Rikki-tikki listened. The house was as still as still, but he thought he could just catch the faintest *scratch-scratch* in the world,—a noise as faint as that of a wasp walking on a window-pane,—the dry scratch of a snake's scales on brickwork.

"That's Nag or Nagaina," he said to himself; "and he is crawling into the bath-room sluice. You're right, Chuchundra; I should have talked to Chua."

He stole off to Teddy's bath-room, but there was nothing there, and then to Teddy's mother's bath-room. At the bottom of the smooth plaster wall there was a brick pulled out to make a sluice for the bath-water, and as Rikki-tikki stole in by the masonry curb where the bath is put, he heard Nag and Nagaina whispering together outside in the moonlight.

"When the house is emptied of people," said Nagaina to her husband, "*he* will have to go away, and then the garden will be our own again. Go in quietly, and remember that the big man who killed Karait is the first one to bite. Then come out and tell me, and we will hunt for Rikki-tikki together."

"But are you sure that there is anything to be gained by killing the people?" said Nag.

"Everything. When there were no people in the bungalow, did we have any mongoose in the garden? So long as the bungalow is empty, we are king and queen of the garden; and remember that as soon as our eggs in the melon-bed hatch (as they may to-morrow), our children will need room and quiet."

"I had not thought of that," said Nag. "I will go, but there is no need that we should hunt for Rikki-tikki afterward. I will kill the big man and his wife, and the child if I can, and come away quietly. Then the bungalow will be empty, and Rikki-tikki will go."

Rikki-tikki tingled all over with rage and hatred at this, and then Nag's head came through the sluice, and his five feet of cold body followed it. Angry as he was, Rikki-tikki was very frightened as he saw the size of the big cobra. Nag coiled himself up, raised his head, and looked into the bath-room in the dark, and Rikki could see his eyes glitter.

"Now, if I kill him here, Nagaina will know; and if I fight him on the open floor, the odds are in his favor. What am I to do?" said Rikki-tikki-tavi.

Nag waved to and fro, and then Rikki-tikki heard him drinking from the biggest water-jar that was used to fill the bath. "That is good," said the snake. "Now, when Karait was killed, the big man had a stick. He may have that stick still, but when he comes in to bathe in the morning he will not have a stick. I shall wait here till he comes. Nagaina—do you hear me?—I shall wait here in the cool till daytime."

There was no answer from outside, so Rikki-tikki knew Nagaina had gone away. Nag coiled himself down, coil by coil, round the bulge at the bottom of the water-jar, and Rikki-tikki stayed still as death. After an hour he began to move, muscle by muscle, toward the jar. Nag was asleep, and Rikki-tikki looked at his big back, wondering which would be the best place for a good hold. "If I don't break his back at the first jump," said Rikki, "he can still fight; and if he fights—O Rikki!" He looked at the thickness of the neck below the hood, but that was too much for him; and a bite near the tail would only make Nag savage.

"It must be the head," he said at last; "the head above the hood; and, when I am once there I must not let go."

Then he jumped. The head was lying a little clear of the water-jar, under the curve of it; and, as his teeth met, Rikki braced his back against the bulge of the red earthenware to hold down the head. This gave him just one second's purchase and he made the most of it. Then he was battered to and fro as a rat is shaken by a dog—to and fro on the floor, up and down, and round in great circles; but his eyes were red, and he held on as the body cartwhipped over the floor, upsetting the tin dipper and the soap-dish and the flesh-brush, and banged against the tin side of the bath. As he held he closed his jaws tighter and tighter, for he made sure he would be banged to death, and, for the honor of his family, he preferred to be found with his teeth locked. He was dizzy, aching, and felt shaken to pieces when something went off like a thunderclap just behind him; a hot wind knocked him senseless and red fire singed his fur. The big man had been wakened by the noise, and had fired both barrels of a shot-gun into Nag just behind the hood.

Rikki-tikki held on with his eyes shut, for now he was quite sure he was dead; but the head did not move, and the big man picked him up and said: "It's the mongoose again, Alice; the little chap has saved *our* lives now." Then Teddy's mother came in with a very white face, and saw what was left of Nag, and Rikki-tikki dragged himself to Teddy's bedroom and spent half the rest of the night shaking himself tenderly to find out whether he really was broken into forty pieces, as he fancied.

When morning came he was very stiff, but well pleased with his doings. "Now I have Nagaina to settle with, and she will be worse than five Nags, and there's no knowing when the eggs she spoke of will hatch. Goodness! I must go and see Darzee," he said.

Without waiting for breakfast, Rikki-tikki ran to the thorn-bush where Darzee was singing a song of triumph at the top of his voice. The news of Nag's death was all over the garden, for the sweeper had thrown the body on the rubbish-heap.

"Oh, you stupid tuft of feathers!" said Rikki-tikki, angrily. "Is this the time to sing?"

"Nag is dead—is dead—is dead!" sang Darzee. "The valiant Rikki-tikki caught him by the head and held fast. The big man brought the bang-stick and Nag fell in two pieces! He will never eat my babies again."

"All that's true enough; but where's Nagaina?" said Rikki-tikki, looking carefully round him.

"Nagaina came to the bath-room sluice and called for Nag," Darzee went on; "and Nag came out on the end of a stick—the sweeper picked him up on the end of a stick and threw him upon the rubbish-heap. Let us sing about the great, the red-eyed Rikki-tikki!" and Darzee filled his throat and sang.

"If I could get up to your nest, I'd roll all your babies out!" said Rikki-tikki. "You don't know when to do the right thing at the right time. You're safe enough in your nest there, but it's war for me down here. Stop singing a minute, Darzee."

"For the great, the beautiful Rikki-tikki's sake I will stop," said Darzee. "What is it, O Killer of the terrible Nag!"

"Where is Nagaina, for the third time?"

"On the rubbish-heap by the stables mourning for Nag. Great is Rikki-tikki with the white teeth."

"Bother my white teeth! Have you ever heard where she keeps her eggs?"

"In the melon-bed, on the end nearest the wall, where the sun strikes nearly all day. She had them there weeks ago."

"And you never thought it worth while to tell me? The end nearest the wall, you said?"

"Rikki-tikki, you are not going to eat her eggs?"

"Not eat exactly; no. Darzee, if you have a grain of sense you will fly off to the stables and pretend that your wing is broken, and let Nagaina chase you away to this bush? I must get to the melon-bed, and if I went there now she'd see me."

Darzee was a feather-brained little fellow who could never hold more than one idea at a time in his head; and just because he knew that Nagaina's children were born in eggs like his own, he didn't think at first that it was fair to kill them. But his wife was a sensible bird, and she knew that cobra's eggs meant young cobras later on; so she flew off from the nest, and left Darzee to keep the babies warm, and continue his song about the death of Nag. Darzee was very like a man in some ways.

She fluttered in front of Nagaina by the rubbish-heap, and cried out, "Oh, my wing is broken! The boy in the house threw a stone at me and broke it." Then she fluttered more desperately than ever.

Nagaina lifted up her head and hissed, "You warned Rikki-tikki when I would have killed him. Indeed and truly, you've chosen a bad place to be lame in." And she moved toward Darzee's wife, slipping along over the dust.

"The boy broke it with a stone!" shrieked Darzee's wife.

"Well! It may be some consolation to you when you're dead to know that I shall settle accounts with the boy. My husband lies on the rubbish-heap this morning, but before night the boy in the house will lie very still. What is the use of running away? I am sure to catch you. Little fool, look at me!"

Darzee's wife knew better than to do *that,* for a bird who looks at a snake's eyes gets so frightened that she cannot move. Darzee's wife fluttered on, piping sorrowfully, and never leaving the ground, and Nagaina quickened her pace.

Rikki-tikki heard them going up the path from the stables, and he raced for the end of the melon-patch near the wall. There, in the warm litter about the melons, very cunningly hidden, he found twenty-five eggs, about the size of a bantam's eggs, but with whitish skin instead of shell.

"I was not a day too soon," he said; for he could see the baby cobras curled up inside the skin, and he knew that the minute they were hatched they could each kill a man or a mongoose. He bit off the tops of the eggs as fast as he could, taking care to crush the young cobras, and turned over the litter from time to time to see whether he had missed any. At last there were only three eggs left, and Rikki-tikki began to chuckle to himself, when he heard Darzee's wife screaming:

"Rikki-tikki, I led Nagaina toward the house, and she has gone into the veranda, and—oh, come quickly—she means killing!"

Rikki-tikki smashed two eggs, and tumbled backward down the melonbed with the third egg in his mouth, and scuttled to the veranda as hard as he could put foot to the ground. Teddy and his mother and father were there at early breakfast; but Rikki-tikki saw that they were not eating anything. They sat stone-still, and their faces were white. Nagaina was coiled up on the matting by Teddy's chair, within easy striking distance of Teddy's bare leg, and she was swaying to and fro singing a song of triumph.

"Son of the big man that killed Nag," she hissed, "stay still. I am not ready yet. Wait a little. Keep very still, all you three. If you move I strike, and if you do not move I strike. Oh, foolish people, who killed my Nag!"

Teddy's eyes were fixed on his father, and all his father could do was to whisper. "Sit still, Teddy. You mustn't move. Teddy, keep still."

Then Rikki-tikki came up and cried: "Turn round, Nagaina; turn and fight!"

"All in good time," said she, without moving her eyes. "I will settle my account with *you* presently. Look at your friends, Rikki-tikki. They are still and white; they are afraid. They dare not move, and if you come a step nearer I strike."

"Look at your eggs," said Rikki-tikki, "in the melon-bed near the wall. Go and look, Nagaina,"

The big snake turned half round, and saw the egg on the veranda. "Ah-h! Give it to me," she said.

Rikki-tikki put his paws one on each side of the egg, and his eyes were blood-red. "What price for a snake's egg? For a young cobra? For a young king-cobra? For the last—the very last—of the brood? The ants are eating all the others down by the melon-bed."

Nagaina spun clear round, forgetting everything for the sake of the one egg; and Rikki-tikki saw Teddy's father shoot out a big hand, catch Teddy by the shoulder, and drag him across the little table with the tea-cups, safe and out of reach of Nagaina.

"Tricked! Tricked! Tricked! *Rikk-tck-tck!*" chuckled Rikki-tikki. "The boy is safe, and it was I—I—I that caught Nag by the hood last night in the bath-room." Then he began to jump up and down, all four feet together, his head close to the floor. "He threw me to and fro, but he could not shake me off. He was dead before the big man blew him in two. I did it. *Rikki-tikki-tck-tck!* Come then, Nagaina. Come and fight with me. You shall not be a widow long."

Nagaina saw that she had lost her chance of killing Teddy, and the egg lay between Rikki-tikki's paws. "Give me the egg, Rikki-tikki. Give me the last of my eggs, and I will go away and never come back," she said, lowering her hood.

"Yes, you will go away, and you will never come back; for you will go to the rubbish-heap with Nag. Fight, widow! The big man has gone for his gun! Fight!"

Rikki-tikki was bounding all round Nagaina, keeping just out of reach of her stroke, his little eyes like hot coals. Nagaina gathered herself together, and flung out at him. Rikki-tikki jumped up and backward. Again and again and again she struck, and each time her head came with a whack on the matting of the veranda and she gathered herself together like a watch-spring. Then Rikki-tikki danced in a circle to get behind her, and Nagaina spun round to keep her head to his head, so that the rustle of her tail on the matting sounded like dry leaves blown along by the wind.

He had forgotten the egg. It still lay on the veranda, and Nagaina came nearer and nearer to it, till at last, while Rikki-tikki was drawing breath, she caught it in her mouth, turned to the veranda steps, and flew like an arrow down the path, with Rikki-tikki behind her. When the cobra runs for her life, she goes like a whiplash flicked across a horse's neck.

Rikki-tikki knew that he must catch her, or all the trouble would begin again. She headed straight for the long grass by the thorn-bush, and as he was running Rikki-tikki heard Darzee still singing his foolish little song of triumph. But Darzee's wife was wiser. She flew off her nest as Nagaina came along, and flapped her wings about Nagaina's head. If Darzee had helped they might have turned her; but Nagaina only lowered her hood and went on. Still, the instant's delay brought Rikki-tikki up to her, and as she plunged into the rat-hole where she and Nag used to live, his little white teeth were clenched on her tail, and he went down with her—and very few mongooses, however wise and old they may be, care to follow a cobra into its hole. It was dark in the hole; and Rikki-tikki never knew when it might open out and give Nagaina room to turn and strike at him. He held on savagely, and struck out his feet to act as brakes on the dark slope of the hot, moist earth.

Then the grass by the mouth of the hole stopped waving, and Darzee said: "It is all over with Rikki-tikki! We must sing his deathsong. Valiant Rikki-tikki is dead! For Nagaina will surely kill him underground."

So he sang a very mournful song that he made up all on the spur of the minute, and just as he got to the most touching part the grass quivered again, and Rikki-tikki, covered with dirt, dragged himself out of the hole leg by leg, licking his whiskers. Darzee stopped with a little shout. Rikki-tikki shook some of the dust out of his fur and sneezed. "It is all over," he said. "The widow will never come out again." And the red ants that live between the grass stems heard him, and began to troop down one after another to see if he had spoken the truth.

Rikki-tikki curled himself up in the grass and slept where he was— slept and slept till it was late in the afternoon, for he had done a hard day's work.

"Now," he said, when he awoke, "I will go back to the house. Tell the Coppersmith, Darzee, and he will tell the garden that Nagaina is dead."

The Coppersmith is a bird who makes a noise exactly like the beating of a little hammer on a copper pot; and the reason he is always making it is because he is the town-crier to every Indian garden, and tells all the news to everybody who cares to listen. As Rikki-tikki went up the path, he heard his "attention" notes like a tiny dinner-gong; and then the steady *"Ding-dong-tock!* Nag is dead— *dong!* Nagaina is dead! *Ding-dong-tock!"* That set all the birds in the garden singing, and the frogs croaking; for Nag and Nagaina used to eat frogs as well as little birds.

When Rikki got to the house, Teddy and Teddy's mother (she looked very white still, for she had been fainting) and Teddy's father came out and almost cried over him; and that night he ate all that was given him till he could eat no more, and went to bed on Teddy's shoulder, where Teddy's mother saw him when she came to look at night.

"He saved our lives and Teddy's life," she said to her husband. "Just think, he saved all our lives."

Rikki-tikki woke up with a jump, for all the mongooses are light sleepers.

"Oh, it's you," said he. "What are you bothering for? All the cobras are dead; and if they weren't, I'm here."

Rikki-tikki had a right to be proud of himself; but he did not grow too proud, and he kept that garden as a mongoose should keep it, with tooth and jump and spring and bite, till never a cobra dared show its head inside the walls.

Serpent Versus Donovan

by ALISTAIR MacCRAE

ON THE THIRD FRIDAY OF SEPTEMBER THE TOWN COUN-
cil of Ballyfintry appointed a committee with extraordinary powers to
deal with the delicate question of Sarah Donovan's attitude to the new
wide road that was coming into the town to bring civilization and a glorious dust-covered, petrol-stinking, man-mind-thyself prosperity to it and
to the whole district. The road was then only two miles away and the
surveyors would soon have to decide whether to bring it marching straight
through the town or make a detour to avoid it. That had been written down
in red ink on the agenda, and Terence O'Shea, conscious of the deep
solemnity of the occasion, had reared himself on his hind legs, given an
introductory cough, and made a motion to appoint a committee to investigate Sarah Donovan's mind, and apply what measures they might
consider necessary to work the miracle of a change in it, and so allow the
new era of milk and honey to come into the place unhindered.

The first they elected to the committee was that little slimy bum of a
lawyer, Aloysius Slaney, and soon he was flanked to east and west by the
corporate wisdom, cunning, and snake's-belly sagacity of Cornelius Rodgers, the proprietor of the Plough Hotel, and Terence Josceyline, the
butcher.

As soon as the meeting was over, this unholy trinity of roguery got into
a huddle and went to a private room in the Plough, where they sat knocking the guts out of a five-gill bottle of Scotch whiskey and bending their
imaginations over the smoke of three cigars.

Slaney put the point to them with commendable brevity. In a nutshell,
it was this. Here was that ould stick Donovan, twelve solid years left
alone, with her man marching out of it and away to the far corners of the
earth, where, for all was known, he might be settled down now with a
handful of naked black women filing his teeth for him, and herself living
a life on a thin string of empty days that made dust and ashes look like
strawberry trifle by comparison, and lighting useless lamps in windows
fore and aft every night the way they would cast a beam of light for his
wayward feet coming back to her.

Aloysius Slaney took a hefty pull at his cigar and blew a reflective ring
of smoke round a ray of sunshine. "That," he said, in his best dehydrated
legal voice, "in so far as it goes, is her own affair and her own funeral,

but now we come to our affair and what looks like being the funeral of our unborn prosperity if we're not careful.

"This Sarah Donovan owns a garden, and that garden, as you gentlemen well know, juts out from her doorstep beyond all Christian proportion to the size of the residence, and at a place that's strategically placed to command the entry of the new wide road that's coming down the valley. But for the same sentimental old foolishness that causes this female martyr to light lamps in her windows and live the frozen life of a celibate nun, she refuses point-blank to allow any alteration to her garden till her man comes back, and when, if ever, that will be, God only knows."

They pondered that over in the depths of a fog of smoke and the biting smell of whiskey. Josceyline said: "Can't we force the issue?"

"No use," said Slaney. "She has all the trumps. She holds that bit of land on a lease that makes it impossible for us to touch it."

"That's what they call democracy," grunted Rodgers. "Democracy means allowin' the random whims of one old woman wipin' her feet on the door mat of madness to hold the whole process of civilization locked up in the hollow of a withered hand. It means the forward march of human progress is to be held at bay by a yellow old face lookin' into the past after the shadow of a man she'll surely never see again." Having got that off his chest, Rodgers turned his face into the whiskey glass again.

"Send a deputation," said Josceyline, "and offer the ould witch money. Money always takes the trick."

"Not with this one," said Slaney. "We've tried it. It was just like shouting into an empty house."

"Did you offer her enough?" said Rodgers.

"Enough and more than enough." Slaney was flat, emphatic, and perfectly final about that.

"This is fanaticism," he said, "and putting money up against it is like popping peas at the Pyramids."

"There's only one thing for it," Josceyline said, "and that's to get her convinced he's dead. If she was convinced he was dead she'd soon soften up."

"That's easy said, but how are we goin' to do it?" said Rodgers. "Are we goin' to produce a homebaked corpse of Michael Donovan an' serve it up on a plate or what? For if you ask me, that ould wan will fall for nothing less."

"Ye'd think," said Josceyline, "ye'd think, in these days of enlightened opinion, that twelve years of unmitigated absence would be a tolerable equivalent for death in even the most stupid of female minds."

"Tach!" said Rodgers. "I'm sick of female minds. They are instruments that don't answer to the logical stimulus of natural common sense. Ye'd need the wisdom of the serpent—"

Aloysius Slaney came to sudden life on that. He jumped to his feet and smashed one claw hand down on the table. "Serpent!" he cried. "Serpent! That's what we want."

2

In the silence that followed, Josceyline started slowly and methodically to rub his long nose while he stared darkly and doubtfully into Slaney's face. After a while Slaney answered the unspoken question that hung thick in the air of the room. He said: "No, I'm not mad."

Rodgers squinted at him over his cigar. "If ye're not itself," he said, "ye're givin' what I would call a damned good impersonation of it. What the devil do ye mean by sayin' we want a serpent?"

Slaney smiled his most slimy smile and weaved a vague pattern in the air with his cigar. "Let me ask *you* one first," he said. "What, now, is the clearest thing you remember about this Michael Donovan?"

Rodgers wrinkled his nose in thought. "Well, it's all damned stupid," he said, "but if ye want to know, my clearest memory of Donovan was him standin' out there in my own bar, mad drunk and roarin' out 'The Wearin' o' the Green' in a voice like ten locomotives runnin' over Fingal's Stones without anny rails."

"And you?" Slaney turned his weasel face on Josceyline.

Josceyline looked down the length of his nose at the lawyer and said: "So far as my memory can descend the ladder of human frailty to mind such a man at all, my clearest recollection—indeed my only recollection of him—was one day he came into my shop and bought a pound of tripe and then went up the middle of the High Street eatin' it raw out of the paper. I thought at the time it was the most glarin' exhibition of sodden, unmannered ignorance I'd ever seen in a civilized Christian town, and the place at the time full of foreign visitors from England."

Slaney listened till they were both finished with their reminiscences. Then he gave a bit of a disparaging grunt. "Well," he said, "there's not much in either of your contributions to help on the matter in hand. Now I'll tell ye what I mind about Michael Donovan. I mind a queer sort of a pin he always wore in his tie. It was made of rolled gold in the shape of a serpent rearing up to strike, with two green stones for eyes. A cruel-looking ornament, but fascinating—damned fascinating. It fascinated me, and I've never seen another like it."

Rodgers said: "Now ye come to mention it I do mind him wearin' a thing like that. He used to call it his lucky pin."

"Of course," said Josceyline, "his lucky pin. He never moved without it stuck into his cravat like a charm. The man was up to the neck in ignor-ant superstition."

Slaney broke in again, his thin reedy voice filling his words with all the double meanings his ferreting mind could dig up. "Exactly," he said. "Donovan never moved without that pin. I want you to remember that because it's important—it's the most important thing that's been said. And beside it I want you to lay the fact that I can mind every detail of that pin, which wouldn't be a wonder, for every time I met the man I found myself lookin' into a snake's head with two green eyes rearin' out at me."

Rodgers thought: "That's because ye've lost the way of lookin' people in the face," but he didn't say it. What he did say was: "All this might be very interesting to you, but I don't see that it's getting us anywhere, Aloysius."

"Ye're damned right," muttered Josceyline, "it isn't. Drawin' pretty pictures of serpents out of a heap of old memories won't ever help us to move the mountain of prejudice and stupid sentiment that ould Sarah Donovan has for a mind."

"Maybe not," said Slaney, "but I've an idea that it might."

"Spill it, then," said Rodgers impatiently, "for God knows there's a remarkable dearth of ideas on the subject round here."

"I was just thinkin'," said Aloysius Slaney softly. "I was just thinkin' that if that pin was to appear in the town here without Donovan's ugly puss stickin' above it, the thought might enter that old fool's head that he was indeed dead, defunct, and finally departed this mortal coil."

Rodgers sat glowering into space, and the birth of a sneer began to visit his ugly mouth. "A tolerable sort of inspiration for the likes of you, Aloysius," he said. "Man, I can just see that pin, which I suppose ye'll conjure up, like Ali Baba, out of the moon, comin' sailin' in to Ballyfintry under its own steam to settle down under the startled eyes of ould Sarah."

"Which statement only goes to prove that ye're even a bigger fool than ye look, Cornelius," said Slaney sweetly. "The aforesaid pin won't come sailin' in anywhere under any sort of steam. Doesn't it strike your mislaid intelligence as possible that I could have a perfect duplicate of that pin made by a jewler I know, and that I could find a stranger to bring it to Sarah Donovan, surrounded and garnished by a suitable story of the lonely death of her useless husband?"

That bit of Slaney's wisdom was followed by a respectful silence while the other two measured the plan in their minds, and took thorough stock of all its implications. At last Josceyline said: "It's a long shot, Aloysius. I don't think she would fall for it."

"Then ye've a lamentable lack of the knowledge of human nature," said Slaney. "Remember the age of the ould stick and the tormentin' way she's lived for the last twelve years."

"Even at that—" said Josceyline. Rodgers said nothing, only blew out a great cloud of blue smoke and stared into it with the wrapped-up look of a fortuneteller.

But Slaney was warming up to his idea now, and didn't care what they said or did. "You leave this to me, and the man I'll get to tell the story," he said. "When she's finally convinced that Donovan's dead, and sees there's no longer any use holdin' the fort for him, she'll be damned glad to take the money we've offered and let the new road cut a way through that jungle wilderness she calls a garden."

Rodgers spoke at last. "You're a cunning devil, Aloysius Slaney," was all he said, but he said it in a tone that was well laced with a mixture of envy and admiration, not to mention the three new glasses of Scotch whiskey he poured out to wet the launching of the idea.

The next day Aloysius Slaney had business in Ballyfergus, about ten miles away, first with a jeweler, and then with an ocher-faced man in a muffler who smelt of dulce and stale beer. That very night the ocher-faced man, who called himself Patrick Tierney, spent a quiet hour or so in the dark prowling round the garden of Sarah Donovan, watching the ceremony of her lighting the lamps and all the other paraphernalia that marked the end of a lonely day. Then, when he was sure she had gone to bed, this Patrick Tierney quietly opened a window and climbed in. Being a careful man he took off his boots before putting his feet on the floor inside the house; then he set about the task of gathering what information he could about Michael Donovan. He didn't get much, but had a good squint at a photograph on the wall in which Donovan stood in all his glory, well plastered up for the occasion and wearing the serpent pin in front of him.

The man stood looking at this for a long while, as if soaking every feature of it into his mind, then he turned and went quietly out by the way he had come in. The only thing he had neglected to take care of was the churned-up mess he had made walking up and down in the garden to keep warm while he waited. But as the garden was well covered in by overgrown bushes and weeds, no one would ever notice that.

Two days later the ocher-faced man again visited Ballyfintry, but this time in daylight. He walked down the street looking this way and that, as a stranger would, and stopping now and again on his way to ask someone for directions to the house of the Widow Donovan. He put a sort of soft, meaning emphasis on the word "Widow," and more than one that he asked noticed that he was wearing in his cravat a gold pin shaped like a rearing serpent—an ornament that seemed vaguely familiar to them.

3

Sarah Donovan looked more every day like a lantern stuck on the end of a thin stick, her face being so hollow and the cheekbones rearing up like two platforms under the deep sockets of her eyes with the dark fever burning away far back in them.

She was thin to gauntness and was never still in her dark shadowy house, drifting like a starved ghost from room to room, always sorting this and arranging that, cleaning what was already clean, burnishing and polishing brass and copper that already shone with a hard malevolence in the dimness of her four rooms.

The overgrown garden and the everlasting curtains over the windows made a formidable barrier for any sunlight that tried to get in. That had been the way of it for so many years now that the place had taken on the look of a mausoleum in which an automatic corpse perambulated around inside. Three times a week she would leave the place for the space of an hour, once to make confession and receive Communion at the Church of Our Lady, the second time to draw her pension at the Post Office, and the third time to buy in what little she needed to keep her spare frame in motion. On all these occasions she would sail through the place like a forlorn derelict ship, bare-masted, her thin face pointed forward the way she was going, and never as much as a look to right or left, let alone the human weakness of a word in the passing.

When she came back again, she would take off her coat and pick up the endless thread of useless duty where she had left off, filling in the slow time till dusk, when she would light a lamp in the front window and one in the back. Only then she would stand still for a little minute, with her eyes closed and her lips moving without any sound coming, before lying down to sleep like the last installment of death till the first gray of the morning. On Tuesday forenoons she would wash clothes and hang them on a big wooden clotheshorse round the fire to dry, and always among them would be some of Michael Donovan's underclothes, maybe a shirt or a pair of drawers, or socks—always some little thing that pinned her mind and activity to the memory of her man.

In that way she was more faithful to the absence of him than many a woman was to the living presence of a man, which was remarkable, considering that Michael Donovan had been a cruel-natured individual who gave her many a bruise when they were in it together. But that is the nature of some women; the more cruel a man is, the better they seem to serve him.

4

It was on one of these Tuesdays that the stranger knocked at the door and she standing in the middle of wringing out a pair of her husband's woolen drawers. When the knock came she stopped in the middle of it, her hands still tightly wrapped round the wool like two great bundles of knotted veins. The sound of the knock seemed a long time in penetrating to her mind, and it was repeated in a louder tone before she stepped, like a yellow wraith, out of the cloud of steam and went to the door. When she opened the door she found a strange man standing there, his face well beaten up with all kinds of weather, and dressed like one who knew more about ships than houses.

But face and body and everything else were lost on Sarah Donovan, whose eyes were fixed in a nailed-down hypnotism on one thing only—a tiepin in the shape of a rearing serpent with two green stones for eyes that looked at her from below the man's unshaven chin.

Patrick Tierney opened his mouth to say what his business was, but before he could get a blessed word out, the long yellow forefinger of the woman was fastened on the tiepin. "Where did ye get that?" she asked, her voice making a low vibration in the still morning air.

The man saw then that the pin was a ticket of admission to this place just as the lawyer had said, so he asked in a quiet, civil way if he could come in and remove the conversation from the handy ears of the town that might be passing and not above loitering a bit to pick up all that was going.

She brought him in then, and he sat down heavily on a horsehair chair beside the highly polished table in the sitting room, where he was facing again the flat-faced likeness of Michael Donovan. As for the old woman, she just stood watching the serpent's head, like a still statue in gray and yellow stone, with never a move out of her.

Patrick Tierney took the pin out then and rolled it over and over between his fingers. "It belonged to a dead man," he said, "a man ye know well, Mrs. Donovan."

The change in her was sudden, like the shudder of an electric shock convulsing the movement into the muscles of her face and hands. She screamed out in a thin shrill cry: "That's a lie! Before God, that's a lie! Michael Donovan's living and coming back again."

"I'm sorry, Missus," said Tierney. "It's a hard thing breakin' it to ye, but I know what ye know, and that is if Michael Donovan ever comes back it'll be carried in the arms of angels he'll be, for I got this off his dead body."

The face of the woman went into a stillness then and did not change any more. It was set the way it would be in death, frozen still in its mold, and her body was quiet so that she did not even seem to breathe. Her eyes were fixed on him with such a look as made Tierney forget forever the rest of the highly colored story Aloysius Slaney had built up for him. All he could do now was look into the horrible dark places of Sarah Donovan's eyes and babble the words: "He's dead, dead. I got this off his body." Then he waited for her to speak, while the silence stretched itself out like a long rope on which was hung the far-away life of the town in little muffled memories of sound. At last, when she did speak, it was only to ask him what his name was and where he lived.

He told her his name was Patrick Tierney and for the passing time he was staying with a Mrs. Stone in the High Street of Ballyfergus, his ship being in Belfast having her bottom scraped. And all the time he cursed himself inside for being such a pulp-brained bum as to allow the eyes of one mad old woman to rob his wits of the ready benefit of using an alias and a false address.

Sarah Donovan pondered over the knowledge of who he was and where he lived, behind the mask of her face; then she said again: "He's not dead. He's coming back." Only this time she said it without any meaning, like a child repeating a parrot lesson in school.

Tierney was still struggling under the paralyzing power of her burning eyes, struggling to remember the next installment of the story Slaney had given him, but in the end nothing would come of it except the words: "Dead. Dead. Dead. You know he's dead, Sarah Donovan."

Then at last he saw a dim waver working over her face, and she turned away from him and went to the window. She pulled the curtains to the side and stood looking out for what seemed to him like ten long eternities. When she turned back, the fierce light had died out of the caves of her eyes, and she sat down. Slowly, heavily, her head sank down. Her voice was as lifeless as old ashes when she said: "I know he's dead. Yes, I know he's dead."

The man went away then on soft feet, his mind in a daze and not knowing properly where he was going, driven by the terrible urge to get out of it, out of the shadows of the house and away from this gaunt shadow of a woman. He set his ocher face with desperate urgency on a course for the public bar of the Plough Hotel.

When he was well gone Sarah Donovan stirred herself and went out to the garden—a thing she had not done for many years. For a while she walked about among the dank vegetation, muttering incessantly to herself, with her scorched eyes looking down. Then she went back into the house, and drew the curtains again, tight over the windows. That night she lit no lamps, and next morning she did not appear in the town to draw her pension.

5

It was four days before Sarah Donovan's absence from confession, added to the accumulated regiment of milk bottles on her step, spurred on the curiosity of the town to have the door knocked in by a policeman.

Then they found her lying her length on the couch, stone dead, and the place stinking like the inside of a gasometer. The only difference in her from the time she was living was that she did not breathe now, and her eyes were frozen in a still mirror of fear.

It was Slaney himself who discovered the sheet of note paper on the table, and he would have crumpled it up quietly and destroyed it, only he was not sure, with all the eyes in the room, if someone else had not seen it as well. On the paper it said that Sarah Donovan left her house and garden to Patrick Tierney, c/o Mrs. Stone, High Street, Ballyfergus, on the sole condition that he would allow no interference with the existing property, but would inherit and live in it just as it was.

That was a shot in the eye for Aloysius Slaney, and he had to call another meeting of the extraordinary committee to deal with the new problems confronting them.

They gathered again in the private room in the Plough Hotel, and Slaney read out Sarah Donovan's last will and testament to them. When he had finished, the three of them sat gathering their thoughts together, trying to see a way out of it.

Josceyline said: "Well, that's the brilliant outside edge of everything.

It's the most remarkable and unique instance of a kick on the behind from the far side of the grave that I've ever heard of."

Cornelius Rodgers waved that bit of wisdom aside impatiently. "What are we goin' to do about it?" he said. "That's what we want to know, and the more precious time we spend philosophizin' and recriminatin' and moanin', the less time we'll have to deal adequately with this man Tierney."

Aloysius Slaney looked his narrowest look at the other two, and then he opened his mind to them slowly, like a man opening up a bag of ferrets.

And out the ferrets came in the shape of a double-crossing idea as flagrant in its simple criminal roguery as had ever fallen on the hard, experienced ears of Rodgers and Josceyline.

"Why not just forget about this fool Tierney? Why not put the whole business on ice till he is well out of the place, and then destroy the will and let the property revert to the town."

At first the other two attempted a sort of circumspect shock for the sake of appearances, but at last they got around to admitting it might be an act of civil benefaction to avoid the risk of this drunken wanderer gaining property in a decent town.

They were in the process of anointing that bit of roguery with three glasses of whiskey when there was the devil of a rumpus from outside, followed in due time by the lumbering drunken body of Patrick Tierney.

He orientated his way around the room and came at last to anchor before the weasel face of Aloysius Slaney. Arrived there, he leered into the face of the lawyer, struck an attitude, and said, "I've had a letter from the dead departed."

Slaney looked at him and saw the serpent tiepin with the green eyes still decorating the scarf under the stubble of his chin. There was something the lawyer did not like about that. He gritted his teeth and said: "You'd better take that pin out now."

With a slow and insolent deliberation Tierney removed the serpent pin, and rolled it over and over between his thick tobacco-stained fingers. He said: "Sure. Sure. I forgot there wouldn't be room in the place for another serpent with all that's in it already."

"What do ye want?" said Rodgers, eying him up and down beneath his heavy lids.

"It's not what I want, it's what I've got," said Tierney. "I told ye I'd had a letter from the dead departed. It's a notification from the late suicide-lamented Sarah Donovan invitin' me to inherit the house and garden which she has just left with such undiscriminatin' haste."

"Let me see that letter." Slaney ground the demand out between his tight teeth. But Tierney gave him a sidelong look and said: "I can't do that, for in my natural stupidity I handed it over to a Protestant lawyer in

Ballyfergus. But I have a copy here ye can look at for your amusement, Mr. Slaney."

Aloysius Slaney took the paper from Tierney's brown paw and in a dull voice read out a duplicate of the will he had lying in his pocket.

It took the three of them a good five minutes to digest the meaning of that one, and then the words began to fly.

"The will would be contested. The woman had been insane. Balance of mind disturbed. No court of law could uphold such a document." To all of which Patrick Tierney replied that the Protestant lawyer thought another way entirely. Out of the storm of words rose his grim ocher face and heavy rampart body, obdurate, obstinate, and undeniably the inheritor of that house and garden—on one condition.

6

When half an hour of it had passed and no impression was made on Tierney except that he began to steer a slow way to the door with the copy of the will in his pocket, Aloysius Slaney swallowed hard and started to eat the dust.

"Of course," he said, "a man like you wouldn't dream of wanting a house like that, especially on those conditions."

"And why wouldn't I?" said Tierney.

"For the simple reason that ye're a natural wanderer on the face of the earth," said Slaney, "a man of the sea and never at rest away from it. What now would the likes of you want with a dark old house and such a wilderness of a garden?"

"There'll come a day when the spirit will move me to settle down," said Tierney, "and what better place could I find to settle in than this— among all my friends," he added, with the ghost of a sneering smile.

Josceyline weighed in then, digging up his best mollifying voice. "Man, man," he said, "surely ye don't contemplate spending the declinin' years of an active life pinin' away in a corner of a damp and dark old house?"

"It wasn't a bad house by what I saw of it," said Tierney. "Not a bad house at all."

Rodgers said: "And what about yourself stuck in it, haunted all your remainin' life by the ghost of an ould woman you druv to death by a fantastic story about her man being dead."

Slaney said: "Indeed, maybe that's what she left it to ye for. Maybe she wanted ye in a place handy for her hauntin' ye."

Tierney looked at him, a long-drawn-out look. "If there's hauntin' in it," he said, "I know who'll be gettin' haunted, an' that's the wan that instigated the story an' planted the seed in me mind to rise up an' drive the livin' burnin' hope out of the face of an oul' woman till in desperation she turns the gas on an' forgets to put a light to it."

Slaney lapped that up, and then, after a minute of silence, he said quietly: "How much, Tierney?"

The ocher face lifted up a heavy look of surprise. "I don't know what ye mean," he said.

Slaney chuckled impatiently with his tongue against his false teeth. "You know you've no shadow of intention of occupying that house," he said. "I'm asking you how much do you want to renounce the inheritance."

Tierney took a look at them all in turn while his brain slowly turned over and pondered the facts of the case—the wide road coming into it, the house standing in the way, these three old crows appointed by the town council to straighten the thing out. He did a quiet sum in his own mind and said six hundred pounds.

Slaney laughed, but it was a very thin laugh. It was even thinner when Josceyline echoed it. Rodgers made no sound, but just lit himself a cigar, which he got well going before he spoke. Then he said: "Surely to God it won't take you all that money to drink yourself to death and you half way there."

For answer, Tierney rotated slowly towards the door. "I'd better go and see about movin' into me new house," he said.

But Aloysius Slaney stopped him. Aloysius Slaney wanted to talk it over as friends. Maybe Rodgers would bring another bottle of whiskey. Rodgers brought the whiskey, and for a while they let the whiskey do the talking; it took the whole five-gill bottle and the three councilors only nibbling a drop here and there, but it did more than all the big brains in Ballyfintry could have done in ten years. Tierney finished up with ten one-pound notes in his pocket, and in Slaney's pocket, lying snugly beside the will, was a signed abdication from the rights of the house, written in a rough uncertain handwriting—but written, and signed. That was the thing. Next day Patrick Tierney weighed anchor with a thick head and a tongue like a door mat, and he was never seen in the place again.

At the end of the week there was a special meeting of the town council at which there was present a man from the road engineers, a man with a tall bald dome of a head like an eggshell, and thin specs on his nose.

Aloysius Slaney made his report, regretting the unfortunate demise of the late Sarah Donovan by a gas accident, and saying that in the absence of any kith or kin the house and property had *ipso facto* reverted to the community.

The mayor, on behalf of the council, thanked Slaney and the extraordinary committee for their noble and disinterested work, and assured the man with the eggshell head that there would now be no hindrance to the new wide road cutting a way through the garden of the old dark house at the end of town.

On hearing that, the man with the eggshell head heaved a sigh of relief because he liked his roads to be straight for the motorcars. He took off his specs to say a few words that fell from his lips like dry biscuits; then he put them on again and went away in a hurry to give the sign that all was clear. So next day, two men with spyglasses on three sticks stood at the end of the town and looked at a distant object along an invisible line that ran straight through the garden of the late Sarah Donovan.

Three weeks later the road came, carried along by three hundred navvies and road makers, who laid it down behind them like a broad gray ribbon. The only snag was that when they came to the garden of the late Sarah Donovan, the proceedings had to be held up for two days while the police held a post-mortem over the body of a man which they found buried there not far in front of the window.

It was lying with its face down, and not very deep, as if the work had been done in a hurry, and maybe by a weak person with no other help.

When they examined the body in the county hospital, they discovered a great gaping hole in the back of the skull—a hole that made the examining doctor say something about a blunt instrument, maybe like a hammer a woman would use ordinarily for breaking coal.

The corpse was in a sad state of decomposition and the doctor said it must have been there for about ten or twelve years, there being nothing much more than a skeleton left, but the cravat it wore round its neck had been made of tougher stuff, it being still there and looking very queer beneath the grinning bones of the face.

It was Aloysius Slaney who identified it as the remains of Michael Donovan when he saw stuck in the cravat, under the rotten face, a tiepin in the shape of a rearing serpent with two green stones for eyes.

Sinbad the Sailor's Third Voyage

from THE ARABIAN NIGHTS' ENTERTAINMENTS

THE PLEASURES OF THE LIFE WHICH I THEN LED SOON made me forget the risks I had run in my two former voyages; but being then in the flower of my age, I grew weary of living without business; and hardening myself against the thought of any danger I might incur, I went from Bagdad, with the richest commodities of the country, to Balsora: there I embarked again with the merchants. We made a long voyage, and touched at several ports, where we drove a considerable trade. One day, being out in the main ocean, we were attacked by a horrible tempest, which made us lose our course. The tempest continued several days, and brought us before the port of an island, where the captain was very unwilling to enter; but we were obliged to cast anchor there. When we had furled our sails, the captain told us that this and some other neighbouring islands were inhabited by hairy savages, who would speedily attack us; and though they were but dwarfs, yet our misfortune was such that we must make no resistance, for they were more in number than the locusts; and if we happened to kill one of them, they would all fall upon us and destroy us.—Here day beginning to appear, Scheherazade broke off her story, and continued it next night, as follows:—

The Seventy-Fifth Night

This discourse of the captain, said Sinbad, put the whole company into a great consternation; and we found very soon, to our cost, that what he had told us was but too true: an innumerable multitude of frightful savages, covered all over with red hair, and about two feet high, came swimming towards us, and encompassed our ship in a little time. They spoke to us as they came near, but we understood not their language; they climbed up the sides of the ship with so much agility as surprised us. We beheld all this with mortal fear, without daring to offer to defend ourselves, or to speak one word to divert them from their mischievous design. In short, they took down our sails, cut the cable, and hauled to the shore, made us all get out, and afterwards carried the ship into another island, from whence they came. All travellers carefully avoided that island where they left us, it being very dangerous to stay there, for a reason you shall hear anon; but we were forced to bear our affliction with patience.

We went forward into the island, where we found some fruits and herbs to prolong our lives as long as we could; but we expected nothing but death. As we went on, we perceived at a distance a great pile of building, and made towards it. We found it to be a palace, well built, and very lofty, with a gate of ebony of two leaves, which we thrust open. We entered the court, where we saw before us a vast apartment, with a porch, having on one side a heap of men's bones and on the other a vast number of roasting pits. We trembled at this spectacle, and being weary with travelling, our legs failing under us, we fell to the ground, being seized with deadly fear, and lay a long time motionless.

The sun was set, and whilst we were in the lamentable condition just mentioned, the gate of the apartment opened with a great noise, and there came out the horrible figure of a black man, as high as a tall palm-tree. He had but one eye, and that in the middle of his forehead, where it looked as red as a burning coal. His fore-teeth were very long and sharp, and stood out of his mouth, which was as deep as that of a horse; his upper lip hung down upon his breast; his ears resembled those of an elephant, and covered his shoulders; and his nails were as long and crooked as the talons of the greatest birds. At the sight of so frightful a giant we lost all sense, and lay like men dead.

At last we came to ourselves, and saw him sitting in the porch, looking at us. When he had considered us well, he advanced towards us, and laying his hand upon me, he took me up by the nape of my neck, and turned me round as a butcher would do a sheep's head. After having viewed me well, and perceiving me to be so lean that I had nothing but skin and bone, he let me go. He took up all the rest, one by one, viewed them in the same manner, and the captain being the fattest, he held him with one hand, as I would do a sparrow, and thrusting a spit through him, kindled a great fire, roasted, and eat him in his apartment for his supper; which being done, he returned to his porch, where he lay and fell asleep, snoring louder than thunder. He slept thus till morning. For our parts, it was not possible for us to enjoy any rest; so that we passed the night in the most cruel fear that can be imagined. Day being come, the giant awaked, got up, went out, and left us in the palace.

When we thought him at a distance, we broke the melancholy silence we had kept all night, and every one grieving more than another, we made the palace resound with our complaints and groans. Though there were a great many of us, and we had but one enemy, we had not at first the presence of mind to think of delivering ourselves from him by his death. This enterprise, however, though hard to put in execution, was the only design we ought naturally to have formed.

We thought of several other things, but determined nothing; so that submitting to what it should please God to order concerning us, we spent the day in running about the island for fruit and herbs to sustain our lives. When evening came, we sought for a place to lie in, but found none; so that we were forced, whether we would or not, to return to the palace.

The giant failed not to come back, and supped once more upon one of our companions; after which he slept and snored till day, and then went out and left us as formerly. Our condition was so very terrible, that several of my comrades designed to throw themselves into the sea, rather than die so strange a death; and those who were of this mind argued with the rest to follow their example: upon which one of the company answered, that we were forbidden to destroy ourselves; but allowing it to be lawful, it was more reasonable to think of a way to rid ourselves of the barbarous tyrant who designed so cruel a death for us.

Having thought of a project for that end, I communicated the same to my comrades, who approved of it. "Brethren," said I, "you know there is a great deal of timber floating upon the coast: if you will be advised by me, let us make several floats of it that may carry us; and when they are done, leave them there till we think fit to make use of them. In the meantime we will execute the design to deliver ourselves from the giant; and if it succeed, we may stay here with patience till some ship pass by that may carry us out of this fatal island; but if it happen to miscarry, we will speedily get to our floats, and put to sea. I confess that by exposing ourselves to the fury of the waves, we run a risk of losing our lives; but if we do, is it not better to be buried in the sea than in the entrails of this monster, who has already devoured two of us?" My advice was relished, and we made floats capable of carrying three persons each.

We returned to the palace towards the evening, and the giant arrived a little while after. We were forced to conclude on seeing another of our comrades roasted. But at last we revenged ourselves on the brutish giant thus: after he had made an end of his cursed supper, he lay down on his back and fell asleep. As soon as we heard him snore, according to his custom, nine of the boldest among us, and myself, took each of us a spit, and putting the points of them into the fire till they were burning hot, we thrust them into his eye all at once, and blinded him. The pain occasioned him to make a frightful cry, and to get up and stretch out his hands, in order to sacrifice some of us to his rage; but we ran to such places as he could not find us; and after having sought for us in vain, he groped for the gate, and went out, howling dreadfully.—Scheherazade stopped here, but next night resumed her story thus:—

The Seventy-Sixth Night.

We went out of the palace after the giant, continued Sindbad, and came to the shore, where we had left our floats, and put them immediately into the sea. We waited till day, in order to get upon them, in case the giant came towards us with any guide of his own species; but we hoped, if he did not appear by sun-rising, and give over his howling, which we still heard, that he would die; and if that happened to be the case, we resolved to stay in that island, and not to risk our lives upon the floats: but day had scarce appeared, when we perceived our cruel enemy, accompanied with two others almost of the same size, leading him, and a great number more coming before him with a very quick pace.

When we saw this, we made no delay, but got immediately upon our floats, and rowed off from the shore. The giants, who perceived this, took up great stones, and running to the shore, entered the water up to the middle, and threw so exactly, that they sunk all the floats but that I was upon; and all my companions, except the two with me, were drowned. We rowed with all our might and got out of the reach of the giants; but when we got out to sea, we were exposed to the mercy of the waves and winds, and tossed about, sometimes on one side, and sometimes on another, and spent that night and the following day under a cruel uncertainty as to our fate; but next morning we had the good luck to be thrown upon an island, where we landed with much joy. We found excellent fruit there, that gave us great relief, so that we pretty well recovered our strength.

In the evening we fell asleep on the bank of the sea, but were awaked by the noise of a serpent as long as a palm-tree, whose scales made a rustling as he crept along. He swallowed up one of my comrades, notwithstanding his loud cries and the efforts he made to rid himself of the serpent; which, shaking him several times against the ground, crushed him; and we could hear him gnaw and tear the poor wretch's bones when we had fled a great distance from him. Next day we saw the serpent again, to our great terror; when I cried out, "O Heaven, to what dangers are we exposed! We rejoiced yesterday at our having escaped from the cruelty of a giant and the rage of the waves, and now are we fallen into another danger altogether as terrible."

As we walked about we saw a large tall tree, upon which we designed to pass the following night for our security; and having satisfied our hunger, we mounted it accordingly. A little while after the serpent came hissing to the root of the tree, raised itself up against the trunk of it, and meeting with my comrade, who sat lower than I, swallowed him at once, and went off.

I stayed upon the tree till it was day, and then came down, more like a dead man than one alive, expecting the same fate with my two companions. This filled me with horror, so that I was going to throw myself into the sea; but nature prompting us to a desire to live as long as we can, I withstood this temptation to despair, and submitted myself to the will of God, who disposes of our lives at his pleasure.

In the meantime I gathered together a great quantity of small wood, brambles, and dry thorns, and making them up into faggots, made a great circle with them round the tree, and also tied some of them to the branches over my head. Having done thus, when the evening came I shut myself up within this circle, with this melancholy piece of satisfaction, that I had neglected nothing which could preserve me from the cruel destiny with which I was threatened. The serpent failed not to come at the usual hour, and went round the tree, seeking for an opportunity to devour me, but was prevented by the rampart I had made; so that he lay till day, like a cat watching in vain for a mouse that has retired to a place of safety. When day appeared he retired; but I dared not to leave my fort until the sun arose.

I was fatigued with the toil he had put me to, and suffered so much by his poisonous breath, that, death seeming more eligible to me than the horror of such a condition, I came down from the tree, and, not thinking on the resignation I had made to the will of God the preceding day, I ran towards the sea, with a design to throw myself into it headlong.—Here Scheherazade stopped because day appeared.

Snake Doctor

by IRVIN S. COBB

IN THE NORTH THEY CALL THEM DEVIL'S DARNING needles. But in the South they are snake doctors, and for a reason. These harmless and decorative dragon-flies with their slim arrow-like bodies, their quick darting flight and their filmy wings, as though the arrows had been fletched with bits of drawn lace, are clothed, down there, with a curious fetish. When a cotton-mouth is sick—and if his feelings match his disposition he must be sick most of the time—the snake doctor comes hurrying to him with the medication for what ails him. Perhaps seventy-five or a hundred years ago some slave newly in from Africa saw a cotton-mouth moccasin sunning its flat, heart-shaped head on top of the yellow creek water, and along the creek came flashing one of these swift creatures seeking a perch upon which to leave its eggs, and the black man saw it suddenly check and hover and stand at poise in the air an inch above the snake's still head, and from that figured this strange bug was a voodoo bug, ministering to the ailing reptile. In such a matter any man's theory is as good as the next one's. The provable thing is that a good many of the whites and more than a good many of the negroes believe in the fable for a fact; and nearly all of them, regardless of color, know the libeled insect as snake doctor.

Now, one of the men I have intent to write about here was known as Snake Doctor, too; and for this, also, there were reasons. To begin with, he was very long and thin, a mere rack of bones held together under the casing of a taut yellow skin; and he had popped, staring eyes, and was amazingly fast in his bodily movements. See him slipping through the willows, so furtive and quick and diffident, with his inadequately small head, his sloped shoulders, his erratic side-steppings this way or that, and thereby inevitably you were reminded of his namesake. You were bound to think of the one when you thought of the other; just naturally you couldn't help it. To top the analogy, he lived right among the moccasins, taking no harm from them and having no fear of them, seemingly.

Along Cashier Creek, where they throve in a wicked abundance, was his regular ranging ground. His cabin stood in the bottoms near a place notorious for its snakes. They were his friends, so to speak. He caught them and with his bare hands he handled them as a butcher might handle links of sausage. He sold them, once in a while, to naturalists or showmen or zoological collectors: there was a taxidermist in Memphis who was an occasional customer of his. In the season he rendered down their soft fat and drew it off in bottles and retailed it; snake oil being held a sovereign remedy for rheumatism.

By such traffickings he was locally reputed to have made large sums of money. But he rarely spent any of this money; so he went by the name of miser, also. Well, in a way of speaking, he was a miser; he zealously coveted what he got and kept it hidden away in the chinking of his log shack. But he was nowhere near so well-off as the community gave him credit for being. The snake business is a confined and an uncertain business and restricted, moreover, to its special markets. A dealer's stock in trade may be plentiful, as in this case, but his patrons must be sought. To be exact, Snake Doctor had ninety-seven dollars in his cache.

But swearing to the truth of this on a stack of Bibles a mile high wouldn't have made the people in the Cashier Creek country have it so. Popular opinion insisted on multiplying his means and then adding naughts. Nor could you, by any argument, have won over his neighbors, white or black, to a fair estimate of the man's real self, which was that here merely was a poor, shy, lonely eccentric touched in the head by hot suns and perhaps by spells of recurrent swamp fevers.

They had contempt for him but mixed in with the contempt was fear. To them he was to be shunned as one having commerce on familiar footing with the most loathly and the most hated of all the creatures that crawl. There was a solitary exception to the current rule of prejudice; a single individual among them who had compassion for him and a measure of understanding and right appraisal of him. This individual, curiously enough, was a woman. She was a minority of one. We'll come to her presently. The rest had forgotten his proper name or else had never heard it. By their majority voice he was Ole Snake Doctor. They knew he was familiar with the ways of the cotton-mouth; they half believed he spoke its language.

In this particular region ordinary folks believed many things that weren't so. Superstition, growing out of ignorance, had twisted honest nature into a myriad of perverted and detractive shapes. The innocent little blue-streaked lizard was a "scorpyun" and its sting killed. A porous white stone found in the bellies of rutting deer was the only known cure for a mad dog's bite; clap it on the wound and it clung fast like a leech and sucked the poison out. You never saw many jay-birds in the woods between dinner-time and dusk on a Friday because then nearly all jay-birds had gone below to tell the news of a malicious world to their master, the devil. You could rarely hit a rain crow with a rifle bullet because this slim, brown, nervous bird enjoyed the special protection of old Nick. If a snapping-turtle clamped his jaws down on your flesh he wouldn't let go till it thundered. A breath of warm air blowing across your path on a cool night in the woods meant a "witch-hag" had passed that way.

Or take snakes: The Prophet of Old put the curse on them forever after when in his story of the Garden he typified evil as a serpent; mankind has been enlarging the slander ever since. Moreover, in these parts, Caucasian ingenuity as regards snakes and their ways had overlaid a deep embroidery of ill-repute upon an already rich background of African folklore. There was the hoop snake, which is mischievous and very deadly, and wears a deadly horn in its head, and there was the joint snake, which is a freak; both fabulous but both accepted as verities. All well-meaning snakes lay under the scandalous ban. Milk snakes, garter snakes, chicken snakes, puff adders, blue racers and coach-whips were to be destroyed on sight; for their licking, forked tongues were "stingers" and dripped venom. If you were bitten by any snake your hope was first to drink all the raw whisky you could get hold of. Or if, within ten minutes after being bitten, you clamped upon the wound the still quivering halves of a young chicken which, while alive, had been split open with a hatchet or a knife, there yet was a chance for you. Lacking either of these cures or both of them, you must expire in torment. The bitten part would swell enormously; the poison spreading and magnifying in your blood would rack you with hideous pains; then swiftly it would reach your heart and you were gone.

Every sort of snake was tricky and guileful but the moccasin of the low grounds the most so of all. Kill a moccasin and spare its mate, and the mate would track you for miles, set on vengeance. It was the habit of the moccasin when meat was scarce to lie beneath the yonkerpads—pond lilies, a Northerner would call them—with its head shoved up among the broad green leaves and its mouth stretched wide and gaping, a living lure for such luckless birds and bees as mistook the snare of the parted jaws with their white linings for a half-opened lily bud.

It was in accord with a quite natural law that the moccasin should be singled out for these special calumnies. Of the four venomous snakes of Temperate North America he is the least personable in looks and behavior. He lacks the grace of his upland cousin, the copperhead, and he lacks the chivalry of his more distant kinsman, the rattler, which gives the enemy due warning before he strikes. He has none of the slimness of form nor patterned beauty of that streak of fanged lightning which lives in the palmetto scrubs, the coral snake. He is mournfully colored and miserably shaped. The tones of dull creek mud and of stale creek slime mingle in his scrofulous mottlings. There is leprosy in the pale foxings of his lips, and dropsy in his bloat amidships. Take him in the dead summer when, with stored-up meanness his belly is monstrous and heavy, and see him then making loopy S's in the torpid water, as he swims, or stretched out, baking himself on the blistered creek-bed and, with his skinny neck and stumpy, inadequate tail joined to that lumpy body, he'll suggest to you a sort of legless malignant lizard rather than a true snake. Only in the eyes of the taxidermist does he redeem himself for these manifold short-comings. Being without bright tints to fade in the mounting, his stuffed skin needs no special varnishing to make it seem authentic. It is a poor compliment, perhaps, but his only one. Of all other counts and for all other qualities he is copiously defamed and folks generally are prone to believe the worst of him.

Japhet Morner did for one. For him, swamp-water athrive with typhoid germs, or rancid corn pones in which the active seeds of pelagra lived, or mosquitoes carrying malaria and ague in their bills, conveyed no sense of peril. The mosquitoes were to be endured, the water was to be drunk. And biliousness was the common lot of man, anyway. At least, in this neck of the woods it was. But snakes, now, were different; any snake and all snakes whatsoever. He accepted for truth all the hard things that might be said of a snake. Certain other things he likewise believed, namely, that first, his nearest neighbor, Snake Doctor, held unwholesome communion with the cotton-mouths; that second, Snake Doctor had a treasure in money hid away in his shack—on this point he was very sure; and that third, the same Snake Doctor was entirely too fond of his, Japhet's wife, Kizzie, and she of him.

So it would appear he had a triplet of reasons for holding the other in disfavor—envy of him for his stored wealth, a gnawing suspicion from seeing in him a potential philanderer, and finally, that emotion of fearsome distrust bred out of stupidity and credulity, which his kind were likely to have for any fellow-man fashioned in different likeness from the run of them. That the shambling, soft-brained Snake Doctor was as sexless as a dirt-clod would have been apparent to any straight-seeing observer; and it should have been as plainly visible even to this husband of hers that Kizzie Morner was a good woman and an honest one. But the jaundiced eye sees everything as yellow, and yellow is the color for jealousy, too, and it suited Japhet Morner's mood to brew jealousy in his mind. Brewing it steadily there was strengthening his will for the putting-through of a private project which for a long time he had been conning over in his thoughts. The issue came to a head on a certain day.

It was a day in that drear season of the year when the birds have quit singing in the daytime and the locusts have started. Summer had sagged as though from the sheer exhaustion of its own wasted fervor. The lowland woods had lost that poisonous green sprightliness which came to them in early April and lasted until the August hot spell set in. Even the weeds, which in the bottoms grew rank and high and close-set, almost as canes in a cane-brake, were wilted and weary-looking. The sun had come up that morning behind clouds. In the middle of the forenoon the clouds still banked together to hide the heavens but the heat seemed intensified, and pressed the unstirring air close down to the burnt earth. As Japhet Morner came out of the timber into the scorched clearing behind his house the sweat dripped from him and he panted in the close still humidity. His two dogs trailed him, their tongues lolling. One of them brushed against his leg. He hauled off and fetched the dog a sound kick in the ribs. He was not in a happy humor.

At sunup, after a breakfast of cold scraps left from the night before, he had gone down to Cashier Creek to get a bait of sunfish. If he were lucky he might catch a catfish for his string. He had no luck, though. The creek was shrunken; it was lower than he ever remembered seeing it. The drought had sucked up its strength. At the shallows it was no more than a thin sluggish trickle. In deeper places there scarcely was current enough to keep twigs and dropped leaves moving on the unrippled coffee-colored surface. Along the edges, wide bare strips of the stream's customary bottom showed. Cooked hard and dry by the sun, the mud here was cracked into irregular squares and parallelograms—the dividing seams always running at rough right angles—and the corners of each crusted segment had crinkled up so that the general effect suggested a bad jog of flagged pavement, scamped in the original contract and now warping apart at all joints. Beyond, right and left, rose sharply the walls of the stream. Cashier Creek was a creek without a valley to it. There was no dip in the ground toward it. The flats came right up to its verges, and then, without warning, the earth was shorn straight away to the scoured-out bed, so that its course ran in what resembled an artificial cutting. In this part of the country many creeks are like that—with abrupt sides that sheer down steep and smooth except where water erosion has scored and runneled the soft earth. Only here and there some glacier has left its autograph in a scour of red gravel to remind parched mankind that once upon a time there was an Age of Ice in the world.

Japhet fished and fished and was rewarded with no nibbles whatsoever; seemingly, even the littlest fishes were too languid to bite at worms he dangled for them in likely spots. He came down stream to the Big Hole, so called, where, an eighth of a mile up from Snake Doctor's shanty, the creek widened to thrice its usual breadth. Here a tight wedge of driftwood blocked the waters. Each successive freshet had added flotsam to the rude dam, lost cross-ties, uprooted trees, corn stalks, chips, fence-rails, sticks. Ordinarily this lesser riffle would cover the pool so thickly that, with the top dressing of cream-colored foam, there was created the simulation of a solid footing; a stranger might have been pardoned for believing he could walk across and keep dry-shod. But now all here was clear of gently eddying debris. The consumed stream, instead of slapping against the spanning driftage, ran under it with an oozy, guzzling sound. Directly in the middle there was a busy little whirlpool, funneling downward.

On one of the lowermost of the bared logs a cotton-mouth was twisted up, taking his ease in the congenial fever-warmth. He was a big fat one—fully two feet long and as thick through his girth as a boy's arm. From the bank edge above, Japhet saw him and looked about for something to throw at him. In a section where gravel is rare and all rock formations are buried a hundred feet down under the silt the verb "to stone" neither is used nor known. Your weapon invariably is a "chunk" and with it—a hard clod or a lump of wood or whatever it is—you "chunk" away at your target.

The man found a sizable missile, a heavy, half-rotted sycamore bough, and he snapped it off to suitable length and flung it, twirling, at the motionless mark. His aim was good. The stricken snake flapped out of coil and dragged its broken loops from sight into an interlacing of naked limbs on the farther side of its log. The stick bounced hard and splashed in the pool. Japhet saw how that it swirled around and around and then, briskly, was sucked beneath the jam. With a quickened curiosity he moved downstream a rod or two and waited. Although the jam was now, so to speak, a suspension bridge, and in places stood inches clear of the water, the stick did not emerge into view below it. No drift showed there, either; the creek for a space flowed clear of rubbish. Evidently, objects caught in that small whirlpool above were carried in and under to lodge and be held fast by some submerged trapwork of soaked and sunken limbs. Probably they would stay there for months, perhaps stay there always. Turning the matter of the phenomenon over in his mind, he flung away his bait can, spun his fishing cane so that the line wrapped around it, and made off through the woods for his home, nearly a mile away. The two dogs racked along at his heels. Coming out of the woods one of them made the mistake of nudging him.

Having disciplined the scrooging dog with his boot toe he slouched out into the six-acre "dead'nin'." His puny patch of corn, for lack of the hoe, was smothering in weeds. In bare spots where the thin soil was washed so close down to the underlying clay-pan that here not even weeds would sprout, the crawfish had pushed up their conical watchtowers of dried mud. Tall ash boles, girdled and dead, threw foreshortened shadows across the clearing—shadows such as gallows trees might cast. His house, of two rooms and built of unpainted up-and-down planking, squatted in the inadequate shade of a stunted hackberry tree. A well was at one corner; a slim pole with a cross-piece, bearing pendent gourds for the martins to nest in, poked above the roof of curled gray shingles. Martins were harbored because they kept the mosquitoes down. There was no flower bed, no truck patch, no fencing. Across the open space, with the heat waves dancing before him, the outlines of the house seemed to waver and twist like an object seen through smoke. It stood a foot from the earth, on log props. Because of seepage there were no cellars in this neighborhood. The inevitable dogs lived under the houses and bred their fleas there, and the hogs, too, if so be a house owner had any hogs.

It was nearly noon now. His wife, bare-footed and in a skimpy blue frock open at the throat, was cooking the midday meal, the principal meal of the three. He came up to the door and she, looking up from the cook stove where she was turning the strips of sizzling meat in the skillet, saw the look on his face. Her mouth twitched apprehensively. By the signs she knew when he was in one of his tantrums.

"Ketch anything, Jafe?" she asked, nervously.

"Ketch anything this weather?—whut'd you expect I'd catch?" From his voice it might be figured that, vicariously, he blamed her for the failure of the expedition.

He hunkered down on the doorstep, his fishing pole still in his hands, and shook his head to free it of the drops which trickled over his face and into his eyes.

"That pore old Mist' Rives come by here a spell ago, mighty nigh shook to pieces with a chill," she said after a bit.

"Oh, he come by, did he?" His tone purposely, was disarming. "Well, did he come in?"

"Jes' fur a minute."

"Jes' fur a minute, heh? And whut did he want?"

"He wanted could I give him somethin' fur his ailment. He jes' about could drag one sorry foot before the other—barely could make it up here frum his place. I reckon hem ust bed own in bed with the fever by now; I could tell by the t'ech it wuz risin' in him when he left here and started back home ag'in. It'll be mighty pitiful, him down flat on his back and nobody there to do nothin' fur his comfort. I give him a dost out of our Butler's Ager Drops. I would a-give him a little smidgin' of licker only— only—" She left the sentence unfinished. "That pore shackly Mist' Rives, he—*Oh,* please don't, Jafe!"

Turning, he had cut viciously at her with the long cane. She shrank back as it whipped through the air, and took the lashing stroke on her forearm, thrown up to fend off the blow.

"Mist' Rives! Mist' Rives!" He mimicked her, furiously. "How many times I got to tell you that there old hoodoo's name is Snake Doctor? Him that'd skin a louse fur its hide and taller and you callin' him 'Mist' Rives'! You'll be callin' him 'Honey' and 'Sugar' next without I learn you better. Pet names, huh? Well, I aim to learn you."

She flinched at the threat, rubbing the welt on her skin; but he made no effort to strike her again. He sat glowering, saying nothing at all as she made hurry to dish up the food and put it before him; she hoped the weight of victuals in his stomach might dull the edge of his temper. For her part, she had the wisdom to keep silent, too. She ate on her feet, serving him between bites and sups, as was the rule in this household.

After dinner he stretched himself on the floor of the inner room. But he did not sleep. He was busy with his thoughts. One thing he had seen that day, and another thing he had heard—he was adding them together, as the first sum in a squalid equation. She drew a cane-bottom chair out-doors and sat under the hackberry tree, fanning herself, and "dipping" snuff with a peach-twig which she scoured back and forth on her gums. After a little while she was driven into the kitchen. It began to rain in sharp violent showers. The rain made the house inside no cooler; merely changed it from a bake-oven to a steam-box.

It was getting along toward four o'clock before Japhet emerged from the front room. He drew on his heavy knee-length boots, which he had removed before lying down, and laced them up. This done, he spoke to her for the first time since noon.

"Where's that there vi'l of licker?" he said. "Fetch it here to me."

They kept a small store of whisky by them—all in that district did the same—for chills and possible snake bites. She brought him a pint flask nearly full and he shoved it into his hip pocket. Then immediately, as though moved by a fresh idea, he hauled it out again and put it down on the kitchen table.

"Come to think about it," he said, "I won't be needin' to tote no sperrits along with me where I'm goin'. Cotton-mouths is all down in the slashes or else along the creek, and where I'll be all this evenin' is up on Bailey's Ridge on the high ground."

He was not given to favoring her with explanations of his motives or accounts of his movements. This departure from fixed habit emboldened his wife to put a question.

"Fixin' to go shootin', Jafe?" she asked, timidly.

"I aim to gun me a mess of young squirrels 'twixt now and dusktime. I heard 'em barkin' all 'round me this mornin'. Ef they're that plenty in the low ground they'll be out thicker'n hops after the mulberries and the young hick'ry nuts up Bailey's Ridge."

He took up his single-shot rifle where it stood in a corner, and from an opened box on a shelf scooped a handful of brass shells. Then he went outside and tied up both his dogs. One was a hound, good for hunting rabbits. It was proper that he should be left behind. But the smaller dog, a black mongrel, was a trained squirrel dog. As his wife stood in the doorway, Japhet read the dumb curiosity which her face expressed.

"With the leaves ez thick ez the way they air, still huntin' is best this time o' year," he explained. "So I won't be needin' Gyp. Don't let neither one of 'em gnaw hisself loose and follow after me. Set me up a snack of cold supper on a shelf. Likely I won't git back till it's plum' night-time— gunnin' fur them squirrels is best jes' before dark, and I'll be away off yonder at the fur end of the Ridge, three miles frum here, when I git ready to start back. 'Tain't ez ef I wuz rangin' in the low ground."

He turned north through the struggling corn rows and in a minute was gone from her sight into the dripping woods. He kept on going north for nearly a mile until he came to where a wild red mulberry tree stood in a small natural opening. Some of the overripe fruit, blackened and shrivelled, still clung to the boughs; and where there are mulberries in the summer woods, there squirrels almost certainly will likewise be. Very neatly he shot two young grays through their heads. Japhet was a master marksman. It was his one gentlemanly accomplishment. In all other regards he was just plain poor white trash, as one of his negro neighbors would have phrased it—behind Japhet's back. But unsuspected by any who knew him, he had a quality of mind which is denied many of his class—an imagination. It was in excellent working order this day. He now was proving that it was.

He tied the brained squirrels together and swung them, tails downward, over a strap of his suspenders. If needed, they were to be evidence in his behalf—part of his alibi. Next he sat down under a tree awhile with his pipe going, partly for solace and partly to keep away the midges and gnats and the ever present plague of mosquitoes. He sat out two brisk showers with the intervals between them. Then, getting up he set off, keeping always to the deeper woodlands, in a swing which would bring him down Bailey's Branch, now wasted to a succession of mere puddles, and along the skirts of Little Cypress Slash to the sunken flats edging Cashier Creek. The arc of his swing was wide. It took him all of two hours, traveling carefully and without haste through the steamy coverts, to reach the point he aimed for.

He came to a halt, cautiously and well sheltered, behind the farthermost fringes of a little jungle of haw bushes where the diminishing woods frayed out in a sort of green promontory fifty yards or so back of Snake Doctor's cabin. This was his chosen destination, so here he squatted himself down in a nest of sodden leaves and grass to wait. It had begun to shower again, good and hard. He was drenched. No matter, though; he figured he would not have so very long to wait. As it turned out he didn't.

There was no house dog to come nosing him out and barking an alarm. That Snake Doctor owned no dog would have marked him, in this part of the land, as a person totally different from his fellows, even had there been lacking other points of variance. What Snake Doctor did own was a mare, or the ruins of one. A wag at the county seat had said once Ole Snake Doctor's nag put him in mind, every time he saw her, of a string band; she had xylophone ribs and a fiddle-shaped head and legs like bass drum sticks. She was housed in a log crib a few rods behind the only slightly larger log cabin of her owner. Where he stood in his point of woods, Japhet could hear her stirring restlessly in her stall. He might have seen her through the cracks between the logs of her shelter except for a brush fence which bounded the small weed-grown clearing.

His plan was simple enough and yet, as he saw it, fault-proof. Feeding time was at hand; soon Snake Doctor, ailing though he was, surely would be coming out from his cabin to bait the old rack-of-bones. Japhet counted on this. He'd get him then, first pop. He'd teach him what the costs were of colleaguing with another man's lawful wedded wife, and the lesson would be the death of him. At a half crouch in his ambush, Japhet told himself that his motive was jealousy; that he was here as a white man and an injured husband for the satisfaction of his personal honor and in the defense of his threatened thresholds. By a conscious effort of his will he kept in the background of his mind the other purpose that had brought him on this errand. In such moments as he let his thoughts dwell on it he strove to regard it as a side-issue, a thing incidental to the main intent. It had to do with money—with Snake Doctor's hoarded money.

The next step after the principal act would be to dispose of the body. That should be easy. He could carry the meager frame over his shoulder for a mile, if needs be. And he wouldn't have to carry it for a mile either— only as far as the Big Hole; then lower the burden into the water and let it slip in under the log jam. The chunk he had killed the moccasin with had stayed under there; skinny old Snake Doctor would stay too. This done, he would come back here to the cabin and hunt out the hidden treasure. He figured it shouldn't take him a great while to find it; he already had a sort of notion as to its whereabouts, a strong clew to start on. Having found it he would circle back up through the woods, reentering his field from the upper or northern side, with two squirrels flapping his flank for proof that he had been hunting on Bailey's Ridge. Suspicion never could touch him. Why should it?

He counted on the rain which was now falling to wipe out his tracks in Snake Doctor's horse lot. Anyhow, it probably would be days or weeks before any one missed the hermit and made search for him; in that time the tracks would have vanished, rain or no. It was greatly in his favor that when Snake Doctor was away from home, or supposed to be, folks religiously refrained from setting foot on the premises. They mightily feared the cotton-mouths with which the recluse was reputed to consort. There was even a story that Snake Doctor kept for a watchman in his house the granddaddy of all created cotton-mouths and set this monster on guard when he stirred abroad. So he needed no locks on his doors nor bar for his single window, the legend amply protecting his belongings in his absences.

Ten minutes passed, fifteen, and Japhet was up on his knees, his rifle at poise, his eyes watching through the tops of the weeds which fringed the ambuscade. Something or other— something quick and furtive— stirred behind him. Startled, he turned his head, saw that the disturber was a belated catbird, and looked front again. In that brief space of time the victim had come into sight. Through the rain and the slackening daylight he could see, above the ragged top of the intervening brush fence, the white patch of Snake Doctor's loppy old straw hat and below the hat the folds of a dark coat drawn over a pair of hunched narrow shoulders as the wearer of these garments came briskly toward the stable, which meant also toward him. At this distance he couldn't miss.

Nor did he. At the shot, the figure jerked backward, then went over face forward. The killer rose upright, exultation contending with tautened nerves within him. He stole up to the fence, set a foot in the tangled brushwood with intent to climb it and then, at what he saw, froze into a poised shape of terror, his eyes bulging, his mouth opened in a square shape, and his rifle dropping from his twitching fingers.

He had just killed Snake Doctor—killed him dead with a 32-caliber slug through the head. And here on his door-sill stood Snake Doctor, whole and sound, and staring at him! And now, Snake Doctor, dead by all rights and rules, yet living, was uttering a cry and starting out of the doorway toward him.

Japhet Morner had sucked in superstitions with his mother's milk. He believed in "ha'nts" and "witch-hags" and "sperrits," believed in "conjures" and "charms" and ghosts and hoop-snakes; believed that those under the favor of infernal forces might only be killed with a bullet molded from virgin silver. And his mistake was, he had used lead out of a brass shell.

Power of motion returned to him. He threw himself backward and whirled and ran into the deeps of the darkening woods, making whimpering sounds like a thrashed puppy as he went.

Terror rode him into the steamy woodlands. Exhaustion, dizziness, the feeling that he must get under the shelter of a sound roof, must have the protection of four walls about him, brought Japhet Morner out again along toward midnight. The rain had ceased; the moon was trying to come forth. A short distance southeast of his place he struck a dirt road which would lead him there. Beyond the next bend he would be in sight of home.

Around the turn he saw coming toward him a joggling light—a lantern hung on a buggy or light wagon, he figured—and heard the creak of wheels turning in the muddied softness. Nameless horrors had made a fugitive of him; the fugitive instinct still possessed him. Anyway, all shocked and shaken and shivering as he was, hatless and wet and dripping with muck, it would be better for him if no prying eyes beheld his present state. He flattened down in a clump of wayside bushes to bide until the approaching traveler passed.

Moving briskly, the rig was almost opposite him when, from the other direction—the same direction he had been following—came a call:

"Hello there!—who's joggin'?" The voice seemed to spring out of the darkness.

"Whoa!—Stiddy, boy!" Whoever was driving, pulled up his horse, which had shied at the sudden hail. "Me—Davis Ware," he answered back, "That you, Tip Bailey?"

"Yep, hoofin' it out from the Junction, and tolerable tired, if anybody should ask you. What's bringin' you out this hour of night, Davis—somebody sick?"

"Sick nothin'! There's been hell poppin' in these bottoms tonight."

Behind the weed screen ten feet away the listener stiffened, his blood drumming in him. He knew the speakers, both neighbors of his, one of them a local leader. The foot passenger hurried up alongside the buggy;

his face, inquisitive and alarmed, showed in the dim circlet of lantern light.

"What do you mean?"

"A killin'—that's whut I mean. An abominable, cold-blooded killin' ef ever there wuz one."

"God! Who's been killed?"

"I'm fixin' to tell you, man. It happened jes' shortly before dusk at ole Snake Doctor's place."

"Was it him was killed?"

"Gimme time, can't you?" This Ware was one who must tell his tale his own way or not at all. "It seems like Snake Doctor's been chillin' lately. He wuz purty bad off to-day—I mean yistiddy. And so, right after supper-time when the rain wuz lullin' a little, Mizz Kizzie Morner she footed it down frum her place to hisn', fetchin' some physic with her and a plate of hot vittles fur him. It seems like she wuzn't feared to go there. I'd 'a' been, I'll own up, but she wuzn't. Well, purty soon after she got there it seems like he tried to git up out of his bed to go feed that old crow-bait sorrel of his'n. It had started in ag'in by then, pourin' down hard and so she made him stay where he wuz. And she put on his old hat and throwed his old coat 'round her to keep off the wust of the wet, and she started out of the back door to do the feedin'. And no more'n she'd got outside in the lot than a shot come frum the aidge of the woods right over the fence and down she went with a bullet through her brains."

"God's sake! Dead?"

"No, not dead, but same ez dead. She barely wuz breathin' here not ten minutes ago when I left her house. Old Doctor Bradshaw, he's there with her now and he says it's a miracle she's lasted this long. Well, it seems like Snake Doctor jumped up at the shot and run out to see whut had happened and there she lay a'welterin'. And him,—well, he's been takin' on like all possessed ever since. I wouldn't 'a' believed he could 'a' had so much feelin' in him ef I hadn't seen him with my own eyes. It wuz him run for help, though—he did have sense enough left to do that. He found me in my tobacco patch and I dropped everything and took out for there, and a bunch of us picked her up and toted her home on a wagon bed. She's shot in the left side of the head just over the temples; the bullet went clean through and come out on the right side."

"But who did it?"

"I'm comin' to that. 'Twuz that low-flung husband of hers done it—that's who. It seems like he must 'a' followed her down to Snake Doctor's and laid in wait fur her and felled her ez she come out. Gawd knows why, onless 'twuz jes' pyure pizen meanness."

"The murderin' dog! They're certain 'twas him, then?"

"Shore ez gun's iron 'twuz him. Snake Doctor ketched a quick look at him over the fence ez he darted off. And right there they found his rifle where he'd dropped it before he whirl't and run—fool thing fur him to do

—and I seen his tracks, myself, in the soft ground, goin' and comin' and where he must 'a' stood when he fired. I seen 'em by lantern light after I got there—and fully half a dozen others seen 'em too. There's a long red streak on her arm where he must 'a' been whuppin' her sometime durin' the day."

"Hangin's a sight too good! Did they catch him?"

"No, but they will. Some thinks he's made fur the slashes and hid out there—his tracks led off that way. There'll be a line of men throwed all the way 'round Little Cypress before sunup. They're organizin' the posse at the Morner place."

"Sheriff got there yet?"

"No, but he's due by daylight or sooner. They telephoned in from Gallup's Mills to him and he's already started with his pack of dogs. The trail ought to lay good, ground bein' damp the way it is. Ole Snake Doctor he's carryin' on and ravin' 'round, sayin' the Lord's goin' to strike the murderer down in his tracks. But I'm puttin' my main dependence on them bloodhounds—on them, first, and then mebbe on a good stout plow line and the limb of a tree. Oh, they'll ketch him, and when they do, I 'low to be there. I'm jes' puttin' out fur my place to roust out my oldest boy and fetch him back with me. There's a good-size crowd mustered already but we'll need every able-bodied hand we can git."

"Don't let me hold you up any longer, then," said the pedestrian, a deadly grimness in his tone. "I'm ready now—got a pistol here in my hip pocket. That poor thing! She always was a good-hearted, hard-workin' woman and mightily put-upon. As for Jafe Morner—well, if I should be so lucky as to be the one to jump him out of the sticks, I'm goin' shoot first and ask questions afterwards. I'll be waitin' there at Morner's when you get back, Davis."

He broke into a half-run.

In the patchy moonlight which sifted through the shredding rain-clouds, Snake Doctor's house made a black square against the lesser blackness of its background. To it, panting in his haste, came the assassin, running. He feared the place—to the bottom of his desperate soul he feared it—but a fear yet greater was driving him hither. Previously it has been stated that this man had a powerful imagination. To a literate person it might have been a gift. To him, in this emergency, it was a curse. It set his already sore and smitten nerves on end; still, it honed his wits to a sharper edge.

What he overheard back there on the dirt road had remodeled his formless flight into a shaped intent. Now he had to deal, not with phantoms and daunting apparitions, but with tangible dangers; dangers not less frightful than those others perhaps, but to be coped with—if his luck held—and outwitted physical devices. There was no remorse in him. After all he was fairly well suited by the outcome of his mistake; getting safely away was what concerned him. In his present plight, weaponless, without a cent in his pocket, with the countryside rousing to hunt him, escape was out of prospect. But with money to buy his way along he'd have a good chance. Let the Sheriff come on with his dogs, then, let the mob form, with their talk of a rope and cold lead! Given any sort of break he'd best them. He would strike through the deep timber for the river; in six hours of steady traveling he could make it. At the river he would hire a shanty-boater to ferry him across to the Arkansas side; in some town over there buy clothes and get his hair cut; then catch a train and travel as far west or as far south as the steam-cars would take him. And it was Snake Doctor's cash that would buy the way for him! Getting this money had been in the angles of his original plan; a seemingly unearthly intervention had diverted him from it. Now he was returning to it, with a tremendous motive, self-preservation, urging him to speed. He had little time, though.

Mighty little. He knew the interior arrangements of Snake Doctor's one room—the pallet in this corner, the fireplace in that, the chair and the table drawn out on the sagging floor. In the one spying visit he ever had paid Snake Doctor two weeks before when this shooting scheme first formed in his mind, he had noted these things in detail. He had marked also the very spot where he was certain the place of concealment for the money was. All through his stay, Snake Doctor, tremulous and plainly apprehensive, had maneuvered to keep between the unbidden, unwelcome caller and the corner where the comforters and blankets were placed. Also, the recluse's eyes had helped to betray him; time and time again they had turned nervously to the wall just beyond and above the bedding, a point, say, five or six feet above it. Just about there, probably in a concealed gap between or behind the logs, the loot surely must be.

He thrust through the planked door, sagging on its leather hinges, and crossed directly to the fireplace. There was no fire in it, but, on stooping and fumbling with his hands, he found chips there ready to be kindled, and under the chips scraps of paper—good! He needed a light of sorts to search by. He had matches in his pocket, corked in a bottle, water-tight. He got them out as quickly as his shaking fingers would let him. There were only four of them. One after another he struck them, applying their points of flame to the paper. But the paper was damp from rain coming down the mud chimney, and no fire caught until the fourth and last match had been struck. Then it merely flickered; it ran slowly along the edge of the charring paper, smoking and threatening to go out.

Alright, then, let it go out, if it wanted to. He could see in the dark as well as the next one, and had hands to feel with. He made for the corner diagonally across the cabin and ran his hands swiftly along the exposed upper surface of a certain log, probing for any deep depressions in the rotted bark adhering to it, nicking the dried clay mortar with his nails. He tried that log without result, started on the log above it—and sucked in his breath as loose scraps of bark fell away at his touch from where they covered a niche in the joining. The cavity thus exposed was roughly circular in shape, the diameter about of a man's arm; he could tell that by fingering its edges. This must be the hole. Greedily he thrust his right hand in. It touched something—something slick and round and firm and smooth —and there came a quick darting sting as pointed things, sharp and keen, jabbed his thumb, tearing the skin as he jerked his hand out.

In that same breath the feeble flame in the fireplace caught well and flared up, its blaze filling the cabin with a wavery, unreliable radiance. Japhet Morner, flinging his hand up before his face, saw by that red brightness that on the inner side of his thumb were two tiny torn punctures, half an inch apart, from which drops of blood had started; and then, on beyond, two feet away, at the level of his stricken eyes he saw the forepart of a thick snake, its hideous dull-marked head lifted and thrust back just within the round of the orifice, its mouth wide open, with the cottony linings revealed, its neck taut and curved as though ready to strike again.

He gave a strangled slobbering howl and leaped to the other side of the room, sobbing, gasping, uttering fragments of wordless sound. The blood jumped and spurted from his flirted thumb to prove the wounds though minute were deep.

He must have whisky to drink or the cloven, hot carcass of a freshly-killed chicken to bind fast to the bite, or he was done for. At his house half a mile away was whisky and there were chickens asleep on their roost. He might make it. He whirled about, then recoiled as though a hard blow had stopped him. He couldn't go where men were assembling, ready and anxious to stretch his neck for him.

Now, then, his brain told him that, already and thus soon, quick pangs were leaping down his thumb, through his hand, flaming along his wrist and up his arm. The poison must be racing in his veins, mounting and growing, as he had heard it would. He had a feeling that his hand was swelling, making the skin tighter and tighter. There was no help, and even did help come now it would come too late. He howled and dropped and rolled on the floor, his head knocking against the rough boards.

Up in the creviced wall the forward length of the snake showed, its head still guardingly reared on its slim neck, its lidless pale eyes, like twin crumbs of blurred glass, aglow in the shifting firelight.

He got upon his feet, and a terrific pain struck at his heart, squeezing and wringing it. His throat closed and he choked. A second pain twisted his heart.

With a drunken leap he cleared the sill of the rear doorway, ran in a wavering course a few strides out across the horse lot and then, as his knees gave way under him, he pitched forward on his face, his lolled mouth full of weeds and muddy grass stems. The drumming fingers of his outstretched right hand almost touched a reddish-black smear where the earth was trampled and the grass flattened down.

"Good reddance by Gravy! I'd call it that; wouldn't you, Doc?"

The speaker was driving Dr. Bradshaw back to his home near Gallup's Mills. The other raised his head wearily. He had been up all night and he was an old man. The rocking motion of the buggy was soothing to him, even though the newly-risen sun did put its slanted rays right into his eyes.

"Well," he said, "I'd not have wished the death he died on any man, no matter what he'd done to deserve it. Yet I reckon there was a sort of rough justice in it, too. Anyway, we've been saved a lynching or else a regular hanging. And one would have been a scandal on the county and the other an expense to the tax-payers. Maybe you have got the right idea about it, Jim Meloan.

"I'm looking at it more from the professional point of view. I've had two strange experiences this past night, Jim. I've seen an undernourished sickly woman, after being shot through the brain, linger for nearly seven hours before she died, and I've examined the body of a man who'd been killed by a snake bite—killed good and quick, too, judging by the evidences."

"Well, Doc, ain't that the way a cotton mouth always does kill a man— sudden like?" asked Meloan. "I've always heared tell—"

"Never mind what you've heard," said the old doctor; he was cross because he was sleepy. "I'm going by the facts, not by fairy-tales. I was born and raised down here and I've been practicing medicine in this county for going on forty-six years and as a country doctor I ought to know something about these things if anybody does. And I tell you that in all my life I've never known of but two or three people actually being bitten by water moccasins, and until this morning I never had personal knowledge of anybody at all dying from the bite of any kind of snake. Horses?—well, yes. Dogs?—maybe so. But not a human being until now.

"Still, the proof is clear enough in this case. I think I'll have to write a paper about it for the next meeting of the State Medical Society. The places where the fangs nipped him were right there in the ball of his thumb —two bloody deep little scratches, side by side. And then there was that look on his face—*ugh!* I'm fairly hardened but I'm not going to forget Jafe Morner's face in a hurry. He died quick, I'd say offhand, but he died hard, too; I'll swear to that part of it. Well, he was the kind who likely would flicker out pretty brisk under certain circumstances. Ever notice the color of his skin and those heavy pouches under his eyes? Bad whisky and bad food and swamp fevers didn't put those signs on him. The late Japhet had a rotten bad heart, Jimmy."

"He shorely did," agreed Meloan fervently. "Yistiddy proved that."

"I don't mean exactly in that sense," explained the physician. "I mean he had an organic weakness. Curious thing, though, there was no swelling 'round the wounds nor any swelling in his hand or arm; no noticeable blotching of the skin, either. And yet, if there's anything in the accepted theories of the toxic effects of a snake's bite, those conditions should have been marked. Oh, I'll have quite a paper to read before the Society!"

"Mebbe the swellin' had done went down before you got to him?" suggested the morbidly interested farmer.

"No, he couldn't have been dead more than a short while when they went down there to set the dogs on the trail and found him; Sheriff Gill tells me he was still warm. And I was there not ten minutes after that. It's a mighty unusual case—several features about it that puzzles me. F'rinstance, now what about the snake that gashed him? Which-a-way did it come from beforehand and where did it head for afterwards? I didn't see any snake tracks in the ground close to where he was laying—I looked for 'em too. Still, the lot was pretty well tromped. Now, that poor forlorn old creature that you people in this neighborhood call Snake Doctor, he's got his own pet theory about it. He keeps on saying it was the Vengeance of the Lord falling upon a red-handed murderer. He thinks the fellow was drawn back to the seat of his crime—well, that might be so; I've heard of such things before—and that the Divine Wrath lit on him. But if I was him I'd be poking under the stable or the cabin for a whopping big snake.

"He tells me, though—and he ought to be an authority on the subject if anybody is—he tells me that a water moccasin never travels many yards away from the water and that night-times they always den up somewhere, being cold-blooded creatures that love the sunshine. And on top of that he swears to me that there never have been any moccasins close about his diggin's unless he'd brought 'em there dead or else as prisoners in a sack."

"Why, looky here, Doc," broke in Meloan; "he lied to you, then. There's always been a sayin' 'round here that Snake Doctor kept a hugeous big cotton-mouth right with him in his house all the time!"

"Yes, that's true. I saw it, myself, not an hour ago," said the doctor, smiling a little. "I reckon the old fellow's smarter than some folks give him credit for being. He took me in his shack and showed it to me."

"But I thought you jes' now said that—"

"Wait till I finish. He took me in and showed it to me, just as I'm telling you. But it was deader than Hector. It was a stuffed snake—with glass eyes and all. It seems a professional taxidermist who was up here from Memphis some years ago mounted it for our eccentric friend. Well, I'll tell the world he made a good job of it. Life-like?—you bet you! See it in a poor light and you'd almost be ready to swear you saw it move its head. I wouldn't have the thing 'round me for any amount of cash. But it seems this old fellow had a purpose in keeping it.

"That point came out in a sort of a peculiar way, too. It's been common gossip, I understand, that Snake Doctor had a store of money laid by. No doubt you've heard exaggerated stories about the size of his wad; but I'm prepared to tell you it wasn't much—just under a hundred dollars, all told. After he'd ca'mmed down he told me he didn't crave to keep it any more. He said he wanted it spent, paying for a proper funeral for that poor woman—said she was the only friend he'd had in the world; the only one that ever gave him a kind look or a kind word. So he asked me and Tip Bailey to take charge of it and then he took us in his shanty and got it out from the secret place where he'd kept it hid. It was tucked down in behind a break in the chinking between two of the side logs. And—listen to this, Jim—right in front of it, just back inside the mouth of the opening, he'd set that stuffed cotton-mouth of his, figuring that the bare sight of it, with its neck all bent like as if it was fixing to lunge and its jaws wide open, would kind of discourage anybody who might take a notion to start exploring in there.

"And, then for a further precaution—oh, he's got plenty of sense in his way—he'd gone and lined the inside of the hole all 'round the edges and half-way down to the bottom with coils of barbed wire, with the points sticking up every which way. Anybody who rammed his hand in there suddenly would certainly get gaffed. Not that anybody would, who'd seen the snake first."

The old doctor yawned heavily. "Purty smart little notion, I'd call it."

MYSTERY STORIES

The Adventure of the Speckled Band

by A. CONAN DOYLE

ON GLANCING OVER MY NOTES OF THE SEVENTY ODD cases in which I have during the last eight years studied the methods of my friend Sherlock Holmes, I find many tragic, some comic, a large number merely strange, but none commonplace; for, working as he did rather for the love of his art than for the acquirement of wealth, he refused to associate himself with any investigation which did not tend towards the unusual, and even the fantastic. Of all these varied cases, however, I cannot recall any which presented more singular features than that which was associated with the well-known Surrey family of the Roylotts of Stoke Moran. The events in question occurred in the early days of my association with Holmes, when we were sharing rooms as bachelors in Baker Street. It is possible that I might have placed them upon record before, but a promise of secrecy was made at the time, from which I have only been freed during the last month by the untimely death of the lady to whom the pledge was given. It is perhaps as well that the facts should now come to light, for I have reasons to know that there are wide-spread rumors as to the death of Dr. Grimesby Roylott which tend to make the matter even more terrible than the truth.

It was early in April in the year '83 that I woke one morning to find Sherlock Holmes standing, fully dressed, by the side of my bed. He was a late riser as a rule, and as the clock on the mantel-piece showed me that it was only a quarter past seven, I blinked up at him in some surprise, and perhaps just a little resentment, for I was myself regular in my habits.

"Very sorry to knock you up, Watson," said he, "but it's the common lot this morning. Mrs. Hudson has been knocked up, she retorted upon me, and I on you."

"What is it, then—a fire?"

"No; a client. It seems that a young lady has arrived in a considerable state of excitement, who insists upon seeing me. She is waiting now in the sitting-room. Now, when young ladies wander about the metropolis at this hour of the morning, and knock sleepy people up out of their beds, I presume that it is something very pressing which they have to communicate. Should it prove to be an interesting case, you would, I am sure, wish to follow it from the outset. I thought, at any rate, that I should call you and give you the chance."

"My dear fellow, I would not miss it for anything."

I had no keener pleasure than in following Holmes in his professional investigations, and in admiring the rapid deductions, as swift as intuitions, and yet always founded on a logical basis, with which he unravelled the problems which were submitted to him. I rapidly threw on my clothes, and was ready in a few minutes to accompany my friend down to the sitting-room. A lady dressed in black and heavily veiled, who had been sitting in the window, rose as we entered.

"Good-morning, madam," said Holmes, cheerily. "My name is Sherlock Holmes. This is my intimate friend and associate, Dr. Watson, before whom you can speak as freely as before myself. Ha! I am glad to see that Mrs. Hudson has had the good sense to light the fire. Pray draw up to it, and I shall order you a cup of hot coffee, for I observe that you are shivering."

"It is not cold which makes me shiver," said the woman, in a low voice, changing her seat as requested.

"What, then?"

"It is fear, Mr. Holmes. It is terror." She raised her veil as she spoke, and we could see that she was indeed in a pitiable state of agitation, her face all drawn and gray, with restless, frightened eyes, like those of some hunted animal. Her features and figure were those of a woman of thirty, but her hair was shot with premature gray, and her expression was weary and haggard. Sherlock Holmes ran her over with one of his quick, all-comprehensive glances.

"You must not fear," said he, soothingly, bending forward and patting her forearm. "We shall soon set matters right, I have no doubt. You have come in by train this morning, I see."

"You know me, then?"

"No, but I observe the second half of a return ticket in the palm of your left glove. You must have started early, and yet you had a good drive in a dog-cart, along heavy roads, before you reached the station."

The lady gave a violent start, and stared in bewilderment at my companion.

"There is no mystery, my dear madam," said he, smiling. "The left arm of your jacket is spattered with mud in no less than seven places. The marks are perfectly fresh. There is no vehicle save a dog-cart which throws up mud in that way, and then only when you sit on the left-hand side of the driver."

"Whatever your reasons may be, you are perfectly correct," said she. "I started from home before six, reached Leatherhead at twenty past, and came in by the first train to Waterloo. Sir, I can stand this strain no longer; I shall go mad if it continues. I have no one to turn to—none, save only one, who cares for me, and he, poor fellow, can be of little aid. I have heard of you, Mr. Holmes; I have heard of you from Mrs. Farintosh, whom you helped in the hour of her sore need. It was from her that I had your address. Oh, sir, do you not think that you could help me, too, and at least throw a little light through the dense darkness which surrounds me? At present it is out of my power to reward you for your services, but in a month or six weeks I shall be married, with the control of my own income, and then at least you shall not find me ungrateful."

Holmes turned to his desk, and unlocking it, drew out a small case-book, which he consulted.

"Farintosh," said he. "Ah yes, I recall the case; it was concerned with an opal tiara. I think it was before your time, Watson. I can only say, madam, that I shall be happy to devote the same care to your case as I did to that of your friend. As to reward, my profession is its own reward; but you are at liberty to defray whatever expenses I may be put to, at the time which suits you best. And now I beg that you will lay before us everything that may help us in forming an opinion upon the matter."

"Alas!" replied our visitor, "the very horror of my situation lies in the fact that my fears are so vague, and my suspicions depend so entirely upon small points, which might seem trivial to another, that even he to whom of all others I have a right to look for help and advice looks upon all that I tell him about it as the fancies of a nervous woman. He does not say so, but I can read it from his soothing answers and averted eyes. But I have heard, Mr. Holmes, that you can see deeply into the manifold wickedness of the human heart. You may advise me how to walk amid the dangers which encompass me."

"I am all attention, madam."

"My name is Helen Stoner, and I am living with my stepfather, who is the last survivor of one of the oldest Saxon families in England, the Roylotts of Stoke Moran, on the western border of Surrey."

Holmes nodded his head. "The name is familiar to me," said he.

"The family was at one time among the richest in England, and the estates extended over the borders into Berkshire in the north, and Hampshire in the west. In the last century, however, four successive heirs were of a dissolute and wasteful disposition, and the family ruin was eventually completed by a gambler in the days of the Regency. Nothing was left save a few acres of ground, and the two-hundred-year-old house, which is itself crushed under a heavy mortgage. The last squire dragged out his existence there, living the horrible life of an aristocratic pauper; but his only son, my step-father, seeing that he must adapt himself to the new conditions, obtained an advance from a relative, which enabled him to take a medical degree, and went out to Calcutta, where, by his professional skill and his force of character, he established a large practice. In a fit of anger, however, caused by some robberies which had been perpetrated in the house, he beat his native butler to death, and narrowly escaped a capital sentence. As it was, he suffered a long term of imprisonment, and afterwards returned to England a morose and disappointed man.

"When Dr. Roylott was in India he married my mother, Mrs. Stoner, the young widow of Major-General Stoner, of the Bengal Artillery. My sister Julia and I were twins, and we were only two years old at the time of my mother's re-marriage. She had a considerable sum of money—not less than £1000 a year—and this she bequeathed to Dr. Roylott entirely while we resided with him, with a provision that a certain annual sum should be allowed to each of us in the event of our marriage. Shortly after our return to England my mother died—she was killed eight years ago in a railway accident near Crewe. Dr. Roylott then abandoned his attempts to establish himself in practice in London, and took us to live with him in the old ancestral house at Stoke Moran. The money which my mother had left was enough for all our wants, and there seemed to be no obstacle to our happiness.

"But a terrible change came over our step-father about this time. Instead of making friends and exchanging visits with our neighbors, who had at first been overjoyed to see a Roylott of Stoke Moran back in the old family seat, he shut himself up in his house, and seldom came out save to indulge in ferocious quarrels with whoever might cross his path. Violence of temper approaching to mania has been hereditary in the men of the family, and in my step-father's case it had, I believe, been intensified by his long residence in the tropics. A series of disgraceful brawls took place, two of which ended in the police-court, until at last he became the terror of the village, and the folks would fly at his approach, for he is a man of immense strength, and absolutely uncontrollable in his anger.

"Last week he hurled the local blacksmith over a parapet into a stream, and it was only by paying over all the money which I could get together that I was able to avert another public exposure. He had no friends at all save the wandering gypsies, and he would give those vagabonds leave to encamp upon the few acres of bramble-covered land which represent the family estate, and would accept in return the hospitality of their tents, wandering away with them sometimes for weeks on end. He has a passion also for Indian animals, which are sent over to him by a correspondent, and he has at this moment a cheetah and a baboon, which wander freely over his grounds, and are feared by the villagers almost as much as their master.

"You can imagine from what I say that my poor sister Julia and I had no great pleasures in our lives. No servant would stay with us, and for a long time we did all the work of the house. She was but thirty at the time of her death, and yet her hair had already begun to whiten, even as mine has."

"Your sister is dead, then?"

"She died just two years ago, and it is of her death that I wish to speak to you. You can understand that, living the life which I have described, we were little likely to see any one of our own age and position. We had, however, an aunt, my mother's maiden sister, Miss Honoria Westphail, who lives near Harrow, and we were occasionally allowed to pay short visits at this lady's house. Julia went there at Christmas two years ago, and met there a half-pay major of marines, to whom she became engaged. My step-father learned of the engagement when my sister returned, and offered no objection to the marriage; but within a fortnight of the day which had been fixed for the wedding, the terrible event occurred which has deprived me of my only companion."

Sherlock Holmes had been leaning back in his chair with his eyes closed and his head sunk in a cushion, but he half opened his lids now and glanced across at his visitor.

"Pray be precise as to details," said he.

"It is easy for me to be so, for every event of that dreadful time is seared into my memory. The manor-house is, as I have already said, very old, and only one wing is now inhabited. The bedrooms in this wing are on the ground floor, the sitting rooms being in the central block of the buildings. Of these bedrooms the first is Dr. Roylott's, the second my sister's, and the third my own. There is no communication between them, but they all open out into the same corridor. Do I make myself plain?"

"Perfectly so."

"The windows of the three rooms open out upon the lawn. That fatal night Dr. Roylott had gone to his room early, though we knew that he had not retired to rest, for my sister was troubled by the smell of the strong Indian cigars which it was his custom to smoke. She left her room, there-fore, and came into mine, where she sat for some time, chatting about her approaching wedding. At eleven o'clock she rose to leave me but she paused at the door and looked back.

" 'Tell me, Helen,' said she, 'have you ever heard any one whistle in the dead of the night?'

" 'Never,' said I.

" 'I suppose that you could not possibly whistle, yourself, in your sleep?'

" 'Certainly not. But why?'

" 'Because during the last few nights I have always, about three in the morning, heard a low, clear whistle. I am a light sleeper, and it has awakened me. I cannot tell where it came from—perhaps from the next room, perhaps from the lawn. I thought that I would just ask you whether you had heard it."

" 'No, I have not. It must be those wretched gypsies in the plantation.'

" 'Very likely. And yet if it were on the lawn, I wonder that you did not hear it also.'

" 'Ah, but I sleep more heavily than you.'

" 'Well, it is of no great consequence, at any rate.' She smiled back at me, closed my door, and a few moments later I heard her key turn in the lock."

"Indeed," said Holmes. "Was it your custom always to lock yourselves in at night?"

"Always."

"And why?"

"I think that I mentioned to you that the doctor kept a cheetah and a baboon. We had no feeling of security unless our doors were locked."

"Quite so. Pray proceed with your statement."

"I could not sleep that night. A vague feeling of impending misfortune impressed me. My sister and I, you will recollect, were twins, and you know how subtle are the links which bind two souls which are so closely allied. It was a wild night. The wind was howling outside, and the rain was beating and splashing against the windows. Suddenly, amid all the hub-bub of the gale, there burst forth the wild scream of a terrified woman. I knew that it was my sister's voice. I sprang from my bed, wrapped a shawl round me, and rushed into the corridor. As I opened my door I seemed to hear a low whistle, such as my sister described, and a few moments later a clanging sound, as if a mass of metal had fallen. As I ran down the passage, my sister's door was unlocked, and revolved slowly upon its hinges. I stared at it horror-stricken, not knowing what was about to issue from it. By the light of the corridor-lamp I saw my sister appear at the opening, her face blanched with terror, her hands groping for help, her whole figure swaying to and fro like that of a drunkard. I ran to her and threw my arms round her, but at that moment her knees seemed to give way and she fell to the ground. She writhed as one who is in terrible pain, and her limbs were dreadfully convulsed. At first I thought that she had not recognized me, but as I bent over her she suddenly shrieked out in a voice which I shall never forget, 'Oh, my God! Helen! It was the band! The speckled band!' There was something else which she would fain have said, and she stabbed with her finger into the air in the direction of the doctor's room, but a fresh convulsion seized her and choked her words. I rushed out, calling loudly for my step-father, and I met him hastening from his room in his dressing-gown. When he reached my sister's side she was unconscious, and though he poured brandy down her throat and sent for medical aid from the village, all efforts were in vain, for she slowly sank and died without having recovered her consciousness. Such was the dreadful end of my beloved sister."

"One moment," said Holmes; "are you sure about this whistle and metallic sound? Could you swear to it?"

"That was what the county coroner asked me at the inquiry. It is my strong impression that I heard it, and yet, among the crash of the gale and the creaking of an old house, I may possibly have been deceived."

"Was your sister dressed?"

"No, she was in her night-dress. In her right hand was found the charred stump of a match, and in her left a match-box."

"Showing that she had struck a light and looked about her when the alarm took place. That is important. And what conclusions did the coroner come to?"

"He investigated the case with great care, for Dr. Roylott's conduct had long been notorious in the county, but he was unable to find any satisfactory cause of death. My evidence showed that the door had been fastened upon the inner side, and the windows were blocked by old-fashioned shutters with broad iron bars, which were secured every night. The walls were carefully sounded, and were shown to be quite solid all round, and the flooring was also thoroughly examined, with the same result. The chimney is wide, but is barred up by four large staples. It is certain, therefore, that my sister was quite alone when she met her end. Besides, there were no marks of any violence upon her."

"How about poison?"

"The doctors examined her for it, but without success."

"What do you think that this unfortunate lady died of, then?"

"It is my belief that she died of pure fear and nervous shock, though what it was that frightened her I cannot imagine."

"Were the gypsies in the plantation at the time?"

"Yes, there are nearly always some there."

"Ah, and what did you gather from this allusion to a band—a speckled band?"

"Sometimes I have thought that it was merely the wild talk of delirium, sometimes that it may have referred to some band of people, perhaps to these very gypsies in the plantation. I do not know whether the spotted handkerchiefs which so many of them wear over their heads might have suggested the strange adjective which she used."

Holmes shook his head like a man who is far from being satisfied.

"These are very deep waters," said he; "pray go on with your narrative."

"Two years have passed since then, and my life has been until lately lonelier than ever. A month ago, however, a dear friend, whom I have known for many years, has done me the honor to ask my hand in marriage. His name is Armitage—Percy Armitage—the second son of Mr. Armitage, of Crane Water, near Reading. My step-father has offered no opposition to the match, and we are to be married in the course of the spring. Two days ago some repairs started in the west wing of the building, and my bedroom wall has been pierced, so that I have had to move into the chamber in which my sister died, and to sleep in the very bed in which she slept. Imagine, then, my thrill of terror when last night, as I lay awake, thinking over her terrible fate, I suddenly heard in the silence of the night the low whistle which had been the herald of her own death. I sprang up and lit the lamp, but nothing was to be seen in the room. I was too shaken to go to bed again, however, so I dressed, and as soon as it was daylight I slipped down, got a dog-cart at the 'Crown Inn,' which is opposite, and drove to Leatherhead, from whence I have come on this morning with the one object of seeing you and asking your advice."

"You have done wisely," said my friend. "But have you told me all?"

"Yes, all."

"Miss Roylott, you have not. You are screening your step-father."

"Why, what do you mean?"

For answer Holmes pushed back the frill of black lace which fringed the hand that lay upon our visitor's knee. Five little livid spots, the marks of four fingers and a thumb, were printed upon the white wrist.

"You have been cruelly used," said Holmes.

The lady colored deeply and covered over her injured wrist. "He is a hard man," she said, "and perhaps he hardly knows his own strength."

There was a long silence, during which Holmes leaned his chin upon his hands and stared into the crackling fire.

"This is very deep business," he said, at last. "There are a thousand details which I should desire to know before I decide upon our course of action. Yet we have not a moment to lose. If we were to come to Stoke Moran to-day, would it be possible for us to see over these rooms without the knowledge of your step-father?"

"As it happens, he spoke of coming into town to-day upon some most important business. It is probable that he will be away all day, and that there would be nothing to disturb you. We have a house-keeper now, but she is old and foolish, and I could easily get her out of the way."

"Excellent. You are not averse to this trip, Watson?"

"By no means."

"Then we shall both come. What are you going to do yourself?"

"I have one or two things which I would wish to do now that I am in town. But I shall return by the twelve o'clock train, so as to be there in time for your coming."

"And you may expect us early in the afternoon. I have myself some small business matters to attend to. Will you not wait and breakfast?"

"No, I must go. My heart is lightened already since I have confided my trouble to you. I shall look forward to seeing you again this afternoon." She dropped her thick black veil over her face and glided from the room.

"And what do you think of it all, Watson?" asked Sherlock Holmes, leaning back in his chair.

"It seems to me to be a most dark and sinister business."

"Dark enough and sinister enough."

"Yet if the lady is correct in saying that the flooring and walls are sound, and that the door, window, and chimney are impassable, then her sister must have been undoubtedly alone when she met her mysterious end."

"What becomes, then, of these nocturnal whistles, and what of the very peculiar words of the dying woman?"

"I cannot think."

"When you combine the ideas of whistles at night, the presence of a band of gypsies who are on intimate terms with this old doctor, the fact that we have every reason to believe that the doctor has an interest in preventing his step-daughter's marriage, the dying allusion to a band, and, finally, the fact that Miss Helen Stoner heard a metallic clang, which might have been caused by one of those metal bars which secured the shutters falling back into their place, I think that there is good ground to think that the mystery may be cleared along those lines."

"But what, then, did the gypsies do?"

"I cannot imagine."

"I see many objections to any such theory."

"And so do I. It is precisely for that reason that we are going to Stoke Moran this day. I want to see whether the objections are fatal, or if they may be explained away. But what in the name of the devil!"

The ejaculation had been drawn from my companion by the fact that our door had been suddenly dashed open, and that a huge man had framed himself in the aperture. His costume was a peculiar mixture of the professional and of the agricultural, having a black top-hat, a long frock-coat, and a pair of high gaiters, with a hunting-crop swinging in his hand. So tall was he that his hat actually brushed the cross bar of the door-way, and his breadth seemed to span it across from side to side. A large face, seared with a thousand wrinkles, burned yellow with the sun, and marked with every evil passion, was turned from one to the other of us, while his deep-set bile-shot eyes, and his high, thin, fleshless nose, gave him somewhat the resemblance to a fierce old bird of prey.

"Which of you is Holmes?" asked this apparition.

"My name, sir; but you have the advantage of me," said my companion, quietly.

"I am Dr. Grimesby Roylott, of Stoke Moran."

"Indeed, doctor," said Holmes, blandly. "Pray take a seat."

"I will do nothing of the kind. My step-daughter has been here. I have traced her. What has she been saying to you?"

"It is a little cold for the time of the year," said Holmes.

"What has she been saying to you?" screamed the old man, furiously.

"But I have heard that the crocuses promise well," continued my companion, imperturbably.

"Ha! You put me off, do you?" said our new visitor, taking a step forward and shaking his hunting-crop. "I know you, you scoundrel! I have heard of you before. You are Holmes, the meddler."

My friend smiled.

"Holmes, the busybody!"

His smile broadened.

"Holmes, the Scotland-yard Jack-in-office!"

Holmes chuckled heartily. "Your conversation is most entertaining," said he. "When you go out close the door, for there is a decided draught."

"I will go when I have said my say. Don't you dare to meddle with my affairs. I know that Miss Stoner has been here. I traced her! I am a dangerous man to fall foul of! See here." He stepped swiftly forward, seized the poker, and bent it into a curve with his huge brown hands.

"See that you keep yourself out of my grip," he snarled, and hurling the twisted poker into the fireplace, he strode out of the room.

"He seems a very amiable person," said Holmes, laughing. "I am not quite so bulky, but if he had remained I might have shown him that my grip was not much more feeble than his own." As he spoke he picked up the steel poker, and with a sudden effort straightened it out again.

"Fancy his having the insolence to confound me with the official detective force! This incident gives zest to our investigation, however, and I only trust that our little friend will not suffer from her imprudence in allowing this brute to trace her. And now, Watson, we shall order breakfast, and afterwards I shall walk down to Doctors' Commons, where I hope to get some data which may help us in this matter."

It was nearly one o'clock when Sherlock Holmes returned from his excursion. He held in his hand a sheet of blue paper, scrawled over with notes and figures.

"I have seen the will of the deceased wife," said he. "To determine its exact meaning I have been obliged to work out the present prices of the investments with which it is concerned. The total income, which at the time of the wife's death was little short of £1100, is now, through the fall in agricultural prices, not more than £750. Each daughter can claim an income of £250, in case of marriage. It is evident, therefore, that if both girls had married, this beauty would have had a mere pittance, while even one of them would cripple him to a very serious extent. My morning's work has not been wasted, since it has proved that he has the very strongest motives for standing in the way of anything of the sort. And now, Watson, this is too serious for dawdling, especially as the old man is aware that we are interesting ourselves in his affairs; so if you are ready, we shall call a cab and drive to Waterloo. I should be very much obliged if you would slip your revolver into your pocket. An Eley's No. 2 is an excellent argument with gentlemen who can twist steel pokers into knots. That and a tooth-brush are, I think, all that we need."

At Waterloo we were fortunate in catching a train for Leatherhead, where we hired a trap at the station inn, and drove for four or five miles through the lovely Surrey lanes. It was a perfect day, with a bright sun and a few fleecy clouds in the heavens. The trees and way-side hedges were just throwing out their first green shoots, and the air was full of the pleasant smell of the moist earth. To me at least there was a strange contrast between the sweet promise of the spring and this sinister quest upon which we were engaged. My companion sat in front of the trap, his arms folded, his hat pulled down over his eyes, and his chin sunk upon his breast, buried in the deepest thought. Suddenly, however, he started, tapped me on the shoulder, and pointed over the meadows.

"Look there!" said he.

A heavily-timbered park stretched up in a gentle slope, thickening into a grove at the highest point. From amid the branches there jutted out the gray gables and high roof-tree of a very old mansion.

"Stoke Moran?" said he.

"Yes, sir, that be the house of Dr. Grimesby Roylott," remarked the driver.

"There is some building going on there," said Holmes; "that is where we are going."

"There's the village," said the driver, pointing to a cluster of roofs some distance to the left; "but if you want to get to the house, you'll find it shorter to get over this stile, and so by the foot-path over the fields. There it is, where the lady is walking."

"And the lady, I fancy, is Miss Stoner," observed Holmes, shading his eyes. "Yes, I think we had better do as you suggest."

We got off, paid our fare, and the trap rattled back on its way to Leatherhead.

"I thought it as well," said Holmes, as we climbed the stile, "that this fellow should think we had come here as architects, or on some definite business. It may stop his gossip. Good-afternoon, Miss Stoner. You see that we have been as good as our word."

Our client of the morning had hurried forward to meet us with a face which spoke her joy. "I have been waiting so eagerly for you," she cried, shaking hands with us warmly. "All has turned out splendidly. Dr. Roylott has gone to town, and it is unlikely that he will be back before evening."

"We have had the pleasure of making the doctor's acquaintance," said Holmes, and in a few words he sketched out what had occurred. Miss Stoner turned white to the lips as she listened.

"Good heavens!" she cried, "he has followed me, then."

"So it appears."

"He is so cunning that I never know when I am safe from him. What will he say when he returns?"

"He must guard himself, for he may find that there is some one more cunning than himself upon his track. You must lock yourself up from him to-night. If he is violent, we shall take you away to your aunt's at Harrow. Now, we must make the best use of our time, so kindly take us at once to the rooms which we are to examine."

The building was of gray, lichen-blotched stone, with a high central portion, and two curving wings, like the claws of a crab, thrown out on each side. In one of these wings the windows were broken, and blocked with wooden boards, while the roof was partly caved in, a picture of ruin. The central portion was in little better repair, but the right-hand block was comparatively modern, and the blinds in the windows, with the blue smoke curling up from the chimneys, showed that this was where the family resided. Some scaffolding had been erected against the end wall, and the stone-work had been broken into, but there were no signs of any workmen at the moment of our visit. Holmes walked slowly up and down the ill-trimmed lawn, and examined with deep attention the outsides of the windows.

"This, I take it, belongs to the room in which you used to sleep, the centre one to your sister's, and the one next to the main building to Dr. Roylott's chamber?"

"Exactly so. But I am now sleeping in the middle one."

"Pending the alterations, as I understand. By-the-way, there does not seem to be any very pressing need for repairs at that end wall."

"There were none. I believe that it was an excuse to move me from my room."

"Ah! that is suggestive. Now, on the other side of this narrow wing runs the corridor from which these three rooms open. There are windows in it, of course?"

"Yes, but very small ones. Too narrow for any one to pass through."

"As you both locked your doors at night, your rooms were unapproachable from that side. Now, would you have the kindness to go into your room and bar your shutters."

Miss Stoner did so, and Holmes, after a careful examination through the open window, endeavored in every way to force the shutter open, but without success. There was no slit through which a knife could be passed to raise the bar. Then with his lens he tested the hinges, but they were of solid iron, built firmly into the massive masonry. "Hum!" said he, scratching his chin in some perplexity; "my theory certainly presents some difficulties. No one could pass these shutters if they were bolted. Well, we shall see if the inside throws any light upon the matter."

A small side door led into the whitewashed corridor from which the three bedrooms opened. Holmes refused to examine the third chamber, so we passed at once to the second, that in which Miss Stoner was now sleeping, and in which her sister had met with her fate. It was a homely little room, with a low ceiling and a gaping fireplace, after the fashion of old country-houses. A brown chest of drawers stood in one corner, a narrow white-counterpaned bed in another, and a dressing-table on the left-hand side of the window. These articles, with two small wicker-work chairs, made up all the furniture in the room, save for a square of Wilton carpet in the centre. The boards round and the panelling of the walls were of brown, worm-eaten oak, so old and discolored that it may have dated from the original building of the house. Holmes drew one of the chairs into a corner and sat silent, while his eyes travelled round and round and up and down, taking in every detail of the apartment.

"Where does that bell communicate with?" he asked, at last, pointing to a thick bell-rope which hung down the bed, the tassel actually lying upon the pillow.

"It goes to the house-keeper's room."

"It looks newer than the other things?"

"Yes, it was only put there a couple of years ago."

"Your sister asked for it, I suppose?"

"No, I never heard of her using it. We used always to get what we wanted ourselves."

"Indeed, it seemed unnecessary to put so nice a bell-pull there. You will excuse me for a few minutes while I satisfy myself as to this floor." He threw himself down upon his face with his lens in his hand, and crawled swiftly backward and forward, examining minutely the cracks between the boards. Then he did the same with the wood-work with which the chamber was panelled. Finally he walked over to the bed, and spent some time staring at it, and in running his eye up and down the wall. Finally he took the bell-rope in his hand and gave it a brisk tug.

"Why, it's a dummy," said he.

"Won't it ring?"

"No, it is not even attached to a wire. This is very interesting. You can see now that it is fastened to a hook just above where the little opening for the ventilator is."

"How very absurd! I never noticed that before."

"Very strange!" muttered Holmes, pulling at the rope. "There are one or two very singular points about this room. For example, what a fool a builder must be to open a ventilator into another room, when, with the same trouble, he might have communicated with the outside air!"

"That is also quite modern," said the lady.

"Done about the same time as the bell-rope?" remarked Holmes.

"Yes, there were several little changes carried out about that time."

"They seem to have been of a most interesting character—dummy bell-ropes, and ventilators which do not ventilate. With your permission, Miss Stoner, we shall now carry our researches into the inner apartment."

Dr. Grimesby Roylott's chamber was larger than that of his step-daughter, but was as plainly furnished. A camp-bed, a small wooden shelf full of books, mostly of a technical character, an arm-chair beside the bed, a plain wooden chair against the wall, a round table, and a large iron safe were the principal things which met the eye. Holmes walked slowly round and examined each and all of them with the keenest interest.

"What's in here?" he asked, tapping the safe.

"My step-father's business papers."

"Oh! you have seen inside, then?"

"Only once, some years ago. I remember that it was full of papers."

"There isn't a cat in it, for example?"

"No. What a strange idea!"

"Well, look at this!" He took up a small saucer of milk which stood on the top of it.

"No; we don't keep a cat. But there is a cheetah and a baboon."

"Ah, yes, of course! Well, a cheetah is just a big cat, and yet a saucer of milk does not go very far in satisfying its wants, I dare say. There is one point which I should wish to determine." He squatted down in front of the wooden chair, and examined the seat of it with the greatest attention.

"Thank you. That is quite settled," said he, rising and putting his lens in his pocket. "Hello! Here is something interesting!"

The object which had caught his eye was a small dog-lash hung on one corner of the bed. The lash, however, was curled upon itself, and tied so as to make a loop of whip-cord.

"What do you make of that, Watson?"

"It's a common enough lash. But I don't know why it should be tied."

"That is not quite so common, is it? Ah, me! it's a wicked world, and when a clever man turns his brains to crime it is the worst of all. I think that I have seen enough now, Miss Stoner, and with your permission we shall walk out upon the lawn."

I had never seen my friend's face so grim or his brow so dark as it was when we turned from the scene of this investigation. We had walked several times up and down the lawn, neither Miss Stoner nor myself liking to break in upon his thoughts before he roused himself from his reverie.

"It is very essential, Miss Stoner," said he, "that you should absolutely follow my advice in every respect. "

"I shall most certainly do so."

"The matter is too serious for any hesitation. Your life may depend upon your compliance."

"I assure you that I am in your hands."

"In the first place, both my friend and I must spend the night in your room."

Both Miss Stoner and I gazed at him in astonishment.

"Yes, it must be so. Let me explain. I believe that that is the village inn over there?"

"Yes, that is the 'Crown.' "

"Very good. Your windows would be visible from there?"

"Certainly."

"You must confine yourself to your room, on pretence of a headache, when your step-father comes back. Then when you hear him retire for the night, you must open the shutters of your window, undo the hasp, put your lamp there as a signal to us, and then withdraw quietly with everything which you are likely to want into the room which you used to occupy. I have no doubt that, in spite of the repairs, you could manage there for one night."

"Oh yes, easily."

"The rest you will leave in our hands."

"But what will you do?"

"We shall spend the night in your room, and we shall investigate the cause of this noise which has disturbed you."

"I believe, Mr. Holmes, that you have already made up your mind," said Miss Stoner, laying her hand upon my companion's sleeve.

"Perhaps I have."

"Then for pity's sake tell me what was the cause of my sister's death."

"I should prefer to have clearer proofs before I speak."

"You can at least tell me whether my own thought is correct, and if she died from some sudden fright."

"No, I do not think so. I think that there was probably some more tangible cause. And now, Miss Stoner, we must leave you, for if Dr. Roylott returned and saw us, our journey would be in vain. Good-bye, and be brave, for if you will do what I have told you, you may rest assured that we shall soon drive away the dangers that threaten you.

Sherlock Holmes and I had no difficulty in engaging a bedroom and sitting-room at the "Crown Inn." They were on the upper floor, and from our window we could command a view of the avenue gate, and of the inhabited wing of Stoke Moran Manor House. At dusk we saw Dr. Grimesby Roylott drive past, his huge form looming up beside the little figure of the lad who drove him. The boy had some slight difficulty in undoing the heavy iron gates, and we heard the hoarse roar of the doctor's voice, and saw the fury with which he shook his clenched fists at him. The trap drove on, and a few minutes later we saw a sudden light spring up among the trees as the lamp was lit in one of the sitting-rooms.

"Do you know, Watson," said Holmes, as we sat together in the gathering darkness, "I have really some scruples as to taking you to-night. There is a distinct element of danger."

"Can I be of assistance?"

"Your presence might be invaluable."

"Then I shall certainly come."

"It is very kind of you."

"You speak of danger. You have evidently seen more in these rooms than was visible to me."

"No, but I fancy that I may have deduced a little more. I imagine that you saw all that I did."

"I saw nothing remarkable save the bell-rope, and what purpose that could answer I confess is more than I can imagine."

"You saw the ventilator, too?"

"Yes, but I do not think that it is such a very unusual thing to have a small opening between two rooms. It was so small that a rat could hardly pass through."

"I knew that we should find a ventilator before ever we came to Stoke Moran."

"My dear Holmes!"

"Oh yes, I did. You remember in her statement she said that her sister could smell Dr. Roylott's cigar. Now, of course that suggested at once that there must be a communication between the two rooms. It could only be a small one, or it would have been remarked upon at the coroner's inquiry. I deduced a ventilator."

"But what harm can there be in that?"

"Well, there is at least a curious coincidence of dates. A ventilator is made, a cord is hung, and a lady who sleeps in the bed dies. Does not that strike you?"

"I cannot as yet see any connection."

"Did you observe anything very peculiar about that bed?"

"No."

"It was clamped to the floor. Did you ever see a bed fastened like that before?"

"I cannot say that I have."

"The lady could not move her bed. It must always be in the same relative position to the ventilator and to the rope—for so we may call it, since it was clearly never meant for a bell-pull."

"Holmes," I cried, "I seem to see dimly what you are hinting at. We are only just in time to prevent some subtle and horrible crime."

"Subtle enough and horrible enough. When a doctor does go wrong, he is the first of criminals. He has nerve and he has knowledge. Palmer and Pritchard were among the heads of their profession. This man strikes even deeper, but I think, Watson, that we shall be able to strike deeper still. But we shall have horrors enough before the night is over; for goodness' sake let us have a quiet pipe, and turn our minds for a few hours to something more cheerful."

About nine o'clock the light among the trees was extinguished, and all was dark in the direction of the Manor House. Two hours passed slowly away, and then, suddenly, just at the stroke of eleven, a single bright light shone out right in front of us.

"That is our signal," said Holmes, springing to his feet; "it comes from the middle window."

As we passed out he exchanged a few words with the landlord, explaining that we were going on a late visit to an acquaintance, and that it was possible that we might spend the night there. A moment later we were out on the dark road, a chill wind blowing in our faces, and one yellow light twinkling in front of us through the gloom to guide us on our sombre errand.

There was little difficulty in entering the grounds, for unrepaired breaches gaped in the old park wall. Making our way among the trees, we reached the lawn, crossed it, and were about to enter through the window, when out from a clump of laurel bushes there darted what seemed to be a hideous and distorted child, who threw itself upon the grass with writhing limbs, and then ran swiftly across the lawn into the darkness.

"My God!" I whispered; "did you see it?"

Holmes was for the moment as startled as I. His hand closed like a vise upon my wrist in his agitation. Then he broke into a low laugh, and put his lips to my ear.

"It is a nice household," he murmured. "That is the baboon."

I had forgotten the strange pets which the doctor affected. There was a cheetah, too; perhaps we might find it upon our shoulders at any moment. I confess that I felt easier in my mind when, after following Holmes's example and slipping off my shoes, I found myself inside the bedroom. My companion noiselessly closed the shutters, moved the lamp onto the table, and cast his eyes round the room. All was as we had seen it in the daytime. Then creeping up to me and making a trumpet of his hand, he whispered into my ear again so gently that it was all that I could do to distinguish the words:

"The least sound would be fatal to our plans."

I nodded to show that I had heard.

"We must sit without light. He would see it through the ventilator."

I nodded again.

"Do not go to sleep; your very life may depend upon it. Have your pistol ready in case we should need it. I will sit on the side of the bed, and you in that chair."

I took out my revolver and laid it on the corner of the table.

Holmes had brought up a long thin cane, and this he placed upon the bed beside him. By it he laid the box of matches and the stump of a candle. Then he turned down the lamp, and we were left in darkness.

How shall I ever forget that dreadful vigil? I could not hear a sound, not even the drawing of a breath, and yet I knew that my companion sat open-eyed, within a few feet of me, in the same state of nervous tension in which I was myself. The shutters cut off the least ray of light, and we waited in absolute darkness. From outside came the occasional cry of a night-bird and once at our very window a long drawn cat-like whine, which told us that the cheetah was indeed at liberty. Far away we could hear the deep tones of the parish clock, which boomed out every quarter of an hour. How long they seemed, those quarters! Twelve struck, and one and two and three, and still we sat waiting silently for whatever might befall.

Suddenly there was the momentary gleam of a light up in the direction of the ventilator, which vanished immediately, but was succeeded by a strong smell of burning oil and heated metal. Some one in the next room had lit a dark-lantern. I heard a gentle sound of movement, and then all was silent once more, though the smell grew stronger. For half an hour I sat with straining ears. Then suddenly another sound became audible—a very gentle, soothing sound, like that of a small jet of steam escaping continually from a kettle. The instant that we heard it, Holmes sprang from the bed, struck a match, and lashed furiously with his cane at the bell-pull.

"You see it, Watson?" he yelled. "You see it?"

But I saw nothing. At the moment when Holmes struck the light I heard a low, clear whistle, but the sudden glare flashing into my weary eyes made it impossible for me to tell what it was at which my friend lashed so savagely. I could, however, see that his face was deadly pale, and filled with horror and loathing.

He had ceased to strike, and was gazing up at the ventilator, when suddenly there broke from the silence of the night the most horrible cry to which I have ever listened. It swelled up louder and louder, a hoarse yell of pain and fear and anger all mingled in the one dreadful shriek. They say that away down in the village, and even in the distant parsonage, that cry raised the sleepers from their beds. It struck cold to our hearts, and I stood gazing at Holmes, and he at me, until the last echoes of it had died away into the silence from which it rose.

"What can it mean?" I gasped.

"It means that it is all over," Holmes answered. "And perhaps, after all, it is for the best. Take your pistol, and we will enter Dr. Roylott's room."

With a grave face he lit the lamp and led the way down the corridor. Twice he struck at the chamber door without any reply from within. Then he turned the handle and entered, I at his heels, with the cocked pistol in my hand.

It was a singular sight which met our eyes. On the table stood a dark-lantern with the shutter half open, throwing a brilliant beam of light upon the iron safe, the door of which was ajar. Beside this table, on the wooden chair, sat Dr. Grimesby Roylott, clad in a long gray dressing-gown, his bare ankles protruding beneath, and his feet thrust into red heelless Turkish slippers. Across his lap lay the short stock with the long lash which we had noticed during the day. His chin was cocked upward and his eyes were fixed in a dreadful, rigid stare at the corner of the ceiling. Round his brow he had a peculiar yellow band, with brownish speckles, which seemed to be bound tightly round his head. As we entered he made neither sound nor motion.

"The band! the speckled band!" whispered Holmes.

I took a step forward. In an instant his strange head-gear began to move, and there reared itself from among his hair the squat diamond-shaped head and puffed neck of a loathsome serpent.

"It is a swamp adder!" cried Holmes; "the deadliest snake in India. He has died within ten seconds of being bitten. Violence does, in truth, recoil upon the violent, and the schemer falls into the pit which he digs for another. Let us thrust this creature back into its den, and we can then remove Miss Stoner to some place of shelter, and let the county police know what has happened."

As he spoke he drew the dog-whip swiftly from the dead man's lap, and throwing the noose round the reptile's neck, he drew it from its horrid perch, and carrying it at arm's length, threw it into the iron safe, which he closed upon it.

Such are the true facts of the death of Dr. Grimesby Roylott, of Stoke Moran. It is not necessary that I should prolong a narrative which has already run to too great a length, by telling how we broke the sad news to the terrified girl, how we conveyed her by the morning train to the care of her good aunt at Harrow, of how the slow process of official inquiry came to the conclusion that the doctor met his fate while indiscreetly playing with a dangerous pet. The little which I had yet to learn of the case was told me by Sherlock Holmes as we travelled back next day.

"I had," said he, "come to an entirely erroneous conclusion, which shows, my dear Watson, how dangerous it always is to reason from insufficient data. The presence of the gypsies, and the use of the word 'band,' which was used by the poor girl, no doubt to explain the appearance which she had caught a hurried glimpse of by the light of her match, were sufficient to put me upon an entirely wrong scent. I can only claim the merit that I instantly reconsidered my position when, however, it became clear to me that whatever danger threatened an occupant of the room could not come either from the window or the door. My attention was speedily drawn, as I have already remarked to you, to this ventilator, and to the bell-rope which hung down to the bed. The discovery that this was a dummy, and that the bed was clamped to the floor, instantly gave rise to the suspicion that the rope was there as bridge for something passing through the hole, and coming to the bed. The idea of a snake instantly occurred to me, and when I coupled it with my knowledge that the doctor was furnished with a supply of creatures from India, I felt that I was probably on the right track. The idea of using a form of poison which could not possibly be discovered by any chemical test was just such a one as would occur to a clever and ruthless man who had had an Eastern training. The rapidity with which such a poison would take effect would also, from his point of view, be an advantage. It would be a sharp-eyed coroner, indeed, who could distinguish the two little dark punctures which would show where the poison fangs had done their work. Then I thought of the whistle. Of course he must recall the snake before the morning light revealed it to the victim. He had trained it, probably by the use of the milk which we saw, to return to him when summoned. He would put it through this ventilator at the hour that he thought best, with the certainty that it would crawl down the rope and land on the bed. It might or might not bite the occupant, perhaps she might escape every night for a week, but sooner or later she must fall a victim.

"I had come to these conclusions before ever I had entered his room. An inspection of his chair showed me that he had been in the habit of standing on it, which of course would be necessary in order that he should reach the ventilator. The sight of the safe, the saucer of milk, and the loop of whip-cord were enough to finally dispel any doubts which may have remained. The metallic clang heard by Miss Stoner was obviously caused by her step-father hastily closing the door of his safe upon its terrible occupant. Having once made up my mind, you know the steps which I took in order to put the matter to the proof. I heard the creature hiss, as I have no doubt that you did also, and I instantly lit the light and attacked it."

"With the result of driving it through the ventilator."

"And also with the result of causing it to turn upon its master at the other side. Some of the blows of my cane came home, and roused its snakish temper, so that it flew upon the first person it saw. In this way I am no doubt indirectly responsible for Dr. Grimesby Roylott's death, and I cannot say that it is likely to weigh very heavily upon my conscience."

TALL TALES

The Fence that Moved

by JULES VERNE ALLEN

ONE NIGHT IN CAMP TWO BOYS, IRA AND TOM, GOT IN rather late. Some of the boys already in camp after having retired to the bunkhouse asked the late comers what they had been doing that day.

Tom sez: "You tell 'em, Iry, 'cause I'm too tired."

Iry sez: "Well, it ain't much to tell, ceptin' that we saved the boss lots of time and money today. He set us out to fence in a section pasture. When we got over there, there wasn't enough fence posts and in going up a draw I smelt a terrible smell and asked Tom what it might be. He said he didn't think, he knowed already what it was. It was a snake den, and the snakes were crawlin' out to get the sunshine. I sed to him, 'There ain't much sunshine, for it's cold today.'"

"Well," sez he, "mebbe they come out yesterday to warm themselves when it was good and warm and stayed out too late last night and got froze to death."

"Shore enough, when we got up to this snake den there was somewhere between five and ten thousand rattlesnakes all the way from six to fourteen feet long, lying stretched out and froze stiff. I sez to Tom, 'Right here's where we get our fence posts,' so we just throwed a rope around a bundle of 'em and drag 'em to where we was goin' to fence the 'trap' and I'd hold the pointed end of the snake with the rattles on it into the ground, and while Tom'd sit on his horse he'd hammer on the blunt end, that is the end his head's on, with a six pound sledge hammer, and drove him in the ground. We got through by about eleven o'clock, and thinkin' we was through so quick that the boss wouldn't care if we laid down and took a nap. Which we did, an' in the meantime the sun came shinin' out and the boss thought he'd ride over to see how we was gettin' along and caught us sleepin'. I told him he needn't to git mad because we had saved him a lot of time and money but I wouldn't tell him just how we done it. I told him to come and go with me and I would show him. Well, sir, I'll be dadgoned if he didn't show his appreciation by tellin' me an' Tom to come on down to the bunkhouse and go to sleep, bein' as how we was in such need of sleep and come to the office in the morning and get our money."

197

One of the boys sed: "Why, Iry, why did he want to fire you, you savin' him all that money expense of cutting fence posts like you did?"

Iry sed: "Oh hell, when that sun commenced to shinin' them damned snakes thawed out and carried off two miles of good barbed wire."

Knute, the Giant Bullsnake

A true account of the adventures of Knute, the biggest Bullsnake that ever lived, and of his meeting with Paul Bunyan, the greatest logger.

by GLEN ROUNDS

KNUTE WAS NO ORDINARY SNAKE. HE WAS NEVER CONtent to be just an ordinary snake, he wanted to be the greatest snake that ever was. From the time he was just a little fellow, he was all the time taking stretching exercises to develop his muscles. So he grew very fast, and it is said that when he was three years old he was able, with his bare tail, to lasso and hogtie a full grown buffalo bull, and that is something that most snakes cannot do even when they are much older.

When he was full grown he was so long that when he was taking a drink out of one of the Great Lakes his tail, likely as not, was scaring the daylights out of homesteaders out by where McCook, Nebraska, now is. What we call the Great Plains was once his bed ground. Tossing in his sleep over the course of some centuries he wore down the trees to sage brush and smoothed off the hills.

During the Indian wars Knute joined up with Custer's army, where a missionary taught him to talk. He was quite a pet with the men because of the tall tales he could spin of the things he'd seen here and there. But he scared the Indians so bad that the soldiers never could catch them, and he was so big that the General was afraid he'd accidentally squash a bunch of men some day, so he asked him please to leave, which was all right with Knute, he being very accommodating. Anyway, he was a little tired of army life.

So he went off up into the Badlands in South Dakota, where no one much lived at that time, to be a hermit. For a while he was quite happy there, game being plentiful, so he had plenty of time to think. Not that he had anything special to think about, but he just liked to think.

However, one day when he was prowling around near Laramie, Wyoming, he came across a railroad track, the first one he'd ever seen. He thought it was some kind of a varmint trail, so he sat himself down to wait for the varmint. Directly along came a freight train a mile and a quarter long, with two engines—and he swallowed the whole thing.

The train crew jumped in time to save themselves, but what a time they had trying to make the boss believe their story when they tried to explain the loss of their train. Finally the boss fined them each a dollar and a quarter. Being as train men were kinda hard to get those days, he hated to fire them.

But poor Knute! It was easy enough for him to digest the freight cars, which were loaded with meat for the army posts, but when he finally digested the boilers, all that steam turned loose in his stomach gave him a bad stomach ache. At first the steam had a pressure of one hundred and ninety pounds to the inch, just as it came from the boilers. But the indigestion gave him fever, and the fever made more steam, and so it went. Before long he had three hundred pounds pressure and it was still a-going up. He felt pretty bad.

He had to have something done, but he couldn't go to the Indian medicine men, as they were scared stiff at the sight of him. Then he thought of Paul Bunyan, the great inventor and logger. As far as anyone knows, Paul never found a problem he couldn't solve. So Knute tore out for his camp. Paul listened to the snake's story and let out a low whistle that blew in the windows of the Sunshine Cafe in Sabinal, Texas.

This was the kind of a problem he liked. So he thought even faster than usual, but even so, he had chewed his nails till the scraps were piled round him nearly to his knees, and his hands were all tangled up in his whiskers, before he thought of anything. By that time, Ole, the Big Swede, had gotten back from replacing the windows of the Sunshine Cafe and Paul right away put him to work taking a safety valve and whistle off an old donkey engine back of the blacksmith shop. Ole was as good a plumber as ever wore hair, so he had no trouble connecting these things up to Knute's neck.

Right away the snake felt better. The valve was set to keep the pressure at one hundred and ten pounds. That was just enough to keep his stomach warm. And he was as tickled with the whistle as a kid with a new red wagon. He wanted to pay Paul for curing him but Paul wouldn't hear of it. Said he was mighty obliged to Knute for bringing him such an interesting problem. Folks all over the country would be telling that story for years.

A few days later Knute was back in camp with another little problem for Paul. He said that, what with his getting along in years, his circulation wasn't what it used to be; and his tail being so far from the rest of him, he was having considerable trouble keeping it warm. That one was nothing at all for Ol' Paul. He just had Ole run a pipe line for the steam from the whistle right down Knute's back to his tail. Along the last mile or two he fastened a lot of old steam radiators he'd picked up somewhere or other. And though that was the beginning of the coldest winter the oldest Indians could remember, Knute came through without a single chilblain.

And more than that, the heat attracted antelope, buffalo and jack rabbits by the thousands, making his hunting a cinch.

Naturally this was the beginning of a very fine friendship that lasted for many years. Knute got into the habit of dropping into camp every now and then with a bait of fresh meat for the men's Sunday dinner. So he was right popular with everyone, even the cooks, and that was something, for it's very, very seldom that anyone is popular with a camp cook.

A couple of years later Ol' Paul was dickering with the Queen of Spain on a lumber deal. It seems that she had options on about four states that she wanted logged off. The price she offered was about right, but the time limit on the job was so short that Johnnie Inkslinger, the bookkeeper, was worried and advised Paul not to try it.

But Paul just grinned in his whiskers and reckoned that he'd try it. He said that if he needed more men there were plenty of good ones yet in Sweden. In the meantime he just sat around whittling, and occasionally went out to the blackksmith shop where Ole, the Big Swede, and a lot of helpers were working on something in the way of a secret contraption. And Johnnie was worrying himself sick.

A few days later a timber cruiser came into camp with the news that Sowbelly Burke, Paul's old enemy, had heard of the deal, and had sent his straw boss, Mike Fink by name, to Sweden and hired all the Swedes there. Johnnie was about fit to be tied by this time, but Paul just sat and whittled.

Later the same day one of Sowbelly's men came in with a message for Paul. It seems that Burke was ready to bet a dollar and a quarter that Paul couldn't finish on time. Paul sent word back that he'd take the bet and raise a quarter. This puzzled Burke, as he knew that under the terms of the contract Ol' Paul had to pay a whale of a penalty if he was late, and he had less than half enough men for a job that size.

By this time the story had spread to every lumber camp and mill town in the country. Bets were being made everywhere on the outcome. Lots of folks thought that at last Sowbelly had gotten the best of Paul. But Paul's men stayed loyal, taking all bets. Even Hot Biscuit Slim bet a dime. But they were worried. They thought a lot of Paul, and working for him meant a lot to them.

However, a couple of weeks later, the straw bosses told the men at breakfast to pack their lunch buckets and get their axes, as work had finally started on the Queen's job.

When they came out of the mess hall there was Knute waiting for them.

But the way he was duded up was a caution. Right back of his shoulder blades were strapped two saw blades each forty feet long, and down his back were the bunks and stakes off three trains of log cars. And there was also a donkey engine and a boom for loading logs from the ground.

Rope ladders hung down his sides and the men climbed these to find places on his back. Ole was sitting by the whistle, and when everyone was loaded he blew the whistle twice and they tore out.

The two saw blades cut a swath through the timber like a mowing machine, and every little way they dropped a crew to top and trim the fallen timber so it would be ready to load on the way back.

That way timber was cut faster than it ever had been before. But after a few days Knute began to limp from the wear and tear of hauling such heavy loads through rough country. So Ole shod him, nailing ninety-three thousand and fourteen pairs of sharp shoes on his belly scales, and from then on there was no trouble.

It was really a stirring sight to see ol' Knute come dusting into camp at night. As far back as you could see was bend after bend of him swinging round the curves of the tote road, and on his back loads and loads of good saw logs with the men riding on top waving their fur caps and hollering. The sparks from his shoes hitting the frozen ground made a solid line of fire the full length of him. The steam flying back from his nostrils almost hid Ole who rode on Knute's head, holding a lantern and blowing the whistle every forty rods.

After they unloaded, it took nine hundred and forty-four men an hour and a quarter to rub him down and cool him off so he would not catch cold.

All winter they worked like that, and the job was finished with three days to spare, winning many bets for the men as well as bonuses all round. But Paul had to chase Sowbelly clear to the Gulf of Mexico to collect his, and then he only got about six bits, as Burke had had to pay his Swedes all winter even though they didn't work, so he was broke.

The Queen of Spain wrote Paul a long letter afterwards, and we all figgered that she probably said some mighty nice things about him, but being as how the letter was written in Spanish, we never did find out, nor did Paul. But the story of how Paul gave Sowbelly Burke his comeuppance was told for years in all the lumber camps in the country.

The Peninsula Python

An Absolutely True Story

by ROBERT BORDNER

1

FROM THE TIME THE PENINSULA PYTHON FIRST CROSSED that Ohio field of sprouting corn before the astonished eyes of Clarence Mitchell in the summer of 1944, until it holed up for the winter, presumably under the overhanging banks of the Cuyahoga River, it left many a mark on the face of the earth.

There were tracks "like those of an auto tire" across the softness of freshly tilled fields. There were tracks in the mud at the river's edge. There were branches broken and bark scuffed from tall trees when it fell, frightened, before still more frightened beholders. His deepest mark was upon the people of the wild, wooded valley between Cleveland and Akron; his longest was a trail that circled the earth.

Clarence Mitchell was hoeing his piece of corn ground between the Everett swamp and the abandoned bed of the old Ohio Canal on June 8. "Two-three days the dogs was nervous, and finally they wouldn't go over there with me at all," he said. "I thought they was acting kind of funny, but I didn't pay it much mind. I don't know what made me look up, but there, about fifteen paces away, was the biggest snake I ever see, sliding along easy and slow in plain sight on the bare ground.

"I just stood quiet, not aiming to attract attention. It seemed like ten minutes I watched. He slid into the river, swam across, and climbed out the other side, heading toward the yellow clay slip on the nose of that hogback up Steele's Corners way.

"He was thick as my thigh, right here, and every bit of fifteen feet long —more like eighteen—sort of brownish spotted. I went over and looked at the track. It was like you'd rolled a spare tire across my field."

Young Mike Bobacek, who had the mules hitched to the cultivator, working the field east of the river, said he saw Clarence light out for home, and that he too saw the snake come out of the river going east.

Nobody paid much attention to the tale except the womenfolk, who canceled plans for blackberrying thereabouts.

Ten days later, Paul and John Szalay fitted a field with disk and culti-packer in the morning. That was in Old Cassidy's Bottom, maybe two miles north of Mitchell's place, and only a couple of miles from Peninsula village. When they came back from lunch to seed the piece, there was a track "like from an auto tire," wavering from the overgrown, swampy canal bed of the river, across the virgin seedbed. They got word to Mayor John Ritch. With his police chief, Art Huey, and the two assistant chiefs, Dale Hall and Dud Watson, the mayor investigated.

"Nothing but a mighty big snake could have made that track," he said, officially.

Two mornings later the fire siren uncoiled its terrifying scream. It was the Roy Vaughn place up the hill east of the river. When the volunteers got there, everybody was housed up tight. Mrs. Vaughn had seen the snake.

"I was up in the second floor of my hen house and looked out into the yard in back," she said. She showed them. "Right there was a great big snake trying to get through the woven wire fence, but he had a lump in him, big as a basket, and the lump wouldn't go through the fence. He reared up and climbed right over the top of that wire fence—three and a half feet high. The last few feet of him fell over, plop—a big plop—on the far side, and he went down the ravine."

Mrs. Vaughn was no hysteric. There was earth on the wire. The weeds were broken flat where she pointed. A chicken was gone.

That settled it for those present; for them the Peninsula Python became a sobering fact. Chief Huey measured the distance Mrs. Vaughn said the snake had extended beside the fence. It was nineteen feet. Mayor Ritch, in a proclamation mobilizing the men of Peninsula, set Sunday for the hunt. The *Cleveland Press* and the *Akron Beacon-Journal* were impressed.

Theories flew. A circus had been in Akron the month before. If a snake had escaped, it was reasoned, the circus would have been anxious to hush it up, because it might have been liable for large damages, and a new snake would cost less than $200. Big snakes cost $10 a foot. The circus was traced, but admitted no escape.

Then it was remembered that two years before, a carnival caravan, lost, cut across the valley. One of the trucks went wild on the Hammond's Corners hill and was wrecked among the tombstones of the Pleasant Valley Cemetery at the bottom. The driver was killed, the contents scattered. Maybe it came from there.

Only tropic constrictors were as long as the Peninsula Python, according to Arthur B. Williams, director of the Cleveland Museum of Natural History. Ohio's biggest native, the blacksnake, never got longer than six feet.

Fletcher Reynolds, director of the Cleveland Zoo, begged for the life of the reptile. "He is harmless unless frightened or cornered," he said. "He can strike only about one-third his length; stay ten feet away from him and he cannot reach you.

"But don't get too close. He has teeth like a dog's and can cut a person up some. The teeth grab when he strikes; then he pulls the victim to him and throws a loop around it; it is only after he gets his tail in the loop that he can tighten enough to kill."

Mr. Reynolds asked anyone finding the snake to be quiet. "Don't scare him. Telephone the location to the Zoo and wait to show me. I will be there in less than thirty minutes. I can easily take him alive."

By that time the radio newscasters were giving bulletins on the snake. United Press and Associated Press were carrying developments out of Akron. All over Ohio the newspapers were carrying the story on page one.

The Columbus Zoo bid $500 for the beast. Carnival men, concessionaires, hunters, "snakeologists," and just plain screwballs began drifting in, snooping, making offers.

2

Schemes for capture were discussed at Scotty's bar, Stebbins's grocery, Sovacool's store, Conger's soda fountain, Early Duffy Ganyard's barbershop.

Dud Watson contrived a large box with an eight-inch hole for entry. He baited it with a hen. "He'll go in, gobble the hen, and be trapped by his breakfast."

Pernel Andrews toted a clothesline prop. "I'll let him strike at the pole, push it down his gullet so he can't coil, and have him at my mercy."

J. H. Bower, the station agent, depended on the charming effects of music. "Snakes love music. Couple of the boys and me used it on hundreds in West Virginia. We would go along the creek, one sawing the fiddle, t'other whanging the banjo, and me picking them off with my .22."

Pierce Monroe Metcalf, the expert frog hunter, explained the sneak-snatch method. "Quick throw a leg over him and start steering. Like as not you can ride him right into town bareback," he said.

Ray Hall, Civilian Defense safety chief, liked the stem-winder way. "All you got to do is keep a snake from coilin. I've used it plenty of times on big blacksnakes. You just grab them by the tail like they was an old Model T Ford and crank. It bewilders them."

Dale, his brother, advocated self-service. "Grab his tail, and when he strikes, just shove his tail down his throat. He'll swaller hisself."

More people kept coming in for the hunt with other ideas. But Mayor Ritch, scared at the sight of the assorted weapons, let out another proclamation: the only firearms permitted would be those in the hands of his police and posse leaders; one gun to a posse. There was danger the hunters would shoot up themselves, especially in the excitement, if the snake were found.

On Sunday, June 25, the weather was beautiful. The church bells were ringing, worshipers were arriving, and Chief Huey was marshaling a crazy assortment of men, boys, weapons, and gadgets in front of the barbershop, assigning each to a posse, giving final instructions.

Just then, across the bridge into town, charged two companies of militia, bayonets fixed. Captain William E. Morris explained that they knew nothing of the snake hunt, but had camped up on Brewery Hill overnight and were "taking" the town for practice.

Newspaper, motion picture, and amateur photographers, together with reporters from the city newspapers, followed the posses deploying on the river bottoms, up ravines, through the woods. Women and children in cars tagged along, sticking to the roads.

It was nearly time for the churches to let out when the siren on the Town Hall howled the prearranged three long blasts. That meant the West Richfield telephone operator had a call the varmint had been located.

It was on the Hudson road, up east of Fred Kelly's. The mayor wrote the directions on the firehouse blackboard and headed for the scene.

The front doors of the churches were pushed open with a rush; the devout had a good head start on the hunters. They piled into cars and, scattering gravel, streamed up the hill.

That siren drained all the loose population of the township down into the village and up Kelly Hill. The posses broke from the woods to the south, jumped on the running boards of cars, roared into town, and brandishing knives and clubs, whirled up the Hudson road.

At the scene, drivers were so anxious to get in on the kill that they ditched their cars or abandoned them, doors open, in the middle of the road. Sunday pants were snagged on barbed wire and brush. City folk scrambled on hands and knees up banks of poison ivy. Girls muddied white dresses in ditches. Patches of hide were skinned off as men slipped in ravines or rolled into the creek.

In the bright June sunshine, through burrs and briars, tangled in thornbush, trampling acres of alfalfa and timothy, the hunters swirled. Meanwhile Mayor Ritch was tracing the call. It was obviously a hoax. But it took an hour to stop the hunt.

Reporters, editorial writers, cartoonists, and radio commentators were hilarious for days. The village split into angry camps. The doubters charged that the township had been made ridiculous and that the story had damaged property values. They twitted the taletellers. The believers, pride bruised, judgment impugned, veracity questioned, decided to go underground.

"It won't be so funny if that snake gets a child next; the jokers would be first to holler," Mayor Ritch warned.

The believers felt cheated by the hoax because Ganyard, the barber and world champion still-hunter of foxes, found evidence that convinced him his posse had been close to the reptile when called off.

The hunt was reorganized in the hands of the few; no more mass hunts, no more siren-blowing, no more information to the newspapers till the python was brought in dead. From then on, these men were out to kill; they wanted proof to fling at their detractors.

Art Huey, the police chief, took charge. Earl Ganyard, most expert as a woodsman, was put on constant alert. Dale and Ray Hall and Dud Watson were the reinforcements. They kept guns in their automobiles, and their automobiles in constant readiness.

The rural operators of all surrounding townships were organized for swift transmission of new reports to the West Richfield telephone exchange. Huey and Ganyard kept themselves constantly available to the exchange, day and night. The strategy was to get to the scene before the frightened reptile had traveled too far.

3

Less than forty-eight hours after the Sunday fiasco, the new posse had its first test. It took place along the river two miles north of Peninsula, near Boston Mills.

Placid and practical Mrs. Pauline Hopko had taken her pail and started down the canal to milk her cows in the pasture Tuesday morning. "The cows were fidgety and I had to tie them to the fence while I milked," she said. "Suddenly there was a crashing in the branches of a willow across the river. The cows jerked loose, breaking halters, and ran, bellowing, leaving me sitting with the pail. I looked over, and there was a snake with a head as big as a man's coming down out of that dead willow. The dogs cowered under my skirts, almost upsetting me."

Bobbie Pollard came along the towpath on his bicycle and she sent him to telephone while she rounded up the cows to finish the milking.

Bobbie neglected to phone, but came back with some more boys instead. Again they saw the snake in a nearer tree across the river. But it was hours before the official snake posse was on the scene. They found freshly broken branches on the two trees, loose bark newly scuffed off, tracks on the ground. But the ten-foot weeds, the rank vines, and the tangled floodplain debris of the river bottoms defeated the hunt.

Two days later, four miles up Brandywine Creek, Ernest Raymond sharpened his scythe and went to mow the fence row. "I noticed a root sticking up in the timothy field. I wondered how that stump got there. Then I saw it move. The snake, coiled like a stump, had his head up looking around.

"I ran to the house for my shotgun and Ray Thompson, my son-in-law. When we came back it was still there, but he lowered his head before I could shoot. We could see the deep grass waving as he went off."

They showed the posse a circle of matted grass in the field. Reporters found out about the incident, and next day Rayy Mitten of the *Akron Beacon-Journal* was hunting Macedonia township in an airplane.

Two days later Mrs. Ralph Griffin went to her back door to call her boy George. "I saw something man-high where the path enters the woods at the back of the yard. It was like a man in a white shirt, till I looked good. It was the snake, reared up and looking around, his throat white and shiny." The posse hunted, but again without luck.

Then the snake headed back down Brandywine to the Cuyahoga river bottoms. Mrs. Katherine Boroutick of Boston Mills saw him next. "I went out back of the house to throw some trash in the river, and just as I turned to come back, there was a crash in the butternut overhead. I turned just as the big snake fell with a thump not ten feet from me."

The posse found limbs the size of your wrist, broken and dangling, their leaves still green, thirty feet from the ground on that butternut tree, and again a track to the river.

By this time the fame of the Peninsula Python had spread around the earth. Boys from the valley, away at war, read about it in *Yank,* in ships' papers at sea, everywhere. Their letters asking about the snake poured in from Iceland, England, the Normandy beachhead, Italy, North Africa, India, Australia, New Guinea, the Pacific fleet, the Aleutians.

And from Idaho Falls, Idaho, Carl Scobie came 2000 miles to help hunt the varmint. A Peninsula boy, he had gone West upon discharge from the Marines after World War I. For twenty-five years he had made snakes a hobby in the oil fields of Texas and Mexico and then in Los Angeles, where he was in real estate. For years he raised rattlers and sold them to a Michigan firm for use on horses in the making of anti-venom serum. He was the expert in that California trial of a man who had murdered his wife by sticking her foot into a box of rattlers. And when the carnival python escaped at Long Beach a few years ago, police called him and he captured the 28-foot reptile under a wharf.

Carl had not been home in a quarter century, but when he read about the Peninsula Python, he hopped a train. He no longer knew where his parents lived, but he found his Aunt Abbie Lee on the farm where she and his Uncle Park had lived for fifty-three years.

Aunt Abbie let the stranger in. She was in the midst of preparations for the Oak Hill picnic to which his parents, aunts, uncles, cousins, and former neighbors were coming on the morrow. In no time she had a plan, and bedded her nephew down for the night.

Next day as some sixty guests arrived, Aunt Abbie introduced the baldish, well-dressed stranger as Mr. Smith. None knew him. "I had a funny feeling," said Charlie Scobie, his father, "but I couldn't tell what was the matter. Then I was flabbergasted."

So Carl Scobie took the field for two weeks armed with nothing but a blanket. "You catch a big snake by letting him strike at the blanket. Then you just wrap it around his head and he is harmless. This one will weigh about 250 pounds. A half-dozen men then can pick him up and carry him stretched out like a timber."

But Carl went home to Idaho in September without the Peninsula Python.

The snake was reported a few more times as the leaves began to fall. The hunters never got word quick enough to see him and shoot, and he traveled too fast, when frightened, to trail. But with the first heavy frost, all trace of him was lost.

The posse watched the skies for the wheel of buzzards to lead them to his carcass, dead of cold. No buzzards circled. "He must have holed up under the overhanging roots of a big tree along the river banks," they reasoned.

They are still waiting for the Peninsula Python to reappear.

"Snake Bit, Snake Bit!"

by HENRY JUNIUS NOTT

DURING 1814 THE WAR WAS GOING ON BETWEEN THE United States and Great Britain, and Charleston was filled with officers beating up for volunteers. One day Singularity had been missing the whole morning, to the no small vexation of Mr. Shepherd, as we had a great press of work. While he was abusing my friend for an idle, dissipated vagabond, we heard military music passing under the window, and looking out, we descried Lieutenant Abram Miller marching before a number of new recruits. I was just withdrawing my head to resume my work, when in spite of the uniform and military cap, I deciphered the features of Tommy himself. Lost in amazement, I exclaimed, "Mercy alive! there's Tom Singularity among 'em." Mr. Shepherd, as soon as he saw that it was in fact he, said, "Good luck to their fishing; they may keep him and welcome. He may make good food for gunpowder, but I am sure he's fit for nothing else."

That night Singularity came to see me, and told me his reasons for embracing the career of arms. He said that he had always felt a martial disposition, but especially at this juncture, when patriotism demanded the services of every true-born American. Moreover, he talked a great deal about glory, chivalry, and other lofty things, all of which I pretended to

take for current coin, as I saw that he was much excited by liberal pota-
tions. It was clear that poor Tommy had been beguiled by Bacchus into
the service of Mars, though he then and ever afterwards spoke of his en-
listment as caused alone by his indomitable spirit and thirst for renown. He
had courage enough, I think, excepting as to dogs and snakes, and I have
seen many men undoubtedly brave that resembled him in this respect.

Singularity made some attempts to draw me into the army, but finding
that I refused with great firmness, he troubled me no more about it. I refused for various reasons. First and foremost, I had conscientious scruples
about breaking my indentures, as I had been well treated. I feared also
for my religious principles among the swearing, drinking, Sabbath-break-
ing roisterers that abound in every army; lastly, I had a constitutional re-
laxation of fiber at the sight of blood, so uncontrollable that I was sure
to faint if a physician attempted to bleed me. Such idiosyncrasies are not
uncommon, as scientific men well know, though the ignorant and malicious have often charged me with cowardice for this defect of my organization. Are there not persons who cannot endure the sight of a cat, or
sicken at the smell of a rose even in the "Persian atargul's perfume?"

In a short time Tommy, to our mutual regret, was ordered off to Can-
ada, and during a couple of years I heard nothing of him; for he always
had a mortal aversion to writing letters of mere friendship. If I mistake
not, he was attached to Scott's brigade. He had not been long at head-
quarters before he was employed as secretary to his captain, and eventually, as his talents were known, he in fact did the writing of the whole regiment. In this manner his life was far from being disagreeable. His time
was mostly spent with the officers, from whom, for his services in writing,
copying, and making out accounts, together with his pay, he received
enough to live comfortably and dress genteelly. He did not content himself with wielding the pen only, but, like Cæsar, wished to serve his country with the sword at the same time. He was in the bloody battles of Chip-
pewa, Erie, and Niagara, and performed unheard-of feats of valor. I may
say *unheard-of,* literally; because I freely admit that he is not mentioned in
the official accounts of those battles, and that his merits, like those of many
other valiant private soldiers, have been, with heartless apathy, con-
signed to oblivion. Neither did he get any promotion during his term of
service. The latter circumstance might have been owing to his fondness
for artificial stimulation, and his consequent neglect of the petty formali-
ties of military routine. I state his heroic conduct from his own mouth,
and I do so with the more particularity, as some malicious persons have
very openly expressed their skepticism respecting it.

At the close of the war he obtained his discharge, and resumed his old
trade of printing. He worked, coming on gradually to the South, in the
offices of the Boston *Sentinel,* New York *Gazette,* Philadelphia *Aurora,*
Nile's Register (in Baltimore), Norfolk *Herald,* and Raleigh *Star.* Some
of these places he quit of his own accord, and from some he was turned

away. In 1816, Thomas Wright Lorrain had established the *Telescope* in Columbia (South Carolina), of which paper I was the foreman. I was one day very busily employed in setting up a handbill about the famous horse "Hephestion," when a man in soiled and tattered attire, with a knapsack on his back, entered the office and looked about composedly at the different parts of the establishment. As it was common enough for country people to step in, out of curiosity, to see printing, the entrance of the man excited so little attention that I continued setting without giving him a second look. By and by he approached where I was, and after looking attentively at me, began to ask me questions that left me in doubt whether they arose from ignorance or a wish to quiz me. I gave him very short answers, without even turning my head, hoping to thus get rid of him. It was useless. He kept interrupting and worrying me till I lost all patience, and stopping short, looked him full in the face. In spite of a beard almost patriarchal, and the bronzing from exposure, I retraced the features of my long-lost friend. Needing journeymen, I proposed to Tommy to remain with us, which he cheerfully consented to, as he was at low-watermark in money. In some things I perceived a considerable change in him. He regularly took a night-cap, as he called it, that is, a stiff drink of grog before going to bed, not unfrequently stimulated in the day, and sometimes indulged in a week's frolicking. His disposition for games of hazard, particularly cards, had increased, and he had caught the mania of buying lottery tickets. In other respects he was the very man he used to be. His old propensity to falling in love, and of thinking all the girls were in love with him, was in no whit diminished. And that my readers may have some idea of this gallant, gay young Lothario, I will try to portray him. He was about five feet four inches high, not badly put together, but of a leanness altogether wonderful, and a slight tendency to being knock-kneed; his face was pale, and somewhat marked with the smallpox; he had light blue eyes, with a very slight squint; a well-shaped nose, and a mouth not amiss, except a disposition to drop the underlip, which, with the obliquity of his vision, gave to his countenance rather a sinister expression. What he mainly prided himself on was his hair. It was abundant and curly, of a flaxen color, verging towards red. He always let it grow to a considerable length, combing it with great care, and madefacting it with pomatums and perfumed oils. Adown either cheek hung a corkscrew curl, that he cherished and nourished with especial affection.

On Sundays and holidays he delighted to exhibit himself in attire more remarkable, in my opinion, for the dandyism of the cut and colors than elegance of taste. Frock-coats he particularly affected, adorned with frogs and worked all over with braid, which he would button up to his chin to set off his form to advantage. "Yet though on pleasure he was bent, still frugal was his mind;" his showy wardrobe was usually of pelisse cloth, or some equally common stuff, in which the workmanship exceeded the material. Though foppish, something always seemed wanting. He would be without gloves, have a rusty hat, foxy boots, or a rumpled collar. Never was he so happy as when attired for conquest, and mounted on some goat of a horse that would kick, plunge, and curvet (for he was proud of his horsemanship), he could exhibit himself to the fair sex. He wrote *billets doux* and poetry to all the milliner-girls and mantua-makers in the place to little purpose; though he was thoroughly satisfied with his success, and related to me some new victory every day.

Our time went on so much to our minds for a few months that we calculated on a long and pleasant sojourn in Columbia. Some untoward circumstances changed all our projects. One Sunday morning, four of us belonging to the *Telescope* office, and one from the office of the *State Gazette,* agreed to set out on a hunting expedition. It is with some shame that I mention the day, as, according to the prejudices and usages of the community, our conduct was anything but proper; still, whatever faults I may have committed, I think it better to leave them fairly to the mercy and forbearance of the world, than to create any distrust of my narrative by a suppression of circumstances well known to many living witnesses. We had passed the back of the college without encountering any game, when some one proposed crossing a marsh at the foot of the hill, and pushing on for the old fields beyond. Singularity objected to the difficulty and almost impossibility of traversing a quagmire, where we could only get along by stepping, and often jumping, on tussocks, which afforded but a narrow and insecure footing. He also faintly intimated there might be snakes, which in fact I readily saw was his only fear. The majority, however, resolved to bulge through. Tommy yielded a most reluctant assent, on one of the young men's agreeing to take his gun over, as he declared he would not undertake it otherwise. He was somewhat under the influence of liquor, or I am sure he would never have consented. I wished to see how the others succeeded, and therefore waited the last, my friend only excepted. By cautious stepping and an occasional spring, the advance got on pretty well through the bog and bushes, and at length we ascertained from their shouts that they were fairly over. Tommy and myself proceeded more cautiously. I had nearly accomplished my journey over, when, making too short a leap, I sank up to my chest in a soft adhesive mud. A few struggles to disengage myself only plunged me a little deeper. Tommy, who was not far from me, burst into a most immoderate fit of laughter, and had I been within striking distance, I could willingly have knocked his teeth down his throat. I told him his merriment was ill timed, but that when he had helped me out, he might laugh his fill. Instead of aiding me, he hallooed as loud as he could to our companions to come and enjoy the sight. Probably they did not hear him, for no one came. Meanwhile I most earnestly entreated him to lay aside his jesting and assist me, as I was afraid of being smothered. It pleased him eventually to yield to my entreaties, and he was approaching me when he suddenly sprang up and shouted, or rather yelled out, "Snake bit, snake bit!" At the same time I beheld a sight that congealed my blood with horror. Not more than ten yards from me lay, coiled for action, a rattlesnake of the most enormous size. His glittering eyes were fixed on my friend, his mouth, from which quivered a forked tongue, hissed in the most venomous manner, while his tail, raised aloft, sounded the horrid rattle with a din that stupefied me. I saw that should I be attacked I had no probability of escaping. "I am a dead man," said Tommy; "for he has bitten me twice on the legs, and the poison will work before I can get to a doctor. But," said he, excited by rage and rum, "I'll not die unrevenged." He thereupon, after looking round, tried to break a small dead sapling which seemed of a suitable size for a pole. With much labor he wrenched it off, and rushed onwards with all the impetuosity of desperate passion. In his trepidation he not only struck beyond where he intended, but hit the ground with such violence that the stick snapped in twain, and, yielding him no support, he pitched forwards at full length, and received, in the twinkling of an eye, another bite on the arm. The serpent never moved from his position, but after each attack again resumed his coil for battle. Doubly sure of death, Tommy now approached more carefully. With the fragment of stick which he retained in his hand, he aimed deliberately a most violent blow at the head of his enemy. The stick did not break this time, but his hand was brought near the ground, and the agile animal, shifting his position as quick as lightning, avoided the danger and struck Singularity on the wrist. Glowing with anger, and stirred up to desperation, he drew out his knife and cut a cudgel that appeared sufficiently long and strong to ensure his purpose. Approaching cautiously, he reconnoitered the locality exactly, and was aiming a stroke with a deadly certainty, when the ground on which his front foot was planted gave away, he sank into the bog, and fell so near the snake that he was bitten full on the cheek. Utterly astounded at this succession of mishaps, and exhausted by his exertions, Singularity desisted from the fight and withdrew some steps. He hallooed again for our companions, who instantly answered, as in fact they were returning in search of us.

The serpent, no longer seeing an enemy in front, turned round as if to retreat. This movement brought him within a few feet of where I stood immovable in the mud. I quickly put my gun almost touching him, and pulled trigger. No report followed. The priming had got wet. The horrible reptile was no sooner aware of my presence than he was thrown into a coil. Again he hissed, his rattle sounded, and he was evidently in the very action of assailing me, when, rallying my strength and raising my gun above my head, I struck him so forcibly that he dropped his head, stunned and disabled. Again he collected his forces and tried to advance, but was stopped by a second blow. From the yielding nature of the bog, my strokes could not have their full effect, and I was becoming more and more exhausted, as much from the intensity of my feelings as the physical exertion. I earnestly implored Singularity to come to my rescue; but he refused positively to venture near the snake again, as he said he felt himself dying. The power of defending myself, and even hope, was lost, when one of my companions came up running, and put an end to my enemy with a load of buckshot. I was speedily extricated from my disagreeable thraldom and set on dry ground.

Before attending to me, Tommy had been laid under a shade-tree, and appeared to be in the last agony. We deliberated whether it would be better to construct an extemporaneous palanquin and bear him into town, or keep him quiet and send for a physician, when one of the young men, who had been examining the snake, cried out, "Halloo, Tom Singularity, get up and take a dram. Why, man, you are more scared than hurt. The snake has not a tooth in his head." And so the fact turned out. The animal from age had lost its fangs, and of course was perfectly harmless. As soon as certified of the truth, Tommy sprang on his feet, and after a swallow from the gin-flask of one of our friends, was himself again. Our joy was not of long duration; for the merciless rascals now commenced a round of jokes on my muddied clothes and Tommy's battle, not much to our comfort. The matter was quickly told in town, with embellishments certainly laughable enough to any but the sufferers.

A Snake Story

by CLAY EMERY

"SPEAKIN' ABOUT SNAKES," SAID CAPTAIN NAT, "THAT last tree I cut down reminds me of an experience I once had the last of my goin' to sea.

" 'Twas in '78. I'd sold my vessil and decided to make one voyage with Cap'n Putnam to the West Indies in the old "North Star," of which I was part owner with him. We warn't more'n two days from port, we figured, if the wind held, when there come up one of those long gales you're so apt to run into when in those waters, and for three days we lay hove to and let her drift. When we took an observation on the fourth day we found we'd drifted out of our course considerable and warn't many miles from a small island that Cap'n Putnam had stopped at once before, so we concluded we'd run in close under the land and get some wood, as we had to have some to keep the galley stove goin.' Cap'n Putnam and I and a couple of Portugee sailors started for shore in the small whale boat. We had a couple of axes with us to cut wood and we landed on the beach all

right, as the wind bein' off shore the water was smooth. Cap'n Putnam
had his gun, and he and I kinder looked around to see if there warn't
some birds to take a shot at while the sailors were at work cutting the
wood. We had walked away from the Portugees probably not more'n forty
rods, when one on 'em let out a yell, and when we looked round, they was
both runnin' for the boat and hollerin' like hellyens. We rushed up and one
on 'em told us in his broken English that he had got a tree about half
chopped down when a snake dropped from one of the limbs and bit him
square on the leg. We pulled off his leather boots but couldn't find no
mark on him, but on the side of his boot leg we found two little marks
showin' where the snake had struck, but his fangs hadn't gone clean
through, and he was more scared than hurt. We finally got them to work
agin, but they made slow progress on account of bein' so frightened, so
Cap and I finally took a hand. I was cuttin' away at the undergrowth when
I saw, not four feet from me, a big snake all coiled up, apparently asleep.
He was the biggest one I ever saw or hearn tell on. He measured a foot
thick, I should think, in the middle, and I wouldn't be surprised if he was
fifty feet long. Wa'al if ever a man's hair riz on his head, mine did. It riz
so that my hat fell off, and that's proof anyway. I didn't dare move for
fear of wakin' him up and havin' him swaller me at one mouthful, and I
didn't dare holler for help neither, so I concluded my only salvation was
to throw my ax quick as lightin' right into him and make for the boat."

"Slowly," continued Captain Nat, "I lifted that ax up without makin'
the least sound and threw it right into the middle of that big coil. It hadn't
no more'n struck 'fore I was runnin' for dear life. The rest saw me and fol-
lered like a blue streak. We all got in the boat and pushed off for a few
rods, and when I told 'em what I had done we expected to see the snake
comin' out of the underbrush every minute ready to eat us all up. Nothin'
happened, however, and finally Cap'n Putnam and I decided I must have
killed him, so we took his gun and started in to where I had been
workin.' We went up mighty careful, I tell you, and the Cap'n had his
gun cocked and had a couple of shells in loaded with thrible B shot, ready
to shoot if the snake showed fight.

"I don't ever expect to see a sight like the one I did there. When we
got to the snake he was stone dead, and the ax was right up to the eyes in
the middle of his body; and, boys, if you'll believe me," every eye was
fixed on the Captain, "that snake was so poisonous that, by gosh, that
ax handle had swelled up as big as my leg."

"Say, Cap, honest, is snakes that poisonous in them foreign countries?
Is that story true?"

"True as preachin,' " said Captain Nat, his eyes twinkling, "and now,
boys, its one o'clock and we must turn to."

Uncle Davy Lane

by H. E. TALIAFERRO ["SKITT"]

I MUST NOT FORGET, IN THESE RANDOM SKETCHES, MY old friend and neighbor, Uncle Davy Lane. Some men make an early and decided impression upon you—features, actions, habits, all the entire man, real and artificial. "Uncle Davy" was that kind of man.

I will mention a few things that make me remember him. His looks were peculiar. He was tall, dark, and rough-skinned; lymphatic, dull, and don't-care-looking in his whole physiognomy. He had lazy looks and movements. Nothing could move him out of a slow, horse-mill gait but snakes, of which "creeturs he was monstrous 'fraid." The reader shall soon have abundant evidence of the truth of this admission in his numerous and rapid flights from "sarpunts."

Uncle Davy was a gunsmith, and, as an evidence of the fact, he carried about with him the last gun he ever made. His gun, a rifle, was characteristic of its maker and owner—rough and unfinished outside, but good within. It was put in an old worm-eaten half-stock which he had picked up somewhere, and the barrel had never been dressed nor ground outside. He would visit a neighbor early in the morning, sit down with his rifle across his knees, in "too great a hurry" to set it aside, would stay all day, would lay it by only at meals, which he seldom refused, but "never was a-hongry."

He had a great fund of long-winded stories and incidents, mostly manufactured by himself—some few he had "hearn"—and would bore you or edify you, as it might turn out, from sun to sun, interspersing them now and then with a dull, guttural, lazy laugh.

He became quite a proverb in the line of big story-telling. True, he had many obstinate competitors, but he distanced them all farther than he did the numerous snakes that "run arter him." He had given his ambitious competitors fair warning thus:

"Ef any on 'um beats me, I'll sell out my deadnin' and hustle off to other deadnin's."

In sheer justice to Uncle Davy, however, and with pleasure I record the fact, that he reformed his life, became a Christian, I hope, as well as a Baptist, and died a penitent man.

As stated, he was never known to get out of a snail's gallop only when in contact with snakes; and the reader shall now have, in Uncle Davy's own style, an account of his flight from a coachwhip snake.

215

The Chase

"I had a hog claim over beyant Moor's Fork, and I concluded I'd take old Bucksmasher (his rifle), and go inter the big huckleberry patch, on Round Hill, in sarch for 'um. Off I trolloped, and toddled about for some time, but couldn't find head nur tail uv 'um. But while I was moseyin' about, I cum right chug upon one uv the biggest, longest, outdaciousest coachwhip snakes I uver laid my peepers on. He rared right straight up, like a May-pole, licked out his tarnacious tongue, and good as said, 'Here's at you, sir. What bizness have you on my grit?' Now I'd hearn folks say ef you'd look a vinimus animil right plump in the eyes he wouldn't hurt you. Now I tried it good, just like I were trying to look through a mill-stone. But, bless you, honey! he had no more respect fur a man's face and eyes than he had fur a huckleberry, sure's gun's iron. So I seed clearly that I'd have to try my trotters.

"I dashed down old Bucksmasher, and jumped 'bout ten steps the fust leap, and on I went wusser nur an old buck fur 'bout a quarter, and turned my noggin round to look fur the critter. Jehu Nimshi! thar he were right dab at my heels, head up, tongue out, and red as a nail-rod, and his eyes like two balls uv fire, red as chain lightnin.' I 'creased my verlocity, jumped logs twenty foot high, clarin' thick bushes, and bush-heaps, deep gullies, and branches. Again I looked back, thinkin' I had sartinly left it a long gap behind. And what do you think? By jingo! he'd hardly begun to run— jist gittin' his hand in. So I jist put flatly down again faster than uver. 'T wasn't long before I run out'n my shot-bag, I went so fast, then out'n my shirt, then out'n my britches—luther britches at that—then away went my drawers. Thus I run clean out'n all my linnen a half a mile afore I got home; and, thinks I, surely the tarnul sarpunt are distanced now.

"But what do you think now? Nebuchadnezzar! thar he were, fresh as a mounting buck jist scared up. I soon seen that wouldn't do, so I jumped about thirty-five foot, screamed like a wildcat, and 'creased my velocity at a monstrous rate. Jist then I begun to feel my skin split, and, thinks I, it's no use to run out'n my skin, like I have'n my linnen, as huming skin are scarce, so I tuck in a leetle.

"But by this time I'd run clean beyant my house, right smack through my yard, scaring Molly and the childering, dogs, cats, chickens—uvrything —half to death. But, you see, I got shet uv my inimy, the sarpunt, fur it had respect fur my house, ef it hadn't fur my face and eyes in the woods. I puffed, and blowed, and sweated 'bout half an hour afore I had wind to tell Molly and the childering what were the matter.

"Poor old Bucksmasher staid several days in the woods afore I could have the pluck to go arter him.' '

When Uncle Davy told one snake story, he must needs exhaust his stock, big and little. After breathing a little from telling his coachwhip story, which always excited him, he would introduce and tell the story of his adventure with

The Horn-Snake

"Fur some time arter I were chased by that sassy coachwhip, I were desput 'fraid uv snakes. My har would stand on eend, stiff as hog's bristles, at the noise uv uvry lizzard that ran through the leaves, and my flesh would jerk like a dead beef's.

"But at last I ventured to go into the face uv the Round Peak one day a-huntin.' I were skinnin' my eyes fur old bucks, with my head up, not thinkin' about sarpunts, when, by Zucks! I cum right plum upon one uv the curiousest snakes I uver seen in all my borned days.

"Fur a spell I were spellbound in three foot uv it. There it lay on the side uv a steep presserpis, at full length, ten foot long, its tail strait out, right up the presserpis, head big as a sasser, right toards me, eyes red as forked lightnin,' lickin' out his forked tongue, and I could no more move than the Ball Rock on Fisher's Peak. But when I seen the stinger in his tail, six inches long and sharp as a needle, stickin' out like a cock's spur, I thought I'd a drapped in my tracks. I'd ruther a had uvry coachwhip on Round Hill arter me en full chase than to a bin in that drefful siteation.

"Thar I stood, petterfied with relarm—couldn't budge a peg—couldn't even take old Bucksmasher off uv my shoulder to shoot the infarnul thing. Nyther uv us moved nor bolted 'ur eyes fur fifteen minits.

"At last, as good luck would have it, a rabbit run close by, and the snake turned its eyes to look what it were, and that broke the charm, and I jumped forty foot down the mounting, and dashed behind a big white oak five foot in diamatur. The snake he cotched the eend uv his tail in his mouth, he did, and come rollin' down the mounting arter me just like a hoop, and jist as I landed behind the tree he struck t'other side with his stinger, and stuv it up, clean to his tail, smack in the tree. He were fast.

"Of all the hissin' and blowin' that uver you hearn sense you seen daylight, it tuck the lead. Ef there'd a bin forty-nine forges all a-blowin' at once, it couldn't a beat it. He rared and charged, lapped round the tree, spread his mouf and grinned at me orful, puked and spit quarts an' quarts of green pisen at me, an' made the ar stink with his nasty breath.

"I seen thar were no time to lose; I cotched up old Bucksmasher from whar I'd dashed him down, and tried to shoot the tarnil thing; but he kep' sich a movin' about and sich a splutteration that I couldn't git a bead at his head, for I know'd it warn't wuth while to shoot him any whar else. So I kep' my distunce tell he wore hisself out, then I put a ball right between his eyes, and he gin up the ghost.

"Soon as he were dead I happened to look up inter the tree, and what do you think? Why, sir, it were dead as a herrin'; all the leaves was wilted like a fire had gone through its branches.

"I left the old feller with his stinger in the tree, thinkin' it were the best place fur him, and moseyed home, 'tarmined not to go out again soon.

"Now folks may talk as they please 'bout there bein' no sich things

as horn-snakes, but what I've seen I've seen, and what I've jist norated is
true as the third uv Mathy.

"I mout add that I passed that tree three weeks arterwards, and the
leaves and the whole tree was dead as a door-nail."

*   *   *   *   *

The Buck-Horned Snake

"I piked out one day," said Uncle Davy, "in sarch uv old bucks, but
they was monstrous scace, and I couldn't find none. I got 'most home, and
thort I hated to return havin' smashed nothin'—didn't like to be laughed
at. Jist then an old sucklin' doe got right smack in my way. I leveled old
Bucksmasher, and down she fell. I tuck her home, and, meat being ruther
scace, we eat her up monstrous quick.

"I furgut to mention that it was on Sunday I smashed that old doe.
My feelings sorter hurt me fur killin' her on Sunday, and frum her young
fawn too, poor critter! So in two ur three days arter, I thort I'd go out
and git the fawn. I made me a blate, went out to the laurel and ivy thicket
whar I'd killed the doe, blated, and the fawn answered me, fur it thought
it was its mammy, poor thing! I kep' blatin' away, and uvry time I'd
blate it would answer me, but it cum to me mighty slow, sartin. I got
onpatient, and moseyed a little to'ads it, and got on a log where I could see
a leetle, which the laurel and ivy was monstrous thick. I blated agin,
which it answered close by. I blated agin, and then I streeched up my
neck liken a scared turkey, lookin' 'mong the laurel and ivy, and what
do you think I seen?"

"I can not imagine," said Taliaferro, to whom he was relating this adventure.

"Well, I'll tell you. Thar lay the biggest, oncommonest black snake the
Lord uver made, sartin—which he has made a many a one—full fifteen
foot long, with a pair of rantankerous big buck's horns, big as antelope's
horns. It fixed its tarnacious eyes on me, but afore it could get its spell
on me I jumped off uv that log, and run so fast that I nuver hev nur nuver
will tell any man—which it is onpossible to tell any man—how fast I did
pike fur home. But sartin it is that the runnin' from the coachwhip on
Round Hill were no more to it than the runnin' uv a snail to a streak uv
lightnin'."

"What do you think it was?" inquired Taliaferro.

"I jist think it were suthin' sent thar to warn me 'bout huntin' on
Sundays. It blated jist like a fawn, and I thort it were the fawn I were
arter; but Jehu Nimshi! it were no more a fawn than I am a fawn, sartin.
But as sure as old Bucksmasher is made uv iron, and is the best gun in the
world, I've nuver hunted on Sunday sense."

FROM THE NOVEL

Elsie Venner Arouses Master Bernard's Suspicions

by OLIVER WENDELL HOLMES

MASTER BERNARD HAD STRUCK UP THE MOUNTAIN obliquely from the western side of the Dudley mansion-house. In this way he ascended until he reached a point many hundred feet above the level of the plain, and commanding all the country beneath and around. Almost at his feet he saw the mansion-house, the chimney standing out of the middle of the roof, or rather, like a black square hole in it,—the trees almost directly over their stems, the fences as lines, the whole nearly as an architect would draw a ground-plan of the house and the inclosures round it. It frightened him to see how the huge masses of rock and old forest-growths hung over the home below. As he descended a little and drew near the ledge of evil name, he was struck with the appearance of a long narrow fissure that ran parallel with it and above it for many rods, not seemingly of very old standing,—for there were many fibres of roots which had evidently been snapped asunder when the rent took place, and some of which were still succulent in both separated portions.

Mr. Bernard had made up his mind, when he set forth, not to come back before he had examined the dreaded ledge. He had half persuaded himself that it was scientific curiosity. He wished to examine the rocks, *to see what flowers grew there*, and perhaps to pick up an adventure in the zoölogical line; for he had on a pair of high, stout boots, and he carried a stick in his hand, which was forked at one extremity so as to be very convenient to hold down a *crotalus* with, if he should happen to encounter one. He knew the aspect of the ledge from a distance; for its bald and leprous-looking declivities stood out in their nakedness from the wooded sides of The Mountain, when this was viewed from certain points of the village. But the nearer aspect of the blasted region had something frightful in it. The cliffs were water-worn, as if they had been gnawed for thousands of years by hungry waves. In some places they overhung their base so as to look like leaning towers which might topple over at any minute. In other parts they were scooped into niches or caverns. Here and there they were cracked in deep fissures, some of them of such width that one might enter them, if he cared to run the risk of meeting the regular tenants, who might treat him as an intruder.

Parts of the ledge were cloven perpendicularly, with nothing but cracks or slightly projecting edges in which or on which a foot could find hold. High up on one of these precipitous walls of rock he saw some tufts of flowers, and knew them at once for the same that he had found between the leaves of his Virgil. Not there, surely! No woman would have clung against that steep, rough parapet to gather an idle blossom. And yet the master looked round everywhere, and even up the side of that rock, to see if there were no signs of a woman's footstep. He peered about curiously, as if his eye might fall on some of those fragments of dress which women leave after them, whenever they run against each other or against anything else,—in crowded ballrooms, in the brushwood after picnics, on the fences after rambles, scattered round over every place which has witnessed an act of violence, where rude hands have been laid upon them. Nothing. Stop, though, one moment. That stone is smooth and polished, as if it had been somewhat worn by the pressure of human feet. There is one twig broken among the stems of that clump of shrubs. He put his foot upon the stone and took hold of the close-clinging shrub. In this way he turned a sharp angle of the rock and found himself on a natural platform, which lay in front of one of the wider fissures,—whether the mouth of a cavern or not he could not yet tell. A flat stone made an easy seat, upon which he sat down, as he was very glad to do, and looked mechanically about him. A small fragment splintered from the rock was at his feet. He took it and threw it down the declivity a little below where he sat. He looked about for a stem or a straw of some kind to bite upon,—a country-instinct,—relic, no doubt, of the old vegetable-feeding habits of Eden. Is that a stem or a straw? He picked it up. It was a hair-pin.

To say that Mr. Langdon had a strange sort of thrill shoot through him at the sight of this harmless little implement would be a statement not at variance with the fact of the case. That smooth stone had been often trodden, and by what foot he could not doubt. He rose up from his seat to look round for other signs of a woman's visits. What if there is a cavern here, where she has a retreat, fitted up, perhaps, as anchorites fitted their cells,—nay, it may be, carpeted and mirrored, and with one of those tiger-skins for a couch, such as they say the girl loves to lie on? Let us look, at any rate.

Mr. Bernard walked to the mouth of the cavern or fissure and looked into it. His look was met by the glitter of two diamond eyes, small, sharp, cold, shining out of the darkness, but gliding with a smooth, steady motion towards the light, and himself. He stood fixed, struck dumb, staring back into them with dilating pupils and sudden numbness of fear that cannot move, as in the terror of dreams. The two sparks of light came forward until they grew to circles of flame, and all at once lifted themselves up as if in angry surprise. Then for the first time thrilled in Mr. Bernard's ears the dreadful sound that nothing which breathes, be it man or brute, can hear unmoved,—the long, loud, stinging whirr, as the huge, thick-bodied reptile shook his many-jointed rattle and adjusted his loops for the fatal stroke. His eyes were drawn as with magnets toward the circles of flame. His ears rung as in the overture to the swooning dream of chloroform. Nature was before man with her anæsthetics: the cat's first shake stupefies the mouse; the lion's first shake deadens the man's fear and feeling, and the *crotalus* paralyzes before he strikes. He waited as in a trance,—waited as one that longs to have the blow fall, and all over, as the man who shall be in two pieces in a second waits for the axe to drop. But while he looked straight into the flaming eyes, it seemed to him that they were losing their light and terror, that they were growing tame and dull; the charm was dissolving, the numbness was passing away, he could move once more. He heard a light breathing close to his ear, and, half turning, saw the face of Elsie Venner, looking motionless into the reptile's eyes, which had shrunk and faded under the stronger enchantment of her own.

*   *   *   *   *

If Master Bernard felt a natural gratitude to his young pupil for saving him from an imminent peril, he was in a state of infinite perplexity to know why he should have needed such aid. He, an active, muscular, courageous, adventurous young fellow, with a stick in his hand, ready to hold down the Old Serpent himself, if he had come in his way, to stand still, staring into those two eyes, until they came up close to him, and the strange, terrible sound seemed to freeze him stiff where he stood,—what was the meaning of it? Again, what was the influence this girl had seemingly exerted, under which the venomous creature had collapsed in such a sudden way? Whether he had been awake or dreaming he did not feel quite sure. He knew he had gone up The Mountain, at any rate; he knew he had come down The Mountain with the girl walking just before him;— there was no forgetting her figure, as she walked on in silence, her braided locks falling a little, for want of the lost hair-pin perhaps, and looking like a wreathing coil of—Shame on such fancies!—to wrong that supreme crowning gift of abounding Nature, a rush of shining black hair, which, shaken loose, would cloud her all round, like Godiva, from brow to instep! He was sure he had sat down before the fissure or cave. He was sure that he was led softly away from the place, and that it was Elsie who had led him. There was the hair-pin to show that so far it was not a dream. But between these recollections came a strange confusion; and the more the master thought, the more he was perplexed to know whether she had waked him, sleeping, as he sat on the stone, from some frightful dream, such as may come in a very brief slumber, or whether she had bewitched him into a trance with those strange eyes of hers, or whether it was all true, and he must solve its problem as he best might.

There was another recollection connected with this mountain adventure. As they approached the mansion-house, they met a young man, whom

Mr. Bernard remembered having seen once at least before, and whom he had heard of as a cousin of the young girl. As Cousin Richard Venner, the person in question, passed them, he took the measure, so to speak, of Mr. Bernard, with a look so piercing, so exhausting, so practised, so profoundly suspicious, that the young master felt in an instant that he had an enemy in this handsome youth,—an enemy, too, who was like to be subtle and dangerous.

Mr. Bernard had made up his mind, that, come what might, enemy or no enemy, live or die, he would solve the mystery of Elsie Venner, sooner or later. He was not a man to be frightened out of his resolution by a scowl, or a stiletto, or any unknown means of mischief, of which a whole armory was hinted at in that passing look Dick Venner had given him. Indeed, like most adventurous young persons, he found a kind of charm in feeling that there might be some dangers in the way of his investigations. Some rumors which had reached him about the supposed suitor of Elsie Venner, who was thought to be a desperate kind of fellow, and whom some believed to be an unscrupulous adventurer, added a curious, romantic kind of interest to the course of physiological and psychological inquiries he was about instituting.

The afternoon on The Mountain was still uppermost in his mind. Of course he knew the common stories about fascination. He had once been himself an eye-witness of the charming of a small bird by one of our common harmless serpents. Whether a human being could be reached by this subtile agency, he had been skeptical, notwithstanding the mysterious relation generally felt to exist between man and this creature, "cursed above all cattle and above every beast of the field,"—a relation which some interpret as the fruit of the curse, and others hold to be so instinctive that this animal has been for that reason adopted as the natural symbol of evil. There was another solution, however, supplied him by his professional reading. The curious work of Mr. Braid of Manchester had made him familiar with the phenomena of a state allied to that produced by animal magnetism, and called by that writer by the name of *hypnotism*. He found, by referring to his note-book, the statement was, that, by fixing the eyes on *a bright object* so placed as *to produce a strain* upon the eyes and eyelids, and to maintain *a steady fixed stare,* there comes on in a few seconds a very singular condition, characterized by *muscular rigidity* and *inability to move,* with a strange *exaltation of most of the senses,* and *generally* a closure of the eyelids,—this condition being followed by *torpor.*

Now this statement of Mr. Braid's, well known to the scientific world, and the truth of which had been confirmed by Mr. Bernard in certain experiments he had instituted, as it has been by many other experimenters, went far to explain the strange impressions, of which, waking or dreaming, he had certainly been the subject. His nervous system had been in a high state of exaltation at the time. He remembered how the little noises that made rings of sound in the silence of the woods, like pebbles dropped in still waters had reached his inner consciousness. He remembered that singular sensation in the roots of the hair, when he came on the traces of the girl's presence, reminding him of a line in a certain poem which he had read lately with a new and peculiar interest. He even recalled a curious evidence of exalted sensibility and irritability, in the twitching of the minute muscles of the internal ear at every unexpected sound, producing an odd little snap in the middle of the head, which proved to him that he was getting very nervous.

The next thing was to find out whether it were possible that the venomous creature's eyes should have served the purpose of Mr. Braid's "bright object" held very close to the person experimented on, or whether they had any special power which could be made the subject of exact observation.

For this purpose Mr. Bernard considered it necessary to get a live *crotalus* or two into his possession, if this were possible. On inquiry, he found that there was a certain family living far up the mountain-side, not a mile from the ledge, the members of which were said to have taken these creatures occasionally, and not to be in any danger, or at least in any fear, of being injured by them. He applied to these people, and offered a reward sufficient to set them at work to capture some of these animals, if such a thing were possible.

A few days after this, a dark, gypsy-looking woman presented herself at his door. She held up her apron as if it contained something precious in the bag she made with it.

"Y'wanted some rattlers," said the woman. "Here they be."

She opened her apron and showed a coil of rattlesnakes lying very peaceably in its fold. They lifted their heads up, as if they wanted to see what was going on, but showed no sign of anger.

"Are you crazy?" said Mr. Bernard. "You're dead in an hour, if one of those creatures strikes you!"

He drew back a little, as he spoke; it might be simple disgust; it might be fear; it might be what we call antipathy, which is different from either, and which will sometimes show itself in paleness, and even faintness, produced by objects perfectly harmless and not in themselves offensive to any sense.

"Lord bless you," said the woman, "rattlers never touches our folks. I'd jest 'z lieves handle them creaturs as so many stripéd snakes."

So saying, she put their heads down with her hand, and packed them together in her apron as if they had been bits of cart-rope.

Mr. Bernard had never heard of the power, or, at least, the belief in the possession of a power by certain persons, which enables them to handle these frightful reptiles with perfect impunity. The fact, however, is well known to others, and more especially to a very distinguished Professor in one of the leading institutions of the great city of the land, whose experiences in the neighborhood of Graylock, as he will doubtless inform the curious, were very much like those of the young master.

Mr. Bernard had a wired cage ready for his formidable captives, and studied their habits and expression with a strange sort of interest. What did the Creator mean to signify, when he made such shapes of horror, and, as if he had doubly cursed this envenomed wretch, had set a mark upon him and sent him forth, the Cain of the brotherhood of serpents? It was a very curious fact that the first train of thoughts Mr. Bernard's small menagerie suggested to him was the grave, though somewhat worn, subject of the origin of evil. There is now to be seen in a tall glass jar, in the Museum of Comparative Anatomy at Cantabridge in the territory of the Massachusetts, a huge *crotalus,* of a species which grows to more frightful dimensions than our own, under the hotter skies of South America. Look at it, ye who would know what is the tolerance, the freedom from prejudice, which can suffer such an incarnation of all that is devilish to lie unharmed in the cradle of Nature! Learn, too, that there are many things in this world which we are warned to shun, and are even suffered to slay, if need be, but which we must not hate, unless we would hate what God loves and cares for.

Whatever fascination the creature might exercise in his native haunts, Mr. Bernard found himself not in the least nervous or affected in any way while looking at his caged reptiles. When their cage was shaken, they would lift their heads and spring their rattles; but the sound was by no means so formidable to listen to as when it reverberated among the chasms of the echoing rocks. The expression of the creatures was watchful, still, grave, passionless, fate-like, suggesting a cold malignity which seemed to be waiting for its opportunity. Their awful, deep-cut mouths were sternly closed over the long hollow fangs which rested their roots against the swollen poison-gland, where the venom had been hoarding up ever since the last stroke had emptied it. They never winked, for ophidians have no movable eyelids, but kept up that awful fixed stare which made the two *unwinking* gladiators the survivors of twenty pairs matched by one of the Roman Emperors, as Pliny tells us, in his "Natural History." Their eyes did not flash, but shone with a cold still light. They were of a pale-golden or straw color, horrible to look into, with their stony calmness, their pitiless indifference, hardly enlivened by the almost imperceptible vertical slit of the pupil, through which Death seemed to be looking out like the archer behind the long narrow loop-hole in a blank turret-wall. On the whole, the caged reptiles, horrid as they were, hardly matched his recollections of what he had seen or dreamed he saw at the cavern. These looked dangerous enough, but yet quiet. A treacherous stillness, however, —as the unfortunate New York physician found, when he put his foot out to wake up the torpid creature, and instantly the fang flashed through his boot, carrying the poison into his blood, and death with it.

Mr. Bernard kept these strange creatures, and watched all their habits with a natural curiosity. In any collection of animals the venomous beasts are looked at with the greatest interest, just as the greatest villains are most run after by the unknown public. Nobody troubles himself for a common striped snake or a petty thief, but a *cobra* or a wife-killer is a centre of attraction to all eyes. These captives did very little to earn their living, but, on the other hand, their living was not expensive, their diet being nothing but air, *au naturel*. Months and months these creatures will live and seem to thrive well enough, as any showman who has them in his menagerie will testify, though they never touch anything to eat or drink.

In the mean time Mr. Bernard had become very curious about a class of subjects not treated of in any detail in those text-books accessible in most country-towns, to the exclusion of the more special treatises, and especially of the rare and ancient works found on the shelves of the larger city-libraries. He was on a visit to old Dr. Kittredge one day, having been asked by him to call in for a few moments as soon as convenient. The Doctor smiled good-humoredly when he asked him if he had an extensive collection of medical works.

"Why, no," said the old Doctor, "I haven't got a great many printed books; and what I have I don't read quite as often as I might, I'm afraid. I read and studied in the time of it, when I was in the midst of the young men who were all at work with their books; but it's a mighty hard matter, when you go off alone into the country, to keep up with all that's going on in the Societies and the Colleges. I'll tell you, though, Mr. Langdon, when a man that's once started right lives among sick folks for five-and-thirty years, as I've done, if he hasn't got a library of five-and-thirty volumes bound up in his head at the end of that time, he'd better stop driving round and sell his horse and sulky. I know the bigger part of the families within a dozen miles' ride. I know the families that have a way of living through everything, and I know the other set that have the trick of dying without any kind of reason for it. I know the years when the fevers and dysenteries are in earnest, and when they're only making believe. I know the folks that think they're dying as soon as they're sick, and the folks that never find out they're sick till they're dead. I don't want to undervalue your science, Mr. Langdon. There are things I never learned, because they came in after my day, and I am very glad to send my patients to those that do know them, when I am at fault; but I know these people about here, fathers and mothers, and children and grandchildren, so as all the science in the world can't know them, without it takes time about it, and sees them grow up and grow old, and how the wear and tear of life comes to them. You can't tell a horse by driving him once, Mr. Langdon, nor a patient by talking half an hour with him."

"Do you know much about the Venner family?" said Mr. Bernard, in a natural way enough, the Doctor's talk having suggested the question.

The Doctor lifted his head with his accustomed movement, so as to command the young man through his spectacles.

"I know all the families of this place and its neighborhood," he answered.

"We have the young lady studying with us at the Institute," said Mr. Bernard.

"I know it," the Doctor answered. "Is she a good scholar?"

All this time the Doctor's eyes were fixed steadily on Mr. Bernard, looking through the glasses.

"She is a good scholar enough, but I don't know what to make of her. Sometimes I think she is a little out of her head. Her father, I believe, is sensible enough;—what sort of a woman was her mother, Doctor?—I suppose of course you remember all about her?"

"Yes, I knew her mother. She was a very lovely young woman."—The Doctor put his hand to his forehead and drew a long breath.—"What is there you notice out of the way about Elsie Venner?"

"A good many things," the master answered. "She shuns all the other girls. She is getting a strange influence over my fellow-teacher, a young lady,—you know Miss Helen Darley, perhaps? I am afraid this girl will kill her. I never saw or heard of anything like it, in prose at least;—do you remember much of Coleridge's Poems, Doctor?"

The good old Doctor had to plead a negative.

"Well, no matter. Elsie would have been burned for a witch in old times. I have seen the girl look at Miss Darley when she had not the least idea of it, and all at once I would see her grow pale and moist, and sigh, and move round uneasily, and turn towards Elsie, and perhaps get up and go to her, or else have slight spasmodic movements that looked like hysterics;—do you believe in the evil eye, Doctor?"

"Mr. Langdon," the Doctor said, solemnly, "there are strange things about Elsie Venner,—very strange things. This was what I wanted to speak to you about. Let me advise you all to be very patient with the girl, but also very careful. Her love is not to be desired, and"—he spoke in a lower tone—"her hate is to be dreaded. Do you think she has any special fancy for anybody else in the school besides Miss Darley?"

Mr. Bernard could not stand the old Doctor's spectacled eyes without betraying a little of the feeling natural to a young man to whom a home question involving a possible sentiment is put suddenly.

"I have suspected," he said,—"I have had a kind of feeling—that she ——Well, come, Doctor,—I don't know that there's any use in disguising the matter,—I have thought Elsie Venner had rather a fancy for somebody else,—I mean myself."

There was something so becoming in the blush with which the young man made this confession, and so manly, too, in the tone with which he spoke, so remote from any shallow vanity, such as young men who are incapable of love are apt to feel, when some loose tendril of a woman's fancy which a chance wind has blown against them twines about them for the want of anything better, that the old Doctor looked at him admiringly, and could not help thinking that it was no wonder any young girl should be pleased with him.

"You are a man of nerve, Mr. Langdon?" said the Doctor.

"I thought so till very lately," he replied. "I am not easily frightened, but I don't know but I might be bewitched or magnetized, or whatever it is when one is tied up and cannot move. I think I can find nerve enough, however, if there is any special use you want to put it to."

"Let me ask you one more question, Mr. Langdon. Do you find yourself disposed to take a special interest in Elsie,—to fall in love with her, in a word? Pardon me, for I do not ask from curiosity, but a much more serious motive."

"Elsie interests me," said the young man, "interests me strangely. She has a wild flavor in her character which is wholly different from that of any human creature I ever saw. She has marks of genius,—poetic or dramatic,—I hardly know which. She read a passage from Keats's 'Lamia' the other day, in the school-room, in such a way that I declare to you I thought some of the girls would faint or go into fits. Miss Darley got up and left the room, trembling all over. Then I pity her, she is so lonely. The girls are afraid of her, and she seems to have either a dislike or a fear of them. They have all sorts of painful stories about her. They give her a name which no human creature ought to bear. They say she hides a mark on her neck by always wearing a necklace. She is very graceful, you know, and they will have it that she can twist herself into all sorts of shapes, or tie herself in a knot, if she wants to. There is not one of them that will look her in the eyes. I pity the poor girl; but, Doctor, I do not love her. I would risk my life for her, if it would do her any good, but it would be in cold blood. If her hand touches mine, it is not a thrill of passion I feel running through me, but a very different emotion. Oh, Doctor, there must be something in that creature's blood which has killed the humanity in her. God only knows the cause that has blighted such a soul in so beautiful a body! No, Doctor, I do not love the girl."

"Mr. Langdon," said the Doctor, "you are young, and I am old. Let me talk to you with an old man's privilege, as an adviser. You have come to this country-town without suspicion, and you are moving in the midst of perils. There are things which I must not tell you now; but I may warn you. Keep your eyes open and your heart shut. If, through pitying that girl, you ever come to love her, you are lost. If you deal carelessly with her, beware! This is not all. There are other eyes on you beside Elsie Venner's.—Do you go armed?"

"I do!" said Mr. Bernard,—and he "put his hands up" in the shape of fists, in such a way as to show that he was master of the natural weapons at any rate.

The Doctor could not help smiling. But his face fell in an instant.

"You may want something more than those tools to work with. Come with me into my sanctum."

The Doctor led Mr. Bernard into a small room opening out of the study. It was a place such as anybody but a medical man would shiver to enter. There was the usual tall box with its bleached, rattling tenant; there were jars in rows where "interesting cases" outlived the grief of widows and heirs in alcoholic immortality,—for your "preparation-jar" is the true *"monumentum ere perennius"*; there were various semipossibilities of minute dimensions and unpromising developments; there were shining instruments of evil aspect, and grim plates on the walls, and on one shelf by itself, accursed and apart, coiled in a long cylinder of spirit, a huge *crotalus,* rough-scaled, flat-headed, variegated with dull bands, one of which partially encircled the neck like a collar,—an awful wretch to look upon, with murder written all over him in horrid hieroglyphics. Mr. Bernard's look was riveted on this creature,—not fascinated certainly, for its eyes looked like white beads, being clouded by the action of the spirits in which it had been long kept,—but fixed by some indefinite sense of the renewal of a previous impression;—everybody knows the feeling, with its suggestion of some past state of existence. There was a scrap of paper on the jar, with something written on it. He was reaching up to read it when the Doctor touched him lightly.

"Look here, Mr. Langdon!" he said, with a certain vivacity of manner, as if wishing to call away his attention,—"this is my armory."

The Doctor threw open the door of a small cabinet, where were disposed in artistic patterns various weapons of offence and defence,—for he was a virtuoso in his way, and by the side of the implements of the art of healing had pleased himself with displaying a collection of those other instruments, the use of which renders the first necessary.

"See which of these weapons you would like best to carry about you," said the Doctor.

Mr. Bernard laughed, and looked at the Doctor as if he half doubted whether he was in earnest.

"This looks dangerous enough," he said,— "for the man who carries it, at least."

He took down one of the prohibited Spanish daggers or knives which a traveller may occasionally get hold of and smuggle out of the country. The blade was broad, trowel-like, but the point drawn out several inches, so as to look like a skewer.

"This must be a jealous bull-fighter's weapon," he said, and put it back in its place.

Then he took down an ancient-looking broad-bladed dagger, with a complex aspect about it, as if it had some kind of mechanism connected with it.

"Take care!" said the Doctor; "there is a trick to that dagger."

He took it and touched a spring. The dagger split suddenly into three blades, as when one separates the forefinger and the ring-finger from the middle one. The outside blades were sharp on their outer edge. The stab was to be made with the dagger shut, then the spring touched and the split blades withdrawn.

Mr. Bernard replaced it, saying, that it would have served for side-arm to old Suwarrow, who told his men to work their bayonets back and forward when they pinned a Turk, but to wriggle them about in the wound when they stabbed a Frenchman.

"Here," said the Doctor, "this is the thing you want."

He took down a much more modern and familiar implement,—a small, beautifully finished revolver.

"I want you to carry this," he said; "and more than that, I want you to practise with it often, as for amusement, but so that it may be seen and understood that you are apt to have a pistol about you. Pistol-shooting is pleasant sport enough, and there is no reason why you should not practise it like other young fellows. And now," the Doctor said, "I have one other weapon to give you."

He took a small piece of parchment and shook a white powder into it from one of his medicine-jars. The jar was marked with the name of a mineral salt, of a nature to have been serviceable in case of sudden illness in the time of the Borgias. The Doctor folded the parchment carefully and marked the Latin name of the powder upon it.

"Here," he said, handing it to Mr. Bernard,—"you see what it is, and you know what service it can render. Keep these two protectors about your person day and night; they will not harm you, and you may want one or the other or both before you think of it."

Mr. Bernard thought it was very odd, and not very old-gentlemanlike, to be fitting him out for treason, stratagem, and spoils, in this way. There was no harm, however, in carrying a doctor's powder in his pocket, or in amusing himself with shooting at a mark, as he had often done before. If the old gentleman had these fancies, it was as well to humor him. So he thanked old Doctor Kittredge, and shook his hand warmly as he left him.

"The fellow's hand did not tremble, nor his color change," the Doctor said, as he watched him walking away. "He is one of the right sort."

*   *   *   *   *

Mr. Langdon to the Professor.

MY DEAR PROFESSOR,—

You were kind enough to promise me that you would assist me in any professional or scientific investigations in which I might become engaged. I have of late become deeply interested in a class of subjects which present peculiar difficulty, and I must exercise the privilege of questioning you on some points upon which I desire information I cannot otherwise obtain. I would not trouble you, if I could find any person or books competent to enlighten me on some of these singular matters which have so excited me.

The leading doctor here is a shrewd, sensible man, but not versed in the curiosities of medical literature.

I proceed, with your leave, to ask a considerable number of questions, —hoping to get answers to some of them, at least.

Is there any evidence that human beings can be infected or wrought upon by poisons, or otherwise, so that they shall manifest any of the peculiarities belonging to beings of a lower nature! Can such peculiarities be transmitted by inheritance? Is there anything to countenance the stories, long and widely current, about the "evil eye"? or is it a mere fancy that such a power belongs to any human being? Have you any personal experience as to the power of *fascination* said to be exercised by certain animals? What can you make of those circumstantial statements we have seen in the papers, of children forming mysterious friendships with ophidians of different species, sharing their food with them, and seeming to be under some subtile influence exercised by those creatures? Have you read, critically, Coleridge's poem of "Christabel," and Keats's "Lamia"? If so, can you understand them, or find any physiological foundation for the story of either?

There is another set of questions of a different nature I should like to ask, but it is hardly fair to put so many on a single sheet. There is one, however, you must answer. Do you think there may be predispositions, inherited or ingrafted, but at any rate constitutional, which shall take out certain apparently voluntary determinations from the control of the will, and leave them as free from moral responsibility as the instincts of the lower animals? Do you not think there may be a *crime* which is not a *sin?*

Pardon me, my dear Sir, for troubling you with such a list of notes of interrogation. There are some *very strange* things going on here in this place, country-town as it is. Country-life is apt to be dull; but when it once gets going, it beats the city hollow, because it gives its whole mind to what it is about. These rural sinners make terrible work with the middle of the Decalogue, when they get started. However, I hope I shall live through my year's school-keeping without catastrophes, though there are queer doings about me which puzzle me and might scare some people. If anything *should* happen, you will be one of the first to hear of it, no doubt. But I trust not to help out the editors of the "Rockland Weekly Universe" with an obituary of the late lamented, who signed himself in life

Your friend and pupil,

BERNARD C. LANGDON.

The Professor to Mr. Langdon.

MY DEAR MR. LANGDON,—

I do not wonder that you find no answer from your country friends to the curious questions you put. They belong to that middle region between science and poetry which sensible men, as they are called, are very shy of meddling with. Some people think that truth and gold are always to be washed for; but the wiser sort are of opinion, that, unless there are so many grains to the peck of sand or nonsense respectively, it does not pay to wash for either, so long as one can find anything else to do. I don't doubt there is some truth in the phenomena of animal magnetism for instance; but when you ask me to cradle for it, I tell you that the hysteric girls cheat so and the professionals are such a set of pickpockets, that I can do something better than hunt for the grains of truth among their tricks and lies. Do you remember what I used to say in my lectures?—or were you asleep just then, or cutting your initials on the rail? (You see I can ask questions, my young friend.) *Leverage* is everything,—was what I used to say;—don't begin to pry till you have got the long arm on your side.

To please you, and satisfy your doubts as far as possible, I have looked into the old books,—into Schenckius and Turner and Kenelm Digby and the rest, where I have found plenty of curious stories which you must take for what they are worth.

Your first question I can answer in the affirmative upon pretty good authority. Mizaldus tells, in his "Memorabilia," the well-known story of the girl fed on poisons, who was sent by the king of the Indies to Alexander the Great. "When Aristotle saw her eyes *sparkling and snapping like those of serpents,* he said, 'Look out for yourself, Alexander! this is a dangerous companion for you!' "—and sure enough, the young lady proved to be a very unsafe person to her friends. Cardanus gets a story from Avicenna, of a certain man bit by a serpent, who recovered of his bite, the snake dying therefrom. This man afterwards had a daughter whom venomous serpents could not harm, though *she had a fatal power over them.*

I suppose you may remember the statements of old authors about *lycanthropy,* the disease in which men took on the nature and aspect of wolves. Attius and Paulus, both men of authority, describe it. Altomaris gives a horrid case; and Fincelius mentions one occurring as late as 1541, the subject of which was captured, still *insisting that he was a wolf,* only that the hair of his hide was turned in! *Versipelles,* it may be remembered, was the Latin name for these "were-wolves."

As for the cases where rabid persons have barked and bit like dogs, there are plenty of such on record.

More singular, or at least more rare, is the account given by Andreas Baccius, of a man who was struck in the hand by a cock, with his beak, and who died on the third day thereafter, looking for all the world *like a fighting-cock,* to the great horror of the spectators.

As to impressions transmitted *at a very early period of existence,* every one knows the story of King James's fear of a naked sword, and the way it is accounted for. Sir Kenelm Digby says,—"I remember when he dubbed me Knight, in the ceremony of putting the point of a naked sword upon my shoulder, he could not endure to look upon it, but turned his face another way insomuch, that, in lieu of touching my shoulder, he had almost thrust the point into my eyes, had not the Duke of Buckingham guided his hand aright." It is he, too, who tells the story of the *mulberry mark* upon the neck of a certain lady of high condition, which "every year, in the mulberry season, did swell, grow big, and itch." And Gaffarel mentions the case of a girl born with the figure of a *fish* on one of her limbs, of which the wonder was, that, when the girl did eat fish, this mark put her to sensible pain. But there is no end to cases of this kind, and I could give some of recent date, if necessary, lending a certain plausibility at least to the doctrine of transmitted impressions.

I never saw a distinct case of *evil eye,* though I have seen eyes so bad that they might produce strange effects on very sensitive natures. But the belief in it under various names, fascination, *jettatura,* etc., is so permanent and universal, from Egypt to Italy, and from the days of Solomon to those of Ferdinand of Naples, that there must be some *peculiarity,* to say the least, on which the opinion is based. There is very strong evidence that some such power is exercised by certain of the lower animals. Thus, it is stated on good authority that "almost every animal becomes panic-struck at the sight of the *rattlesnake,* and seems at once deprived of the power of motion, or the exercise of its usual instinct of self-preservation." Other serpents seem to share this power of fascination, as the *Cobra* and the *Bucephalus Capensis.* Some think that it is nothing but fright; others attribute it to the

> "strange powers that lie
> Within the magic circle of the eye,"—

as Churchill said, speaking of Garrick.

You ask me about those mysterious and frightful intimacies between children and serpents, of which so many instances have been recorded. I am sure I cannot tell what to make of them. I have seen several such accounts in recent papers, but here is one published in the seventeenth century, which is as striking as any of the more modern ones:—

"Mr. *Herbert Jones* of *Monmouth,* when he was a little Boy, was used to eat his Milk in a Garden in the Morning, and was no sooner there, but a large Snake always came, and eat out of the Dish with him, and did so for a considerable time, till one Morning, he striking the Snake on the Head, it hissed at him. Upon which he told his Mother that the Baby (for so he call'd it) cry'd *Hiss* at him. His Mother had it kill'd, which occasioned him a great *Fit of Sickness,* and 'twas thought would have dy'd, but did recover."

There was likewise one "*William Writtle,* condemned at *Maidston Assizes* for a double murder, told a Minister that was with him after he was condemned, that his mother told him, that when he was a Child, there crept always to him a Snake, wherever she laid him. Sometimes she would convey him up Stairs, and leave him never so little, she should be sure to find a Snake in the Cradle with him, but never perceived it did him any harm."

One of the most striking alleged facts connected with the mysterious relation existing between the serpent and the human species is the influence which the poison of the *Crotalus*, taken internally, seemed to produce over the *moral faculties*, in the experiments instituted by Dr. Hering at Surinam. There is something frightful in the disposition of certain ophidians, as the whip-snake, which darts at the eyes of cattle without any apparent provocation or other motive. It is natural enough that the evil principle should have been represented in the form of a serpent, but it is strange to think of introducing it into a human being like cow-pox by vaccination.

You know all about the *Psylli*, or ancient serpent-tamers, I suppose. Savary gives an account of the modern serpent-tamers in his "Letters on Egypt." These modern jugglers are in the habit of making the venomous *Naja* counterfeit death, lying out straight and stiff, *changing it into a rod*, as the ancient magicians did with their serpents, (probably the same animal,) in the time of Moses.

I am afraid I cannot throw much light on "Christabel" or "Lamia" by any criticism I can offer. Geraldine, in the former, seems to be simply a malignant witch-woman with the *evil eye* but with no absolute ophidian relationship. Lamia is a serpent transformed by magic into a woman. The idea of both is mythological, and not in any sense physiological. Some women unquestionably suggest the image of serpents; men rarely or never. I have been struck, like many others, with the ophidian head and eye of the famous Rachel.

Your question about inherited predispositions, as limiting the sphere of the will, and, consequently, of moral accountability, opens a very wide range of speculation. I can give you only a brief abstract of my own opinions on this delicate and difficult subject. Crime and sin, being the *preserves* of two great organized interests, have been guarded against all reforming poachers with as great jealousy as the Royal Forests. It is so easy to hang a troublesome fellow! It is so much simpler to consign a soul to perdition, or say masses, for money, to save it, than to take the blame on ourselves for letting it grow up in neglect and run to ruin for want of humanizing influences! They hung poor, crazy Bellingham for shooting Mr. Perceval. The ordinary of Newgate preached to women who were to swing at Tyburn for a petty theft as if they were worse than other people,—just as though he would not have been a pickpocket or shoplifter, himself, if he had been born in a den of thieves and bred up to steal or starve! The English law never began to get hold of the idea that a crime was not necessarily a sin, till Hadfield, who thought he was the Saviour of mankind, was tried for shooting at George the Third;—lucky for him that he did not hit his Majesty!

It is very singular that we recognize all the bodily defects that unfit a man for military service, and all the intellectual ones that limit his range of thought, but always talk at him as if all his moral powers were perfect. I suppose we must punish evil-doers as we extirpate vermin; but I don't know that we have any more right to judge them than we have to judge rats and mice, which are just as good as cats and weasels, though we think it necessary to treat them as criminals.

The limitations of human responsibility have never been properly studied, unless it be by the phrenologists. You know from my lectures that I consider phrenology, as taught, a pseudo-science, and not a branch of positive knowledge; but, for all that, we owe it an immense debt. It has melted the world's conscience in its crucible, and cast it in a new mould, with features less like those of Moloch and more like those of humanity. If it has failed to demonstrate its system of special correspondences, it has proved that there are fixed relations between organization and mind and character. It has brought out that great doctrine of moral insanity, which has done more to make men charitable and soften legal and theological barbarism than any one doctrine that I can think of since the message of peace and good-will to men.

Automatic action in the moral world; the *reflex movement* which *seems* to be self-determination, and has been hanged and howled at as such (metaphorically) for nobody knows how many centuries: until somebody shall study this as Marshall Hall has studied reflex nervous action in the bodily system, I would not give much for men's judgments of each others' characters. Shut up the robber and the defaulter, we must. But what if your oldest boy had been stolen from his cradle and bred in a North-Street cellar? What if you are drinking a little too much wine and smoking a little too much tobacco, and your son takes after you, and so your poor grandson's brain being a little injured in physical texture, he loses the fine moral sense on which you pride yourself, and doesn't see the difference between signing another man's name to a draft and his own?

I suppose the study of automatic action in the moral world (you see what I mean through the apparent contradiction of terms) may be a dangerous one in view of many people. It is liable to abuse, no doubt. People are always glad to get hold of anything which limits their responsibility. But remember that our moral estimates come down to us from ancestors who hanged children for stealing forty shillings' worth, and sent their souls to perdition for the sin of being born,—who punished the unfortunate families of suicides, and in their eagerness for justice executed one innocent person every three years, on the average, as Sir James Mackintosh tells us.

I do not know in what shape the practical question may present itself to you; but I will tell you my rule in life, and I think you will find it a good one. *Treat bad men exactly as if they were insane.* They are *in-sane,* out of health, morally. Reason, which is food to sound minds, is not tolerated, still less assimilated, unless administered with the greatest caution; perhaps, not at all. Avoid collision with them, so far as you honorably can; keep your temper, if you can,—for one angry man is as good as another; restrain them from violence, promptly, completely, and with the least possible injury, just as in the case of maniacs,—and when you have got rid of them, or got them tied hand and foot so that they can do no mischief, sit down and contemplate them charitably, remembering that nine tenths of their perversity comes from outside influences, drunken ancestors, abuse in childhood, bad company, from which you have happily been preserved, and for some of which you, as a member of society, may be fractionally responsible. I think also that there are *special influences* which *work in the blood like ferments,* and I have a suspicion that some of those curious old stories I cited may have more recent parallels. Have you ever met with any cases which admitted of a solution like that which I have mentioned?

Yours very truly

————— —————

Bernard Langdon to Philip Staples.

MY DEAR PHILIP,—

I have been for some months established in this place, turning the main crank of the machinery for the manufactory of accomplishments superintended by, or rather worked to the profit of, a certain Mr. Silas Peckham. He is a poor wretch, with a little thin fishy blood in his body, lean and flat, long-armed and large-handed, thick-jointed and thin-muscled,—you know those unwholesome, weak-eyed, half-fed creatures, that look not fit to be round among live folks, and yet not quite dead enough to bury. If you ever hear of my being in court to answer to a charge of assault and battery, you may guess that I have been giving him a thrashing to settle off old scores; for he is a tyrant, and has come pretty near killing his principal lady-assistant with over-working her and keeping her out of all decent privileges.

Helen Darley is this lady's name,—twenty-two or -three years old, I should think,—a very sweet pale woman,—daughter of the usual country clergyman,—thrown on her own resources from an early age, and the rest: a common story, but an uncommon person,—very. All conscience and sensibility, I should say,—a cruel worker,—no kind of regard for herself,—seems as fragile and supple as a young willow-shoot, but try her and you find she has the spring in her of a steel crossbow. I am glad I happened to come to this place, if it were only for her sake. I have saved that girl's life; I am as sure of it as if I had pulled her out of the fire or water.

Of course I'm in love with her, you say,—we always love those whom we have benefited, "saved her life,—her love was the reward of his devotion," etc., etc., as in a regular set novel. In love, Philip? Well, about that,—I love Helen Darley—very much: there is hardly anybody I love so well. What a noble creature she is! One of those that just go right on, do their own work and everybody else's, killing themselves inch by inch without ever thinking about it,—singing and dancing at their toil when they begin, worn and saddened after a while, but pressing steadily on, tottering by-and-by, and catching at the rail by the way-side to help them lift one foot before the other, and at last falling, face down, arms stretched forward——

Philip, my boy, do you know I am the sort of man that locks his door sometimes and cries his heart out of his eyes,—that can sob like a woman and not be ashamed of it? I come of fighting-blood on one side, you know; I think I could be savage on occasion. But I am tender—more and more tender as I come into my fulness of manhood. I don't like to strike a man (laugh, if you like,—I know I hit hard when I do strike,)—but what I can't stand is the sight of these poor, patient, toiling women, who never find out in this life how good they are, and never know what it is to be told they are angels while they still wear the pleasing incumbrances of humanity. I don't know what to make of these cases. To think that a woman is never to be a woman again, whatever she may come to as an unsexed angel,—and that she should die unloved! Why does not somebody come and carry off this noble woman, waiting here all ready to make a man happy? Philip, do you know the pathos there is in the eyes of un-sought women, oppressed with the burden of an inner life unshared? I can see into them now as I could not in those earlier days. I sometimes think their pupils dilate on purpose to let my consciousness glide through them; indeed, I dread them, I come so close to the nerve of the soul itself in these momentary intimacies. You used to tell me I was a Turk,—that my heart was full of pigeonholes, with accommodations inside for a whole flock of doves. I don't know but I am still as Youngish as ever in my ways,—Brigham-Youngish, I mean; at any rate, I always want to give a little love to all the poor things that cannot have a whole man to them-selves. If they would only be contented with a little!

Here now are two girls in this school where I am teaching. One of them, Rosa M., is not more than sixteen years old, I think they say, but Nature has forced her into a tropical luxuriance of beauty, as if it were July with her, instead of May. I suppose it is all natural enough that this girl should like a young man's attention, even if he were a grave school-master; but the eloquence of this young thing's look is unmistakable,—and yet she does not know the language it is talking,—they none of them do; and there is where a good many poor creatures of our good-for-nothing sex are mistaken. There is no danger of my being rash, but I think this girl will cost somebody his life yet. She is one of those women men make a quarrel about and fight to the death for,—the old feral instinct, you know.

Pray, don't think I am lost in conceit, but there is another girl here who I begin to think looks with a certain kindness on me. Her name is Elsie

V., and she is the only daughter and heiress of an old family in this place. She is a portentous and almost fearful creature. If I should tell you all I know and half of what I fancy about her, you would tell me to get my life insured at once. Yet she is the most painfully interesting being,—so handsome! so lonely!—for she has no friends among the girls, and sits apart from them,—with black hair like the flow of a mountain-brook after a thaw, with a low-browed, scowling beauty of face, and such eyes as were never seen before, I really believe, in any human creature.

Philip, I don't know what to say about this Elsie. There is something about her I have not fathomed. I have conjectures which I could not utter to any living soul. I dare not even hint the possibilities which have suggested themselves to me. This I will say,—that I do take the most intense interest in this young person, an interest much more like pity than love in its common sense. If what I guess at is true, of all the tragedies of existence I ever knew this is the saddest, and yet so full of meaning! Do not ask me any questions,—I have said more than I meant to already; but I am involved in strange doubts and perplexities,—in dangers too, very possibly, —and it is a relief just to speak ever so guardedly of them to an early and faithful friend.

Yours ever,
BERNARD.

Huckleberry Finn Discovers What Comes of Handlin' Snake Skin

by SAMUEL L. CLEMENS

AFTER BREAKFAST I WANTED TO TALK ABOUT THE DEAD man and guess out how he come to be killed, but Jim didn't want to. He said it would fetch bad luck; and besides, he said, he might come and ha'nt us; he said a man that warn't buried was more likely to go a-ha'nting around than one that was planted and comfortable. That sounded pretty reasonable, so I didn't say no more; but I couldn't keep from studying over it and wishing I knowed who shot the man, and what they done it for.

We rummaged the clothes we'd got, and found eight dollars in silver sewed up in the lining of an old blanket overcoat. Jim said he reckoned the people in that house stole the coat, because if they'd 'a 'knowed the money was there they wouldn't 'a 'left it. I said I reckoned they killed him, too; but Jim didn't want to talk about that. I says:

"Now you think it's bad luck; but what did you say when I fetched in the snake-skin that I found on the top of the ridge day before yesterday? You said it was the worst bad luck in the world to touch a snakeskin with my hands. Well, here's your bad luck! We've raked in all this truck and eight dollars besides. I wish we could have some bad luck like this every day, Jim."

"Never you mind, honey, never you mind. Don't you git too peart. It's a-comin'. Mind I tell you, it's a-comin'."

It did come, too. It was a Tuesday that we had that talk. Well, after dinner Friday we was laying around in the grass at the upper end of the ridge, and got out of tobacco. I went to the cavern to get some, and found a rattlesnake in there. I killed him, and curled him up on the foot of Jim's blanket, ever so natural, thinking there'd be some fun when Jim found him there. Well, by night I forgot all about the snake, and when Jim flung himself down on the blanket while I struck a light the snake's mate was there, and bit him.

He jumped up yelling, and the first thing the light showed was the varmint curled up and ready for another spring. I laid him out in a second with a stick, and Jim grabbed pap's whisky-jug and begun to pour it down.

He was barefooted, and the snake bit him right on the heel. That all comes of my being such a fool as to not remember that wherever you leave a dead snake its mate always comes there and curls around it. Jim told me to chop off the snake's head and throw it away, and then skin the body and roast a piece of it. I done it, and he eat it and said it would help cure him. He made me take off the rattles and tie them around his wrist, too. He said that that would help. Then I slid out quiet and throwed the snakes clear away amongst the bushes; for I warn't going to let Jim find out it was all my fault, not if I could help it.

Jim sucked and sucked at the jug, and now and then he got out of his head and pitched around and yelled; but every time he come to himself he went to sucking at the jug again. His foot swelled up pretty big, and so did his leg; but by and by the drunk begun to come, and so I judged he was all right; but I'd druther been bit with a snake than pap's whisky.

Jim was laid up for four days and nights. Then the swelling was all gone and he was around again. I made up my mind I wouldn't ever take a-holt of a snake-skin again with my hands, now that I see what had come of it. Jim said he reckoned I would believe him next time. And he said that handling a snake-skin was such awful bad luck that maybe we hadn't got to the end of it yet. He said he druther see the new moon over his left shoulder as much as a thousand times than take up a snake-skin in his hand. Well, I was getting to feel that way myself, though I've always reckoned that looking at the new moon over your left shoulder is one of the carelessest and foolishest things a body can do. Old Hank Bunker done it once, and bragged about it; and in less than two years he got drunk and fell off of the shot-tower, and spread himself out so that he was just a kind of a layer, as you may say; and they slid him edgeways between two barn doors for a coffin, and buried him so, so they say, but I didn't see it. Pap told me. But anyway it all come of looking at the moon that way, like a fool.

The Rattlesnake

by WILLIAM GILMORE SIMMS

[The heroine, Bess Matthews, in the wood waits the coming of her lover.]

"HE IS NOT COME," SHE MURMURED, HALF DISAP-pointed as the old grove of oaks with all its religious solemnity of shadow lay before her. She took her seat at the foot of a tree, the growth of a century, whose thick and knotted roots, started from their sheltering earth, shot even above the long grass around them, and ran in irregular sweeps for a considerable distance upon the surface. Here she sat not long, for her mind grew impatient and confused with the various thoughts crowding upon it—sweet thoughts it may be, for she thought of him whom she loved,—of him almost only; and of the long hours of happy enjoyment which the future had in store. Then came the fears, following fast upon the hopes, as the shadows follow the sunlight. The doubts of existence—the brevity and the fluctuations of life; these are the contemplations even of happy love, and these beset and saddened her; till, starting up in that dreamy confusion which the scene not less than the subject of her musings had inspired, she glided among the old trees scarce conscious of her movement.

"He does not come—he does not come," she murmured, as she stood contemplating the thick copse spreading before her, and forming the barrier which terminated the beautiful range of oaks which constituted the grove. How beautiful was the green and garniture of that little copse of wood. The leaves were thick, and the grass around lay folded over and over in bunches, with here and there a wild flower, gleaming from its green, and making of it a beautiful carpet of the richest and most various texture. A small tree rose from the centre of a clump around which a wild grape gadded luxuriantly; and, with an incoherent sense of what she saw, she lingered before the little cluster, seeming to survey that which, though it seemed to fix her eye, yet failed to fill her thought. Her mind wandered—her soul was far away; and the objects in her vision were far other than those which occupied her imagination. Things grew indistinct beneath her eye. The eye rather slept than saw. The musing spirit had given holiday to the ordinary senses, and took no heed of the forms that rose, and floated, or glided away, before them. In this way, the leaf detached made no impression upon the sight that was yet bent upon it; she saw not the bird, though it whirled, untroubled by a fear, in wanton circles around her head—and the black snake, with the rapidity of an arrow, darted over her path without arousing a single terror in the form that otherwise would have shivered at its mere appearance. And yet, though thus indistinct were all things around her to the musing eye of the maiden, her eye was yet singularly fixed—fastened as it were, to a single spot—gathered and controlled by a single object, and glazed, apparently, beneath a curious fascination. Before the maiden rose a little clump of bushes,—bright tangled leaves flaunting wide in glossiest green, with vines trailing over them, thickly decked with blue and crimson flowers. Her eye communed vacantly with these; fastened by a star-like shining glance— a subtle ray, that shot out from the circle of green leaves—seeming to be their very eye—and sending out a lurid lustre that seemed to stream across the space between, and find its way into her own eyes. Very piercing and beautiful was that subtle brightness, of the sweetest, strangest power. And now the leaves quivered and seemed to float away, only to return, and the vines waved and swung around in fantastic mazes, unfolding ever-changing varieties of form and color to her gaze; but the star-like eye was ever steadfast, bright and gorgeous gleaming in their midst, and still fastened, with strange fondness, upon her own. How beautiful, with wondrous intensity, did it gleam, and dilate, growing larger and more lustrous with every ray which it sent forth. And her own glance became intense, fixed also; but with a dreaming sense that conjured up the wildest fancies, terribly beautiful, that took her soul away from her, and wrapt it about as with a spell. She would have fled, she would have flown; but she had not power to move. The will was wanting to her flight. She felt that she could have bent forward to pluck the gem-like thing from the bosom of the leaf in which it seemed to grow, and which it irradiated with its bright white gleam; but ever as she aimed to stretch forth her hand, and bend forward, she heard a rush of wings, and a shrill scream from the tree above her—such a scream as the mock-bird makes, when, angrily, it raises its dusky crest, and flaps its wings furiously against its slender sides. Such a scream seemed like a warning, and though yet unawakened to full consciousness, it startled her and forbade her effort. More than once in her survey of this strange object, had she heard that shrill note, and still had it carried to her ear the same note of warning, and to her mind the same vague consciousness of an evil presence. But the star-like eye was yet upon her own—a small, bright eye, quick like that of a bird, now steady in its place, and observant seemingly only of hers, now darting forward with all the clustering leaves about it, and shooting up towards her, as if wooing her to seize. At another moment, riveted to the vine which lay around it, it would whirl round and round, dazzlingly bright and beautiful, even as a torch, waving hurriedly by night in the hands of some playful boy;—but, in all this time, the glance was never taken from her own—there it grew, fixed—a very principle of light—and such a light—a subtle, burning, piercing, fascinating gleam, such as gathers in vapor above the old grave, and binds us as we look—shooting, darting directly into her eye, dazzling her gaze, defeating its sense of discrimination, and confusing strangely that of perception. She felt dizzy, for, as she looked, a cloud of colors, bright, gay, various colors, floated and hung like so much drapery around the single object that had so secured her attention and spell-bound her feet. Her limbs felt momently more and more insecure—her blood grew cold, and she seemed to feel the gradual freeze of vein by vein, throughout her person. At that moment a rustling was heard in the branches of the tree beside her, and the bird, which had repeatedly uttered a single cry above her, as it were of warning, flew away from his station with a scream more piercing than ever. This movement had the effect, for which it really seemed intended, of bringing back to her a portion of the consciousness she seemed so totally to have been deprived of before. She strove to move from before the beautiful but terrible presence, but for a while she strove in vain. The rich, star-like glance still riveted her own, and the subtle fascination kept her bound. The mental energies, however, with the moment of their greatest trial, now gathered suddenly to her aid; and, with a desperate effort, but with a feeling still of most annoying uncertainty and dread, she succeeded partially in the attempt, and threw her arms backwards, her hands grasping the neighboring tree, feeble, tottering, and depending upon it for that support which her own limbs almost entirely denied her. With her movement, however, came the full development of the powerful spell and dreadful mystery before her. As her feet receded, though but a single pace, to the tree against which she now rested, the audibly articulated ring, like that of a watch when wound up with the verge broken, announced the nature of that splendid yet dangerous presence, in the form of the monstrous rattlesnake, now but a few feet before her, lying coiled at the bottom of a beautiful shrub, with which, to her dreaming eye, many of its own glorious hues had become associated. She was, at length, conscious enough to perceive and to feel all her danger; but terror had denied her the strength necessary to fly from her dreadful enemy. There still the eye glared beautifully bright and piercing upon her own; and, seemingly in a spirit of sport, the insidious reptile slowly unwound himself from his coil, but only to gather himself up again into his muscular rings, his great flat head rising in the midst, and slowly nodding, as it were, towards her, the eye still peering deeply into her own;—the rattle still slightly ringing at intervals, and giving forth that paralysing sound, which, once heard, is remembered for ever. The reptile all this while appeared to be conscious of, and to sport with, while seeking to excite her terrors. Now, with his flat head, distended mouth, and curving neck, would it dart forward its long form towards her,—its fatal teeth, unfolding on either side of its upper jaws, seeming to threaten her with instantaneous death, whilst its powerful eye shot forth glances of that fatal power of fascination, malignantly bright, which, by paralysing, with a novel form of terror and of beauty, may readily account for the spell it possesses of binding the feet of the timid, and denying to fear even the privilege of flight. Could she have fled! She felt the necessity; but the power of her limbs was gone! And there still it lay, coiling and uncoiling, its arching neck glittering like a ring of brazed copper, bright and lurid; and the dreadful beauty of its eye still fastened, eagerly contemplating the victim, while the pendulous rattle still rang the death note, as if to prepare the conscious mind for the fate which is momently approaching to the blow. Meanwhile the stillness became death-like with all surrounding objects. The bird had gone with its scream and rush. The breeze was silent. The vines ceased to wave. The leaves faintly quivered on their stems. The serpent once more lay still; but the eye was never once turned away from the victim. Its corded muscles are all in coil. They have but to unclasp suddenly, and the dreadful folds will be upon her, its full length, and the fatal teeth will strike, and the deadly venom which they secrete will mingle with the life-blood in her veins.

The terrified damsel, her full consciousness restored, but not her strength, feels all the danger. She sees that the sport of the terrible reptile is at an end. She cannot now mistake the horrid expression of its eye. She strives to scream, but the voice dies away, a feeble gurgling in her throat. Her tongue is paralysed; her lips are sealed—once more she strives for flight, but her limbs refuse their office. She has nothing left of life but its fearful consciousness. It is in her despair, that, a last effort, she succeeds to scream, a single wild cry, forced from her by the accumulated agony; she sinks down upon the grass before her enemy—her eyes, however, still open, and still looking upon those which he directs for ever upon them. She sees him approach—now advancing, now receding—now swelling in every part with something of anger, while his neck is arched beautifully like that of a wild horse under the curb; until, at length, tired as it were of play, like the cat with its victim, she sees the neck growing larger and becoming completely bronzed as about to strike—the huge jaws unclosing almost directly above her, the long tabulated fang charged with venom, protruding from the cavernous mouth—and she sees no more. Insensibility came to her aid, and she lay almost lifeless under the very folds of the monster.

In that moment the copse parted—and an arrow, piercing the monster through and through the neck, bore his head forward to the ground, alongside the maiden, while his spiral extremities, now unfolding in his own agony, were actually, in part, writhing upon her person. The arrow came from the fugitive Occonestoga, who had fortunately reached the spot in season, on his way to the Block House. He rushed from the copse as the snake fell, and, with a stick, fearlessly approached him where he lay tossing in agony upon the grass. Seeing him advance the courageous reptile made an effort to regain his coil, shaking the fearful rattle violently at every evolution which he took for that purpose; but the arrow, completely passing through his neck, opposed an unyielding obstacle to the endeavor; and finding it hopeless, and seeing the new enemy about to assault him, with something of the spirit of the white man under like circumstances, he turned desperately round, and striking his charged fangs, so that they were riveted in the wound they made, into a susceptible part of his own body, he threw himself over with a single convulsion, and, a moment after, lay dead beside the utterly unconscious maiden.

PERSONAL ADVENTURES

The Ancient Enmity

by MARJORIE KINNAN RAWLINGS

"AND THE LORD GOD SAID UNTO THE SERPENT, BECAUSE thou hast done this, thou art cursed above all cattle, and above every beast of the field; upon thy belly shalt thou go, and dust shalt thou eat all the days of thy life:

"And I will put enmity between thee and the woman, and between thy seed and her seed; it shall bruise thy head, and thou shalt bruise his heel."

GENESIS 3:14–15

Fear of the serpent is inherent in most animals. A placid mare has bolted under me like any wild filly at sight of a coiled moccasin by the road. I have seen my cat jump with arched back like a witch's cat, at the unexpected movement of a garter snake. All hunters have seen their bird dogs tumble backward to avoid a snake. If avoidance is impossible, the dog comes to an unforgettable point, obviously not on birds, a point that is one long tense quiver of distress.

I believe that, contrary to Biblical implications, fear of snakes is not inherent in human beings, but is planted at an age so early that memory draws no line for its beginnings. Fear is the most easily taught of all lessons, and the fight against terror, real or imagined, is perhaps the history of man's mind. The average man or woman says, and believes it, "I have an instinctive horror of snakes." Yet babies and small children, who might be instinctively terrified at sight of a large animal such as a cow or dog, show no fear of snakes, but reach out their hands to them, and have even been known to handle venomous snakes without harm.

I came to Cross Creek with such a phobia against snakes that a picture of one in the dictionary gave me what Martha calls "the all-overs." I had the common misconception that in Florida they were omnipresent. I thought, "If anything defeats me, sends me back to urban civilization, it will be the snakes." They were not ubiquitous as I expected, but I saw one often enough to keep my anxiety alive. A black snake actually ran at me, and a chicken snake thrust his face into mine from a pantry shelf. These were harmless, I knew, but none the less revolting. I took my first faltering steps of progress through sheer shame. In a section where the country women possess great physical fearlessness, I felt feeble-minded

245

to find myself screaming at sight of a king snake that asked nothing more than a chance to destroy the rats that infested the old barn. I forced myself to stand still when I saw a snake in the weeds of the neglected house yard, at least long enough to determine its non-venomous nature. The only poisonous reptiles in Florida, I knew, were the rattlesnake and the cotton-mouth moccasin, which I had already seen with horror, and the coral snake, which I did not know.

My determination to use common sense might have been my undoing. One late winter day in my first year I discovered under the palm tree by the gate a small pile of Amaryllis bulbs. The yard was desperate for flowers and greenery and I began separating the bulbs to set out for spring blooming. I dug with my fingers under the pile and brought out in my hand not a snake, surely, but a ten-inch long piece of Chinese lacquer. The slim and inert reptile was an exquisite series of shining bands of yellow and black and vermilion, with a tiny black nose. I thought, "Here is a snake, in my hands, and it is as beautiful as a necklace. This is the moment in which to forget all nonsense." I let it slide back and forth through my fingers. Its texture was like satin. I played with it a long time, then killed it reluctantly with a stick, not for fear or hate, but because I decided to cure the skin for an ornament on the handle of a riding crop. I salted the hide and tacked it to a sunny wall. I showed it proudly to my friend Ed Hopkins, who was teaching me the Florida flora and fauna.

He said, "God takes care of fools and children."

The snake was the deadly coral snake. Its venom is of the cobra type, killing within a few minutes by a paralyzing of the nerves. The old terror was back again, and it seemed to me that I should never now be able to pass beyond it. I had no fear of death as death, but the medium was another matter, and one is certainly entitled to one's prejudices in so personal a matter. I found that I had still the blind, unthinking, "instinctive" horror of coming on a poisonous serpent. Nothing could warm the frozen column that replaced my spine at the thought of finding myself face to face with a Florida diamond-back rattler. In a varied life I had discarded one physical fear after another, finding them harmless when confronted. I said, "I am only afraid of the intangibles." Yet even such intangibles as poverty and loneliness might be, simply, accepted, and so disarmed. I discovered that for me rattlesnakes represented the last outpost of physical fear.

I discovered this when Ross Allen, a young Florida herpetologist, invited me to join him on a hunt in the upper Everglades—for rattlesnakes. At the moment I was passing through one of those periods of emotional distress that all of us experience, when some personal catastrophe has tumbled our house of cards about our ears. My small world had crumbled. I should have said offhand that there was nothing left to frighten me. Instantly I realized that I was numb all over at the thought of going out of my way to encounter rattlesnakes.

I am something of a fatalist, in that I believe in a fatalism that stems from one's own adjustment, or lack of it, to circumstance. The Chinese call this "luck character," and it is the same thing. This rather out of the way invitation had been laid on my doorstep like an unwanted foundling. There was no better time to see the thing through; to go down in defeat and hysteria before my fear; or, by facing it, to rip away the veil of panic that stood, perhaps, between me and the facts. I got out of bed, where my mental agony was causing physical symptoms, and packed my bag.

Ross and I drove to Arcadia in his coupé on a warm January day.

I said, "How will you bring back the rattlesnakes?"

"In the back of my car."

My courage was not adequate to inquire whether they were thrown in loose and might be expected to appear between our feet. Actually, a large portable box of heavy close-meshed wire made a safe cage. Ross wanted me to write an article about his work and on our way to the unhappy hunting grounds I took notes on a mass of data that he had accumulated in years of herpetological research. The scientific and dispassionate detachment of the material and the man made a desirable approach to rattlesnake territory. As I had discovered with the insects and varmints, it is difficult to be afraid of anything about which enough is known, and Ross' facts were fresh from the laboratory.

The hunting ground was Big Prairie, south of Arcadia and west of the northern tip of Lake Okeechobee. Big Prairie is a desolate cattle country, half marsh, half pasture, with islands of palm trees and cypress and oaks. At that time of year the cattlemen and Indians were burning the country, on the theory that the young fresh wire grass that springs up from the roots after a fire is the best cattle forage. Ross planned to hunt his rattlers in the forefront of the fires. They lived in winter, he said, in gopher holes, coming out in the midday warmth to forage, and would move ahead of the flames and be easily taken. We joined forces with a big Cracker named Will, his snake-hunting companion of the territory, and set out in early morning, after a long rough drive over deep-rutted roads into the open wilds.

I hope never in my life to be so frightened as I was in those first few hours. I kept on Ross' footsteps, I moved when he moved, sometimes jolting into him when I thought he might leave me behind. He does not use the forked stick of conventional snake hunting, but a steel prong, shaped like an L, at the end of a long stout stick. He hunted casually, calling my attention to the varying vegetation, to hawks overhead, to a pair of the rare whooping cranes that flapped over us. In mid-morning he stopped short, dropped his stick, and brought up a five-foot rattlesnake draped limply over the steel L. It seemed to me that I should drop in my tracks.

"They're not active at this season," he said quietly. "A snake takes on the temperature of its surroundings. They can't stand too much heat for that reason, and when the weather is cool, as now, they're sluggish."

The sun was bright overhead, the sky a translucent blue, and it seemed to me that it was warm enough for any snake to do as it willed. The sweat poured down my back. Ross dropped the rattler in a crocus sack and Will carried it. By noon, he had caught four. I felt faint and ill. We stopped by a pond and went swimming. The region was flat, the horizon limitless, and as I came out of the cool blue water I expected to find myself surrounded by a ring of rattlers. There were only Ross and Will, opening the lunch basket. I could not eat. Ross never touches liquor and it seemed to me that I would give my hope of salvation for a dram of whiskey. Will went back and drove his truck closer, for Ross expected the hunting to be better in the afternoon. The hunting was much better. When we went back to the truck to deposit two more rattlers in the wire cage, there was a rattlesnake lying under the truck.

Ross said, "Whenever I leave my car or truck with snakes already in it, other rattlers always appear. I don't know whether this is because they scent or sense the presence of other snakes, or whether in this arid area they come to the car for shade in the heat of the day."

The problem was scientific, but I had no interest.

That night Ross and Will and I camped out in the vast spaces of the Everglades prairies. We got water from an abandoned well and cooked supper under buttonwood bushes by a flowing stream. The camp fire blazed cheerfully under the stars and a new moon lifted in the sky. Will told tall tales of the cattlemen and the Indians and we were at peace.

Ross said, "We couldn't have a better night for catching water snakes."

After the rattlers, water snakes seemed innocuous enough. We worked along the edge of the stream and here Ross did not use his L-shaped steel. He reached under rocks and along the edge of the water and brought out harmless reptiles with his hands. I had said nothing to him of my fears, but he understood them. He brought a small dark snake from under a willow root.

"Wouldn't you like to hold it?" he asked. "People think snakes are cold and clammy, but they aren't. Take it in your hands. You'll see that it is warm."

Again, because I was ashamed, I took the snake in my hands. It was not cold, it was not clammy, and it lay trustingly in my hands, a thing that lived and breathed and had mortality like the rest of us. I felt an upsurgence of spirit.

The next day was magnificent. The air was crystal, the sky was aquamarine, and the far horizon of palms and oaks lay against the sky. I felt a new boldness and followed Ross bravely. He was making the rounds of the gopher holes. The rattlers came out in the mid-morning warmth and were never far away. He could tell by their trails whether one had come out or was still in the hole. Sometimes the two men dug the snake out. At times it was down so long and winding a tunnel that the digging was hopeless. Then they blocked the entrance and went on to other holes. In an hour or so they made the original rounds, unblocking the holes. The rattler in every case came out hurriedly, as though anything were preferable to being shut in. All the time Ross talked to me, telling me the scientific facts he had discovered about the habits of the rattlers.

"They pay no attention to a man standing perfectly still," he said, and proved it by letting Will unblock a hole while he stood at the entrance as the snake came out. It was exciting to watch the snake crawl slowly beside and past the man's legs. When it was at a safe distance he walked within its range of vision, which he had proved to be no higher than a man's knee, and the snake whirled and drew back in an attitude of fighting defense. The rattler strikes only for paralyzing and killing its food, and for defense.

"It is a slow and heavy snake," Ross said. "It lies in wait on a small game trail and strikes the rat or rabbit passing by. It waits a few minutes, then follows along the trail, coming to the small animal, now dead or dying. It noses it from all sides, making sure that it is its own kill, and that it is dead and ready for swallowing."

A rattler will lie quietly without revealing himself if a man passes by and it thinks it is not seen. It slips away without fighting if given the chance. Only Ross' sharp eyes sometimes picked out the gray and yellow diamond pattern, camouflaged among the grasses. In the cool of the morning, chilled by the January air, the snakes showed no fight. They could be looped up limply over the steel L and dropped in a sack or up into the wire cage on the back of Will's truck. As the sun mounted in the sky and warmed the moist Everglades earth, the snakes were warmed too, and Ross warned that it was time to go more cautiously. Yet having learned that it was we who were the aggressors; that immobility meant complete safety; that the snakes, for all their lightning flash in striking, were inaccurate in their aim, with limited vision; having watched again and again the liquid grace of movement, the beauty of pattern, suddenly I understood that I was drinking in freely the magnificent sweep of the horizon, with no fear of what might be at the moment under my feet. I went off hunting by myself, and though I found no snakes, I should have known what to do.

The sun was dropping low in the west. Masses of white cloud hung above the flat marshy plain and seemed to be tangled in the tops of distant palms and cypresses. The sky turned orange, then saffron. I walked leisurely back toward the truck. In the distance I could see Ross and Will making their way in too. The season was more advanced than at the Creek, two hundred miles to the north, and I noticed that spring flowers were blooming among the lumpy hummocks. I leaned over to pick a white violet. There was a rattlesnake under the violet.

If this had happened the week before, if it had happened the day before, I think I should have lain down and died on top of the rattlesnake, with no need of being struck and poisoned. The snake did not coil, but lifted its head and whirred its rattles lightly. I stepped back slowly and put the violet in a buttonhole. I reached forward and laid the steel L across the snake's neck, just back of the blunt head. I called to Ross:

"I've got one."

He strolled toward me.

"Well, pick it up," he said.

I released it and slipped the L under the middle of the thick body.

"Go put it in the box."

He went ahead of me and lifted the top of the wire cage. I made the truck with the rattler, but when I reached up the six feet to drop it in the cage, it slipped off the stick and dropped on Ross' feet. It made no effort to strike.

"Pick it up again," he said. "If you'll pin it down lightly and reach just back of its head with your hand, as you've seen me do, you can drop it in more easily."

I pinned it and leaned over.

"I'm awfully sorry," I said, "but you're pushing me a little too fast."

He grinned. I lifted it on the stick and again as I had it at head height, it slipped off, down Ross' boots and on top of his feet. He stood as still as a stump. I dropped the snake on his feet for the third time. It seemed to me that the most patient of rattlers might in time resent being hauled up and down, and for all the man's quiet certainty that in standing motionless there was no danger, would strike at whatever was nearest, and that would be Ross.

I said, "I'm just not man enough to keep this up any longer," and he laughed and reached down with his smooth quickness and lifted the snake back of the head and dropped it in the cage. It slid in among its mates and settled in a corner. The hunt was over and we drove back over the uneven trail to Will's village and left him and went on to Arcadia and home. Our catch for the two days was thirty-two rattlers.

I said to Ross, "I believe that tomorrow I could have picked up that snake."

Back at the Creek, I felt a new lightness. I had done battle with a great fear, and the victory was mine.

It would be impossible for me ever to feel affection for a snake. One may be ever so interested and tolerant, but prefer work dogs to lap dogs, dogs to cats, cats to horses, and almost any living thing at all, to snakes. But with the conquering of the horror, it has been possible to watch the comings and goings of various reptiles with conjectures as to their habits and to consider them as personalities.

A king snake lived for several years in a hole beside the front gate. When the first strong sun of spring, in February or early March, struck into the ground, he appeared, a majestic fellow, fresh shed, in yellow and black. His favorite place was coiled on top of the first post to the right of the gate. This was probably a good vantage point over the passing of rats and mice, frogs and smaller snakes. He seemed to enjoy being within sight of human activity and lifted his slim bright-eyed head with interest when any one went in or out of the gate. He was very ornamental and when he did not appear on his post I felt a certain anxiety about him. I had sweet-peas planted on the fence one year and often worked and weeded among them as he watched me a few feet away. Sometimes he slid gracefully into his hole, leaving a careless half-foot of tail hanging out, as though hostage to his friendly confidence. He was itchy one season at shedding time and nothing pleased him more than to have fingers stroke his back. He lay quietly, rippling his muscles as one does under the touch of a masseur. He had some sort of rapprochement with my cat, for I often saw Jib pat the exposed tail playfully but gently. The king snake withdrew it without hurry and Jib followed with an unmolesting claw-sheathed paw. Perhaps they divided their extra rats.

Jib's relation with black snakes did not seem so friendly. The one who lived under the kitchen came out one morning with a broken tail, tell-tale slashes at its tip. The innocuous black snake is both brave and impudent. I walked close to a slim ebony beauty with its smooth narrow head high above the grass. My purpose was only to admire at close range but he resented my attention. He made a running attack at me. Quite naturally, I jumped out of his way. It reminded me of the utterly ignominious evening when a skunk chased me down the road for several hundred yards. Discretion in both cases seemed the better part of valor. The black snake turned and ran at me again. He switched himself arrogantly as long as I stood near. When I went away, he retired in the opposite direction, probably well pleased with himself as a ferocious and awe-inspiring fellow. The fastest living thing I have ever seen was a black snake crossing a bed of hot ashes with a mouse in his mouth. We use the expression here, "Fast as a black snake," and I can amend it to, "Fast as a black snake with his belly burning."

I have been obliged to wage unceasing war on the chicken or oak snakes. If I left them to themselves, we should never raise a biddy or a young Mallard duck. The snakes ignore nests of new-laid eggs through the winter. When nesting time comes and the peanut hay in the loft of the barn is full of the game hens setting, and the Mallards begin to set under the Turk's-cap bushes and along the fence row, the chicken snakes appear from nowhere. Usually they wait for their feast until the night the hatching begins and swallow the wet chicks and ducklings as they pip their shells and emerge, for an instant, into the unfriendly world. It is heart-breaking to leave one of the Mallard mothers hovering her new brood contentedly one night, and in the morning to find her childless, fluttering and crying in her distress, the trail of a chicken snake leading away from the nest. Little Will and I watch with constant vigilance at these times and at the first squawk of a hen, the first almost human cry of a female Mallard, one or the other of us dashes to the nest. I once shot a very large chicken snake who came to a nest in one corner of the duck pen while the mother was out getting a bit of green for herself. He had a duck egg in his mouth and rolled his yellow eyes at me as he distended his jaws to swallow it. I did not want to shoot and destroy the other eggs and poked him with the gun barrel to force him to a place more convenient for my purposes. He merely wrapped his tail around the mesh of the wire pen, for purchase, gulped down his egg and opened his jaws over another. This was too insulting and I gave him one shot in the tail. He withdrew then, the egg still in his mouth. It was halfway down before I managed to destroy him.

I have never actually seen a rattlesnake on my land, though the east hammock is a crossing place for them. I see them sometimes on the road at the edge of my place, always moving too rapidly for me to get hold of a hoe or a shotgun. One was killed at the corner where my house grove joins that of Old Boss, and the hoe-hands in summer, or Snow and Little Will on the tractor, come across half a dozen or so in the grove in season. I admire the great beauty of the diamond-back rattler and feel that as snakes go, he is very much of a gentleman.

The cottonmouth moccasins make free of the house yard and I have killed several large ones a few feet from the house. My friend Ross feels that I fail him in not taking them alive for him. I have a guilty moment, thinking of the wasted venom that he would milk from them for scientific and medical purposes, but I am forced to prefer the death of a poisonous snake in my yard to not knowing at what moment it will strike the dog, the cat, one of the Creek children coming for milk, or appear under my own feet in the darkness. I have no particular fear of the cottonmouth, for he is sluggish and easily killed, but he is revolting in appearance. He is darkly nondescript in color, he is fat and greasy. He slithers. When I look at him I think of Martha's shuddering summing up of the reasons for her dislike of all snakes, "Ain't got no footses an' kin slide so!"

I think the motion of all snakes, if watched and studied long enough, would move any lover of rhythm. I can understand why a cobra sways to music. The way of the serpent is the way of music. I have sat on the veranda watching the movement of a green tree snake rippling in and out among the orange boughs; watching a black snake flow like water in a dream among the leaves of a poinsettia, or lie like a Japanese brush stroke along a spider-lily leaf, and felt that I watched the poetry of motion. Ruth St. Denis caught this serpentine grace in some of her Oriental dances. I should like to have seen her use, as the Hopi Indians use the rattlesnake, the coral snake, in all its jewelled enamel—properly de-fanged, of course, as a scientist has recently discovered the Hopi rattlers to be.

I shall always feel an interest in snakes, after my exposure to Ross' wisdom and knowledge, but it will never extend to making one welcome in the house. I was obliged to deal unconventionally a few nights ago with a small cottonmouth in the guest bathroom. The screen door leading on one side to the porch had been left ajar and he had wandered in, attracted perhaps by the light burning there. If the light had not been on, I should have stepped on him in the dark on my way to my own quarters, for he was directly in my path. He was small and young but he was belligerent and quite as venomous as though he had been six feet long. My first thought was of my .22 rifle or my shotgun on the back porch, but I knew that if I left the visitor he would slip away, and I could think of many places where he might reappear that would be less convenient than his present one. Too, it seemed absurd to fill the bathroom floor full of holes. The Negroes would be sound asleep in the tenant house and could not hear me call. It seemed to me also that I should feel very foolish having Little Will come from his bed, hoe in hand, to face so small a creature. I looked around the room behind me. On the chest of drawers were two books. One was the Sears Roebuck catalogue, a hefty volume. I heaved it at the moccasin. It hurt him enough so that he went into convulsive coils instead of slipping under the bathtub and I knew I could approach closer. The other book was a copy of one of my own writings, *The Yearling.* I took it and finished off the moccasin. I told Little Will next morning of the encounter, and the method by which I had dispatched the intruder. He chuckled.

"It sho' do come in handy to write books," he said.

A Black Snake Attacks a Catbird's Nest

by JOHN BURROUGHS

I HARDLY KNOW WHETHER I AM MORE PLEASED OR AN-noyed with the catbird. Perhaps she is a little too common, and her part in the general chorus a little too conspicuous. If you are listening for the note of another bird, she is sure to be prompted to the most loud and protracted singing, drowning all other sounds; if you sit quietly down to observe a favorite or study a new-comer, her curiosity knows no bounds, and you are scanned and ridiculed from every point of observation. Yet I would not miss her; I would only subordinate her a little, make her less conspicuous.

She is the parodist of the woods, and there is ever a mischievous, bantering, half-ironical undertone in her lay, as if she were conscious of mimicking and disconcerting some envied songster. Ambitious of song, practicing and rehearsing in private, she yet seems the least sincere and genuine of the sylvan minstrels, as if she had taken up music only to be in the fashion, or not to be outdone by the robins and thrushes. In other words, she seems to sing from some outward motive, and not from inward joyousness. She is a good versifier, but not a great poet. Vigorous, rapid, copious, not without fine touches, but destitute of any high, serene melody, her performance, like that of Thoreau's squirrel, always implies a spectator.

There is a certain air and polish about her strain, however, like that in the vivacious conversation of a well-bred lady of the world, that commands respect. Her maternal instinct, also, is very strong, and that simple structure of dead twigs and dry grass is the centre of much anxious solicitude. Not long since, while strolling through the woods, my attention was attracted to a small densely grown swamp, hedged in with eglantine, brambles, and the everlasting smilax, from which proceeded loud cries of distress and alarm, indicating that some terrible calamity was threatening my sombre-colored minstrel. On effecting an entrance, which, however, was not accomplished till I had doffed coat and hat, so as to diminish the surface exposed to the thorns and brambles, and, looking around me from a square yard of terra firma, I found myself the spectator of a loathsome yet fascinating scene. Three or four yards from me was the nest, beneath which, in long festoons, rested a huge black snake; a bird two thirds grown was slowly disappearing between his expanded jaws. As he seemed unconscious of my presence, I quietly observed the proceedings. By slow degrees he compassed the bird about with his elastic mouth; his head flattened, his neck writhed and swelled, and two or three undulatory movements of his glistening body finished the work. Then he cautiously raised himself up, his tongue flaming from his mouth the while, curved over the nest, and, with wavy, subtle motions, explored the interior. I can conceive of nothing more overpoweringly terrible to an unsuspecting family of birds than the sudden appearance above their domicile of the head and neck of this arch-enemy. It is enough to petrify the blood in their veins. Not finding the object of his search, he came streaming down from the nest to a lower limb, and commenced extending his researches in other directions, sliding stealthily through the branches, bent on capturing one of the parent birds. That a legless, wingless creature should move with such ease and rapidity where only birds and squirrels are considered at home, lifting himself up, letting himself down, running out on the yielding boughs, and traversing with marvelous celerity the whole length and breadth of the thicket, was truly surprising. One thinks of the great myth of the Tempter and the "cause of all our woe," and wonders if the Arch One is not now playing off some of his pranks before him. Whether we call it snake or devil matters little. I could but admire his terrible beauty, however; his black, shining folds, his easy, gliding movement, head erect, eyes glistening, tongue playing like subtle flame, and the invisible means of his almost winged locomotion.

The parent birds, in the mean while, kept up the most agonizing cry, —at times fluttering furiously about the pursuer, and actually laying hold of his tail with their beaks and claws. On being thus attacked, the snake would suddenly double upon himself and follow his own body back, thus executing a strategic movement that at first seemed almost to paralyze his victim and place her within his grasp. Not quite, however. Before his jaws could close upon the coveted prize the bird would tear herself away, and, apparently faint and sobbing, retire to a higher branch. His reputed powers of fascination availed him little, though it is possible that a frailer and less combative bird might have been held by the fatal spell. Presently, as he came gliding down the slender body of a leaning alder, his attention was attracted by a slight movement of my arm; eying me an instant, with that crouching, utter, motionless gaze which I believe only snakes and devils can assume, he turned quickly,—a feat which necessitated something like crawling over his own body,—and glided off through the branches, evidently recognizing in me a representative of the ancient parties he once so cunningly ruined. A few moments after, as he lay carelessly disposed in the top of a rank alder, trying to look as much like a crooked branch as his supple, shining form would admit, the old vengeance overtook him. I exercised my prerogative, and a well-directed missile, in the shape of a stone, brought him looping and writhing to the ground. After I had completed his downfall and quiet had been partially restored, a half-fledged member of the bereaved household came out from his hiding-place, and, jumping upon a decayed branch, chirped vigorously, no doubt in celebration of the victory.

Every Stick a Snake

by E. TEMPLE-PERKINS

A FRIEND OF MINE IN ENGLAND, WHO WOULD HAVE GIVEN all he possessed to go to the wild places of the world, said to me one day, "There is one thing about Africa I should hate, though, and that is the constant danger of snakes."

I disillusioned him on that point. I explained that weeks might pass without any snakes being seen, and that in any case I seldom walked in the bush without at least two natives in front. The foremost followed or cut the track, and the second watched for game; their four eyes should be enough to spot any snakes ahead, leaving me free to look at the country without having to pick my way along.

But, of course, things do not always work to plan, and there are times when the orthodox methods are abandoned. On my very first encounter with the deadly cobra I was in front! In a dried-up marsh at midday I came upon a ten- to twelve-foot cobra, one of the worst snakes in Africa, lying curled up in the shade of a small bush about a dozen feet from where I halted. At the moment I saw the snake it saw me, and reared up in the grass—as I thought at the time, preparatory to attacking.

I half turned to the rear to get some form of defence from my servant, but he was too far behind to be of immediate assistance, and I dared not take my eyes off the snake. It continued to rear up, and then in a second or two it made its attack. It appeared to be coming straight at me, but through some extraordinary piece of luck it suddenly swerved and flashed off between me and my gun-bearer, who had just handed me a rifle.

Another time I met with a cobra when I was stalking some eland in grass about waist high. My tracker in front suddenly swerved to the right, and I did likewise but was unable to evade the thing altogether. The cobra, about eight to ten feet, reared up and looked frighteningly aggressive. I was so much on top of it that I made an instantaneous decision to jump, and as I went over my right foot touched its neck. It was fortunate my tracker had swerved to the right, as the snake had its home in an ant-hill to our left, and if we had intercepted it the brute would most certainly have got one of us.

The cobra is the best known and most feared of all African snakes—mainly because it is so often wrongly called the mamba, a snake that has the most sinister reputation in South Africa, although it is not nearly so aggressive here. The cobra (*Naja*) and mamba (*Dendroaspis*) are two different kinds of snake.

There are four species of cobra in Uganda, of which the big black-lipped *N. melanoleuca* is the commonest. Though relatively massive, the cobra is amazingly speedy and agile, and also apt to be inquisitive and aggressive. An angry or startled cobra will spread a hood two or three times the normal size of the head, and rear up from the ground on the least provocation. It remains poised and menacing, and the spilling of its venom can be seen as dribbling, almost frothy, at the jaws. It is an awe-inspiring sight. When it strikes it moves with lightning speed, and hangs on to its victim, worrying or chewing the bitten area and at the same time squirting a succession of discharges of poison. Its venom is particularly deadly.

The mamba has its fangs right forward under the nostrils. There are only two species of this snake in Uganda: the green (*D. jamesonii*) and the larger black (*D. augusticeps*). Even the experts sometimes say they are the same species, the green changing to black (or more accurately dark brown) when fully grown; but in my opinion this does not make sense, as they seem to be always in different habitats. The green mamba—which I have seen described as the "tree cobra"—grows to an astonishing length:

specimens up to fourteen feet have been known. It is seen mostly in bushes and low trees, where it lies in wait for birds, but it also comes to ground in search of small rodents. Its speed is fantastic. It moves through foliage and bushes literally like the wind, too fast to be seen, its passage betrayed only by a rustling of the leaves. Among some South African tribes its name means "shadow of death."

The python is sometimes even longer, but it is non-poisonous and the African species is generally disinclined to attack human beings. But it is said that when a python is defending itself from intrusion or molestation its blow can have the force of a sledge-hammer, and one authority had the alarming experience of a fourteen-feet specimen he was trying to capture striking at him on a level with his chest and throat. When intimidating, the python makes short lunges with open jaws, something like a dog baring its teeth. It lives mainly on small mammals like rats and on birds.

The Edward flats near Kichwamba are infested with snakes of many species. I have killed as many as seven in one day—and at other times I have gone for days without seeing one. As I emerged from a particularly nasty swamp one day in pursuit of elephant I came on a patch of pleasant green reeds, and, as I was enjoying the luxury of comparatively easy walking after struggling through a wide belt of date palms in deep black mud, I noticed a movement in the reeds, obviously not that of a quadruped. It turned out to be a large python. Taking a spear from one of my porters I took careful aim at the centre of the coil and was successful in pinning it to the ground. An equally well-directed hit on the reptile's head with a long heavy stick finished the operation.

The python had been more or less somnolent, no doubt because it had just swallowed an otter which was found still fresh and intact in its interior.

That evening, as the snake's skin and the otter were hanging on a sapling just outside my tent, the boys called to me to bring a rifle as there were two hyaenas after the meat. While I was engaged in close combat with one hyaena near the fire, the other went to the front of my tent and made off with the otter, which it proceeded to eat within hearing distance.

That otter, then, had the unusual distinction of being eaten twice in one day.

A much smaller and much more dangerous reptile than the python is the puff-adder. Its poison glands are possibly more rapidly fatal than those of any other viper, including the cobra. It looks evil and sluggish, but the latter part of its appearance is deceptive. It throws its head sideways and backward with an instantaneous movement, swifter than the eye can follow, to get its long fangs into striking position. I like Ditmar's description of puff-adders (in *The Snakes of the World*). "In appearance they are the personification of deadliness and as dangerous as they look. Their fangs are enormously developed, and they strike with a lightning-like flash, injecting their poison by a combination strike and bite, as do the pit vipers." Pitman, describing their eyes, says: "Their rather pallid gleaming golden or silvery colour combines with the slit-like pupils to produce the effect of a fixed malevolent stare, imparting the appearance of extraordinary deadliness."

Frightening as their appearance is, the greatest danger comes from not seeing them. They have a habit of lying amongst the dead leaves on a path, and are easy to miss. I tripped over one once while stalking elephants, but luckily I was able to whirl round and cut it in half with a spear. To my astonishment the front half went off at surprising speed and disappeared. That was especially surprising, for if I had hit it hard with a stick it would not have moved a foot. But I know of a man in Teso who found a black cobra in his room and cut it in half with a butcher's knife and deeply regretted it—the front half gained amazing speed and careered round the room for some minutes, presumably still able to eject its deadly venom.

I also had the experience of finding a large snake slithering round the room I was in. I was sitting writing in a rest camp, a thatched mud house, when I became aware of a rather strange noise on the floor. Then I discovered that a green snake about five feet long and an inch and a half thick was in the room trying to get out. It was going round the edges, over or under anything in the way and occasionally rearing up and looking for an exit. I dispatched it in due course when I had succeeded in making a boy outside realize my predicament and come to light with the necessary stout stick.

A bright moonlight night is an eerie time for meeting a snake. After dinner one night, about 9 P.M., I was strolling along a wide road, gravelled in the centre with a wide, smooth, native-worn track on each side of it. Smoking my pipe and enjoying the still, peaceful evening, my thoughts were far from the reptiles of this earth. There were some small trees on each side of the road, and the moon behind those on my right was casting thin shadows across my path. At one moment my eyes happened to catch sight of a single dark line across my way, about a foot in front of me. For a second I took it to be a shadow of a tree—and then in a flash I realized there was no tree, and I awoke to the fact that the "shadow" was shining black. It was a snake, and I was almost on it, and I was unarmed. It turned to look at me and my heart went to my shoes. While I cautiously prepared to take one of them off for defence, the reptile slid into the grass and my heart back to its proper place.

Snakes, it is said, are nocturnal in their habits—as a rule. There are exceptions.

I once used a track near a lake so often by day—and fairly often after dark—that it came as a rude shock one morning to hear the sudden scurry of a living thing in the grass to my left, only two or three feet from where I was walking. It was obviously the movement of a very large snake, probably a python or possibly a cobra; they were both prevalent in that region. It did not go far at once, for after I had retreated with some alacrity, and approached cautiously from the other direction with better light from the rising sun, I heard it again in the tangle of grass and leaves as it made its way farther into the darkness of the forest. I failed to get even a glimpse of it.

That same afternoon I thought I would stroll along the lake shore as far as possible to see if a certain croc had returned to its lie-up. As I was passing through the first patch of forest on the way I thought of snakes again. I had crossed a small trickle of water in a natural drain from a rise in the forest, and at once looked for the most unlikely sight of a water cobra; I had found what I thought was the slough of one some days before. I saw nothing, but as I made my way along a track by the lake shore, through a pretty stretch of forest thick with ferns and grassy undergrowth, I felt a little jumpy again. I picked up a branch blown down by the recent gale, and tried to make a walking-stick of it, but it was too brittle. I picked up another more likely stick, and to test it gave it a sharp bang against the trunk of a tree; it snapped with a noise like a Christmas cracker. "Oh, it doesn't matter," I told myself. "There won't be any snakes about at this time of the day. Nocturnal in their habits, aren't they? Might be lying in the sun, but not in a dark forest."

I went on, and as usual kept my eyes steadily on the track. At one place a large tree was leaning over the narrow path and obscured my view in front for a second, until I stooped to pass under its trunk. As I got clear I looked a little farther ahead than I had been doing, so as to get a general idea of the ground ahead. I could hardly believe I was awake. There, just ahead of me, only a few paces, was a shining object lying across the path glistening in the sun like a burnished piece of metal or piping. Only two feet of it were visible, as there were ferns and waist-high grass on each side of the track—but I did not want to see any more. For the second time in a few hours I experienced that shock to the system that strikes you so seldom—when you suddenly realize you are near to deadly peril. The thing across the track was a huge black cobra, one of the most venomous and aggressive snakes in the world, said to be the nearest rival to the ghastly king cobra of the east.

Nocturnal habits be damned, I thought. This one was anything but inactive at two o'clock in the afternoon. It seemed to be deliberately waiting for me. It might have been enjoying the sun or even the view, but I never thought of that then. It was lying ominously still and straight and, I thought, no doubt listening, having heard the snap of that stick I had broken on the tree.

My first thought was to procure another stick, and I remembered a large, supple piece of liana I had seen as I crossed the trickle a few yards back. Before I went I gazed for a second or two, horribly fascinated, at those two feet of shining body. For all I knew the snake could see me quite well through the cover above its head, but I could see only its smooth dorsal scales. Its body was about two inches in diameter, and possibly ten feet or even more in length.

I turned to go back—and at the same moment the cobra glided off to my left. I saw it again a few yards farther on, and then it disappeared down the overgrown bank of the lake shore among the exposed roots of large trees leaning out over the water. I found a suitable stick, and for some time made a cautious search in the vicinity, all the time feeling that the appalling reptile's departure had been deceptive and that it would approach me from behind as I was foolishly peering ahead. But it had gone for good. No doubt I had flattered myself in thinking it was interested in me.

I wondered afterwards what I would have done if I had had a stick when I first saw the thing. Would I have had the nerve to deal the requisite blow? An accurate hit with the full force of a heavy stick would probably have caused the brute to remain where it was, or at the most gain the water a few yards ahead of it; but anything like a mis-hit would have brought it into action without doubt. Before it moved I did not know which side of the track its head was, although I guessed it would be on my left as it was almost certainly making for the water; and any aggression on its part in that thick undergrowth would have put me at a perilous disadvantage. But I would have given a good deal to have had the satisfaction of adding that shining, gun-metal skin to my collection of trophies.

It is encounters of that sort that make you jumpy, although you may have been several weeks without sight or even thought of snakes. Suddenly the bush seems full of hidden dangers, and you keep your eyes on the track, stopping to peer at every branch in front and overhead, instinctively ducking low if any liana happens to sway festooned above like the waiting python. Then:

> Do you know what it is to shudder; do you know what it is to shake;
> When one thing after another makes every stick a snake?

Fortunately such moods do not last, or life in Africa would be unbearable. In many regions you hardly ever see a snake; and, after all, most of these reptiles can be put out of action with an ordinary stick. Life goes on normally even in the notoriously snake-infested parts. I was in one such area for a time, and during the rainy season—to be precise, two months and one week—my diary shows—"snakes encountered, 36; killed, 25 (species, 15)—the first venomous one in my bedroom." But I will say frankly that I would rather meet any wild animal I know than a snake.

I said so to a man I met who was taking a large collection of various snakes to the Adelaide Zoo. He had come from Fitzsimon's snake park in Port Elizabeth, and we met on the ship after leaving Cape Town. In the evening he used to let his snakes loose on a well deck to feed them, and once he gave a demonstration in the saloon of the correct application of Fitzsimon's snake-bite antidote. He let a snake bite his arm during the demonstration, explaining that when you were bitten by that snake the venom might be ejected beyond the punctures of the fangs if you caught it in time, and then you could brush off the venom away from the wounds. I accompanied him to the zoo, and when saying good-bye suggested that he should be extra-cautious with the Australian tiger snake. Four months later I was in Adelaide again, and meant to pay him a call; but the morning paper of the day I arrived gave the sad news that he had just died—as the result of a bite by a tiger snake.

There are lesser lights in the African snake world, and I had one down my neck. I was stalking a bushbuck through a channel in very close undergrowth when a snake fell out of a bush and landed with a plop, cold and repulsive, on the back of my neck. The instantaneous feeling was truly appalling—until I realized it was not there to stay. I caught a glimpse of it as it darted away in the grass, and recognized it as probably a harmless, bright-green tree snake (*Chlorophis*).

The twig snake or bird snake is another smaller reptile, but I should not like that down my neck. The natives of Northern Rhodesia have a name for it that means "the little bit of wood that bites," and they say "he who has been bitten can get as far as to see the roofs of the village but no farther." It is held by them to be deadly poisonous, as venomous as the mamba, death occurring in one minute if no antidote is administered.

I found one of these little pests in my bedroom recently. I was stooping low to get something out of a suitcase, which was on a tin trunk and only eight inches from the floor, when I heard a faint hiss; and there, only two feet from my face, was the raised head of an angry twig snake. It was on the floor behind another trunk about a foot from the one that held my suitcase.

I dodged my head to the left in a second, thus getting my face out of its line of fire. In its customary manner it inflated its neck to at least three times the width of its head, showing up the yellow colour with lateral black stripes, and all the time its tongue was extended. My boys and I at length despatched the venomous little gentleman. It was just under four feet long and very slender and apparently pretty courageous, as it reared and hissed several times before the fatal blow was delivered. It had a most distinctive bright green head, a pale brownish body, and a pinkish underpart. Six inches of its 13½-inch tail was as thin as string.

It gives you a shock to have this kind of experience so unexpectedly in your room. The bungalow was thatched and had no ceilings, the grass roof in each room going up to a point so that the supporting timber and grass was visible from the inside. The snake could have entered from the roof just as easily as by the door—and for a day or two I was expecting its mate to appear. By lamplight at night those rafters and struts often assumed sinister shapes.

This kind of thing makes you ponder at times, and when you are jumpy you wish yourself in safer places. The mind conjures up visions of more open surroundings—even to the extreme of a snake-proof dwelling-place in the centre of a huge bare space! But then I think of the monkeys and squirrels that share my haunts. I often wonder how frequently these nimble and cunning little creatures come into conflict with snakes—and who wins.

My most recent experience with snakes is more amusing in retrospect than it was at the time. The other day a friend of mine, who knows I am interested in all forms of wild life, brought me a "present." He arrived one evening at my bungalow with a large cardboard box, which I noticed was most securely tied with string. "I got this one in the channel," he said, meaning Kazinga. "I thought you might like to have it. But," he added, as he began untying the string, "I don't think it is quite dead."

I knew at once what he had brought me, as he is working on the new bridge at Katunguru, and black-lipped cobras are quite common in the channel. "Tip it out carefully, and I'll finish it off," I said.

As he dropped it on the ground I gave it two or three blows with a big stick, but not on the head as I wanted to examine the fangs. It was indeed a black-lipped cobra, six feet in length, with some broad pink bands, peculiar to the local species, across the under forepart of the body and neck. Having "dispatched it," my friend picked it up by the back of the neck while I opened its mouth with a twig and exposed the fangs. After this operation I put the snake back in the box and told my boy to leave it in the bungalow.

Next morning I was busy on other things, and did not think about the snake until about half-past eleven. Then I cautiously opened the box, shook it, and decided that all was well: there was no sound or movement inside. I took the box out onto my verandah, opened the lid again and looked in; still no movement, so I began to tip the snake out on to a small table for detailed examination.

As the curled-up body touched the table I suddenly realized that it was uncurling more rapidly than I expected. Still not quite aware of the truth, I found the long, shining black body was not only uncurling but was moving towards my side of the table. The snake was very much alive, and the next moment it fell off the table onto my feet.

I kicked it away a foot or two, and hastily made my retreat, almost tripping over my dog as I did so. Then, having seized the dog and called a boy to tie him up, I went in search of a weapon. By this time the snake was looking most aggressive, with its head raised about a foot from the floor and its hood extended. It was a fearsome sight, poised among table and chairs in my favourite corner of the verandah. The boys all shouted and the dog barked—but I suppose the snake was more frightened than they were.

Deciding that a stick would be difficult to manipulate just there, I dashed round the house, got my .22 rifle, and then stalked my quarry from the back. I took careful aim at the back of the neck at six feet range, and one shot was enough.

The sequel was amusing. After recording measurements I told my boy to dispose of the corpse, and to be careful to bury it fairly deep to avoid unpleasantness. Later in the day I went into the garden to make sure he had done the job properly, and found a neat grave—with a wooden cross on it! The boy explained very seriously that as the *nyoka* had not poisoned any of us it deserved a proper grave. A Christian snake.

The Psylli and the Serpents

by THE DUCHESS D'ABRANTES

THE CHIEF OF THE PSYLLI LOST NO TIME IN ANSWERING the summons (of Napoleon). As soon as he arrived, the general-in-chief told him, through the medium of the interpreter, "There are two serpents in this house; find them and thou shalt have two sequins (12 francs) for thyself, and as much for thy followers."

The Psylle prostrated himself, and requested two troughs filled with water. When they were brought he stripped himself naked as at his birth, then filled his mouth with water, laid himself flat on his face, and began creeping, in imitation of the reptile he was in search of, and shooting water through his closed teeth to mimic its hissing. When he had in this manner made the tour of the ground-floor, sweeping the house with his person, he returned, and placing himself, all naked and dirty as he was, before the general-in-chief, said to him with a savage laugh, "Mafiche, Mafiche," which signifies, "there is none." The general-in-chief echoed his laugh and said, *Comment Diable!* can this idiot really play the magician with some truth?" And he ordered the interpreter to give the Psylle to understand that the serpent had been seen. "Oh! I know that," said the Psylle. "I felt it on entering the house."

"There, now," said the general-in-chief, "now the comedy is beginning. Well; seek thy serpent, and if thou findest it thou shalt have two additional sequins." The Psylle returned to his artifices, climbed with the same maneuvers a staircase which led to the upper story, where Bourrienne lodged, pursued by a troop of inquisitors with the general-in-chief at their head, who determined not to lose sight of his magician. The corridor was lighted by a loophole overlooking the country, and through which the perfect and unvarying azure of the beautiful Egyptian sky was distinguishable. The Psylle closed his eyes and shuddered. "There is your actor beginning his part," said the First Consul to Junot. The serpent-detector,

however, after several repetitions of his antics, said in a low voice,—
"There he is!" "I shall be delighted to have the pleasure of paying him the
honors of hospitality," said the general-in-chief; "but, my friend, I think
thou art mocking us. Dost know that this animal, with his hissing music,
has completely mystified us for the last hour, making us run about without parasols after his imaginary serpentship?" The Psylle, nowise dis-
couraged, still crept and hissed about, till presently an actual serpent was
seen to interpose its opaque line across the loophole, and was heard answering with fraternal goodwill the hissing of the Psylle; it was six feet
in length, and Junot has assured me that its eyes sparkled through the
dusty corridor with a fire almost sanguine. It approached the Psylle, and
was no sooner within his reach than he caught it with incredible address,
in one hand, just below the jaw-bone, in such a manner as to oblige the
mouth to open, when, spitting into it, the effect was like magic; the reptile
appeared struck with instant death, and during his lethargy, his enchanter,
by some peculiar operation, extracted the venom from his teeth, or rather
from his gums.

"Well, my general, what say you to this adventure?" asked Junot of the
general-in-chief.

"What would you have me answer to an effect of chance? Your Psylle
is a lucky imposter, that it all."

*   *   *   *   *

All men possess in their bodies a poison which acts upon serpents; and
the human saliva, it is said, makes them take to flight, as though they had
been touched with boiling water. The same substance, it is said, destroys
them the moment it enters their throat.—Pliny, the Elder

Snakes as Pets

by CLIFFORD B. MOORE

OUR NATIVE NON-POISONOUS SNAKES OFFER COMPARA-
tively few problems as to care in captivity. Snakes are not slimy as many
people would have us believe, but clean and smooth. The harmless
varieties can easily be caught in the field with the hands or with a three-
foot stick having a "Y" or prongs at the end, this arrangement being
used to pin the reptiles to the ground. If captured individuals are vicious
and disposed to bite, as may the large Blacksnakes and a few of the

Garter snakes (they can do nothing more than scratch the skin), leather pigskin gloves should be worn; and to control them better after being grasped, the right hand should be slipped gradually up over the body to a position behind the neck while the reptile is being held in the middle by the left hand. While being held, a snake should never be squeezed.

It is highly desirable that the inside walls and floor of snake boxes be painted cream color or white. This will show the reptiles up well, being dark-bodied as they generally are. Whatever screening you may have, it should be of very fine mesh so small flies will not get in and make life miserable for the snakes by flying on and around their eyes.

EASTERN GARTER SNAKES (*Thamnophis sirtalis*)

Garter snakes are easily tamed and are ready to meet anyone's advances half-way. They are the most common snakes in North America, there being around twenty species of them altogether. They vary a good deal in color; the underparts are generally of a greenish white, and down the center of the back is usually a darker band of ground-color. On each side is a similar stripe, but not so brightly colored; sometimes the middle stripe, and sometimes the side stripes are broken into spots or are absent entirely. The checkered pattern is a most common one. When fully grown this snake is about three feet in length.

The garters assemble in good numbers in places favorable for hibernation—rocky ledges and stony side hills. Here each snake finds some crevice between rocks and soil and often burrows in as far as three feet. In the sunny noon hours of warm fall days, these winter hermits crawl out to bask themselves in the full glory of the sun. When the cold weather comes, they retire to go into a sleep and do not awaken till the first warm days of spring; then, if the sun shines hot, they come out on the ledges to bask in its welcome rays.

With the middle of April, the garter snakes scatter to other localities in search of food—the edges of woods, and banks of streams, where earthworms, toads, frogs, insects, and salamanders are plentiful. The young garters emerge from the body of the mother in July and are about six inches long at birth. One mother may have in her litter from a dozen to fifty little snakelings. When in danger the little ones do not crawl into the mother's mouth for safety, as the superstition goes. The young snakes shift for themselves as soon as they are able to get about, the diet consisting for the most part of earthworms, and often small toads and insects. If food conditions are good and predacious hawks, crows, weasels, skunks and small boys spare them, garter snakes will mature in a year's time.

When first captured, garter snakes often make it unpleasant by pouring out an offensive-smelling fluid from glands near the base of the tail. A pet snake will often learn to associate your hand with food and kind treatment after awhile, and will refrain from biting and giving off the fluid when handled.

A packing box about 2′ x 3′ and 1½′ high will make good quarters for one or two garter snakes. The front and top should be of plate glass and the upper part of the back screened, while the lower part should have a hinged door opening to the outside and allowing for the cleaning and sweeping out of waste. The inside floor and sides should be painted cream white or white to show the snakes up well. Several sticks and a stone or two might be put in the box; the former to assist the snake in shedding its skin (which is done once every month or two). Garter snakes do not require direct sunlight, but this can be given once a day for an hour or so, providing the temperature in the box does not go above 85° F.

Earthworms are quite generally acceptable to garter snakes throughout life, and they can easily be stored and also easily reared. We used to go out on rainy days, pick up a plentiful supply from the wet sidewalks and put them in a box of dirt to use over a period of several weeks. Small live toads are acceptable to large garter snakes, as are less agile small frogs. It is occasionally possible to get garter snakes to take raw meat, when this is drawn across the floor of the box on a loose thread. An easily obtained food for garter snakes in winter is "live bait" minnows and shiners purchased from live bait dealers or caught in your own minnow trap. In an emergency, small live goldfish as sold in the ten-cent store can be used.

RIBBON SNAKE (*Thamnophis saurita*)

The Ribbon species is one of the most slender of American snakes. The vivid, yellow stripe on its dark brown or black body surface, together with a similar stripe on each side, produces a ribbon-like aspect, and hence the popular name. This snake is found in scattered localities east of the Mississippi and south of the St. Lawrence River. It does not seem very abundant in any one place and favors damp places, generally the grassy banks of ponds and streams, where it feeds on small frogs, tadpoles, sluggish fish and salamanders. It is an excellent swimmer and diver, has all the agility of the water snakes, and will seek refuge beneath aquatic plants, remaining under the surface for some minutes.

As to food in captivity, the ribbon snake will devour many kinds of small frogs, tadpoles, and salamanders, but doesn't "take" to earthworms. Minnows can be introduced to the pool of the semi-aquatic terrarium from time to time or thrown alive onto the soil of a woodland terrarium in front of the snake, and they will often be snapped up. But as a principal article of diet is frogs, it would be wise to catch a large number of smaller ones, especially of the pickerel and leopard species, and make over a large box with a moss floor and shallow tank or sink full of water to keep them in during the winter. One ribbon snake will take from one to two small frogs a week as an average, besides other smaller food.

The interest in moving objects apparently prompts captive ribbon snakes and other frog-eating species to show what appears to be profound intelligence in a serpent. Ditmars has said of this: "When many of these reptiles are kept in the same cage and food is introduced, the snakes first seizing the small frogs or fishes, as the case may be, at once begin to thrash their tails in a most vigorous fashion, seemingly to attract the attention of their associates that are voraciously searching for food, having scented the same, to the commotion of the caudal appendage and away from what the reptile thus performing, is swallowing. There is, of course, a possibility that the snakes thus maneuvering are merely displaying nervous symptoms in the anticipation that their feeding will meet interference, but so invariable are these antics that the first theory appears to be more logical."

SMOOTH-SCALED GREEN OR GRASS SNAKE (*Liopeltis vernalis*)

This insectivorous snake, which reaches an adult length of about 15 inches, is found in open fields and along fence rows, usually perfectly camouflaged against its grassy backgrounds. It is an ideal pet for the terrarium and can be handled by children and even babes (care being taken it isn't swallowed) without its biting and attempting to escape. The green snake naturally feeds upon crickets, katydids, grasshoppers, green hairless caterpillars and spiders. Besides these items in captivity, it will take cockroaches, which you can rear or which you can obtain from any local exterminator. We kept a green snake in a large clump of young evergreen trees, including cedars and hemlocks, and growing together in a crowded way, for a whole summer. This clump of trees was set up against a stone museum building and was surrounded on the outside by a thin border of grass and a sidewalk. Any time we wanted to show the snake to visitors, all we had to do was search for a moment among the lower branches of the hemlocks and pick it up. This snake found plenty of food and dainties by robbing the low-hanging webs of hammock and funnel-web spiders and by snapping up the many crickets that hopped up against the walls of the building. Another captive green snake kept in a terrarium would occasionally grab a small piece of raw beefsteak dangled on a loose thread, but it took a great deal of time and patience in the process.

For exhibition purposes the best arrangement for keeping green snakes is the snake box as previously described for the garter snake: here the snake has no soil to burrow in. You can put a flowerpot with an evergreen or fern growing in it inside the box and your snake will usually show appreciation for such by posing on it. For food, it might be well advised to capture a lot of crickets before the frost sets in. These can be kept in a screen-covered box, fed on bread and fruit, and given to the snake at the rate of three or four a day.

EASTERN RING-NECKED SNAKE (*Diadophis punctatus edwardsi*)

The handsome Ring-necked snake with its slate-gray body and yellow-ringed neck is a small species and usually grows to a length of around 10 or 12 inches. It is secretive and nocturnal, concealing itself and taking refuge under rocks and logs as well as under the loose bark of fallen trees. Its natural food includes earthworms, salamanders, lizards and small snakes. Because of its carnivorous tastes it is advisable not to lodge small salamanders and lizards with it in the terrarium.

Earthworms, small toads and salamanders can be put in the terrarium for your ring-necked snake, but the feeding will generally be done during the night when you are not present to observe it.

One thing that commends the ring-necked snake to the beginning reptile enthusiast is the fact that it is very docile and can be handled with impunity. Its smooth, sleek skin is easy to touch: it is a characteristic that is present in all burrowing reptiles and salamanders and is successful in keeping dirt and foreign particles from adhering to the skin.

COMMON HOG-NOSED SNAKE (*Heterodon contortrix*)

In various localities, this snake has the descriptive names of "Puff Adder," "Blow Snake," and "Spreading Viper." Because of its unusual habit of "playing dead" or of puffing up and hissing, done to discourage its enemies, this snake makes an interesting subject for study and observation in the terrarium. The protective devices or "bluffs" it resorts to are quite necessary, for in the open places it frequents, such as fields and sandy stretches where it unearths toads and mice, it is continually exposed to attack from natural enemies and cannot escape by flight on the ground.

Even though the hog-nosed snake may strike terror into the heart of the nature novice through its surprising behavior, it is really a gentle and harmless creature. Whenever on exhibit, or in places where it may be observed by children and people untutored in the ways of making advances toward strange pets, it is wise to have a sign put up, or make an introductory explanation designed to prevent the individuals from tapping on the box or vivarium and annoying the reptiles. Repeated annoyances of this kind will result in the snake's continued hostility and antagonism toward human beings with little possibility of their becoming desirable pets.

While the hog-nosed snakes eat newts and salamanders, their food is largely confined to toads and frogs. Ditmars says in this respect: ". . . . The light specimens occur usually in very dry, sandy places, while the darker forms are found in woods or moist locations. The dark specimens will usually eat both frogs and toads; the light specimens, with few exceptions, refuse frogs altogether and confine their diet to toads. The species feeds voraciously in captivity. The majority of specimens will so gorge themselves that further feeding is temporarily impossible. The wide head and great elasticity of the jaws enable this snake to swallow very large prey in proportion to its size. It is not unusual for a small snake to engage in a struggle with a very large toad; the toad may be possibly three or four times the diameter of the thickest part of the snake's body, and the little reptile may be rolled and dragged about by the batrachian for nearly an hour, but finally engulfs the toad, which so distends and weighs down the serpent's body that it drags itself with great difficulty to a place of concealment to await assimilation of the meal. During the process of swallowing a large and vigorous toad, the reptile is greatly aided by a pair of large teeth in the rear of the mouth, which, being sharply recurved, holds the struggling prey in a grip that seldom fails."

BLACKSNAKE OR BLACK RACER (*Coluber constrictor.*)

It is not to be inferred, as the scientific name would suggest, that this reptile is a true constrictor (squeezing its prey to death). The Blacksnake, which in its adult state reaches a 5- or 6-foot length, is ordinarily too large for the woodland terrarium and must be kept in a large packing box with a glass or screen front and screened-door top. This reptile is not suitable as a pet unless given an unusually large amount of room to exercise in. It does, however, make an excellent pet in a short time and deserves the best of room and care.

The blacksnake is found in open situations and in the vicinity of woodland swamps where there is an abundance of bird life, frogs, wild mice, and chipmunks. It frequently enters holes in the ground in search of eggs and takes the young of ground and low-nesting birds. More intelligence is displayed than with the average run of our native serpents. Ditmars has described an incident where he saw a pet blacksnake follow its owner, who was holding a dead mouse by the tail, up a ladder to a lift, and then down again. The snake was finally allowed to crawl up the owner's free arm, whereupon it took the mouse and swallowed it, showing no fear of the actions of the man.

The eggs of the blacksnake are elongated and cylindrical in shape and measure about 2 inches in length. When found together in shallow earth and brush nests on pond edges, or when laid in captivity,—they can be placed in a pail containing a composition of decaying pulp from the interior (preferably the core) of a decaying tree, mixed with sphagnum moss. The period of incubation is usually two months.

As stated before, the food of the blacksnake consists of birds, wild mice, chipmunks, and frogs. Besides furnishing these (and especially the latter article in a live state) to captive specimens, one can usually induce them to accept raw meat when such is jiggled on a loose thread. The author has had considerable success in satisfying the appetite of a captive blacksnake by catching mice for it in wire-cage traps. He found that a liberal supply of these rodents could be obtained by setting the traps in a nearby dump after nightfall and likewise by securing the coöperation of neighborhood store managers and janitors, who were usually more than willing to let him set traps in their places at frequent intervals. In the spring and summer seasons, this same snake was fed on frogs which were caught with a net along a nearby pond.

BULL SNAKE (*Pituophis sayi*)

One of the most valuable serpents in the United States is the big Bull Snake of the Central States and Texas. It is a powerful constrictor which captures, crushes to death, and swallows countless injurious rodents, including gophers and ground squirrels, rats, mice and rabbits. Farmers are beginning to realize the real services performed by the bull snake and are protecting it where they destroyed it before.

The bull snake may reach an adult length of anywhere from four to nine feet. It is yellowish-brown above with a row of large rectangular reddish-brown or black patterns on the back and smaller ones on the sides. The head is pointed. As a hisser, the bull snake is much superior to the puff adder and it can be heard at a distance of over fifty feet. The eggs are creamy white and a dozen or more may be laid by a female.

Due to the fact that the bull snakes are hardy in captivity and very good natured, they are sold extensively as pets. They are the most popular and common of all snakes used by so-called snake charmers in side-shows and, as a rule, cannot be induced to bite. Being fond of both snake and bird eggs in a wild state, the bull snake can be fed for the most part on hen eggs in captivity. Rats and mice caught alive in wire traps set in neighborhood dumps and stores can also be given daily. It is always interesting to watch a bull snake eat. When an egg has passed down the throat for about a foot, the reptile presses its body firmly against the ground, contracts the muscles in advance and posteriorly to the egg and breaks it. This action is entirely a deliberate one and may consume as much as ten seconds. The egg collapses with an externally discernible crunch and the fragments of shell are ingested. Bull snakes can be housed in a box arrangement similar to that described for the blacksnake and garter snake, except on a larger scale.

DEKAY'S OR BROWN SNAKE (*Storeria dekayi*)

These snakes are of a dull brown color and seldom over 14 inches in length. When discovered, they are generally exposed from concealment under flat stones, or the bark of dead trees and logs. In the springtime, DeKay's, like other snake species, are given to exposing themselves and basking in the sunlight for extended periods of time. The diet consists of small salamanders, soft-shelled beetles and their grubs, slugs, and earthworms. In the terrarium, they will live in harmony with full-grown toads and, possibly, grasshoppers and crickets. Earthworms can be fed them regularly.

WORM SNAKE (*Carphophis amænus*)

This is such a secretive species, both naturally and in captivity, that it is hardly worth while to keep it in the terrarium. The adult is brown above and pink below, and the eyes are very small. The length is about 9 inches, while the body diameter is generally around a quarter of an inch. The worm snake's diet consists of earthworms, the soft-bodied grubs and larvæ of beetles and other ground insects.

KING SNAKES, INCLUDING THE CHECKERED ADDER

All the snakes in this group or genus are constrictors and feed largely upon rodents and smaller snakes. They possess comparatively small heads and attractively marked bodies, the brilliant coloration being arranged in transverse bands or rings. The ruggedness and cylindrical shape of the bodies moreover make them especially adapted to an under-ground existence, and they are often found in or near the nests or tunnels of rodents and other snakes.

Some years ago, when the food habits of the checkered adder or milk snake (*Lampropeltis triangulum*) were unknown to farmers, their presence in barns and farmyards, where they were freely killed, was attributed to an inordinate desire on their part to suck milk from the udders of cows. Their presence in such places has since been explained by the fact that they were in search of mice and rats. Unfortunately, though, the appellation of "Milk Snake" has persisted.

A female checkered adder will sometimes lay from 8 to 10 oval white eggs in captivity, and if these are put in a pail or bowl of loose earth, and wood pulp or sawdust, and moistened slightly from time to time, they should hatch in a little less than 3 months. In captivity, the checkered adders are quite hardy and make good pets, especially the larger ones. A full-grown individual which measures over two feet in length will do best in the type of box previously described for garter snakes and into which live or freshly killed mice may frequently be dropped. To prevent your adders from escaping, and they are especially adept at it, all crevices and apertures must be securely stopped up.

The king snake, or chain snake (*Lampropeltis getulus*) inhabits the eastern part of the United States and is found in moist and shady locations, but does not go in for climbing trees and swimming. The common name is very appropriate, for king snakes do not hesitate to attack and vanquish other snakes larger than themselves, including such poisonous species as rattlers, copperheads and moccasins. An adult six-foot king snake is a match for practically any snake that lives in America. In addition to other snakes, rats, mice, birds, lizards and various species of small animals are captured and squeezed to death before being swallowed. The venom of the poisonous snakes swallowed does not appear to have any deleterious effects on the king snake.

In captivity, king snakes are unusually gentle, making excellent and interesting pets. They are hardy and will live for years in confinement. As to the nature of their food, they are not particular, and will eat dead animals and pieces of raw beef alike.

The colors of the king snake vary somewhat according to the part of the country in which they live. A common color is black, with narrow or white cross-bands.

RED COLUBER; CORN SNAKE; MOUSE SNAKE; HOUSE SNAKE; RED CHICKEN SNAKE (*Elapphe guttata*)

This beautiful snake is easily distinguished for its crimson saddles against a pale red background on the upper surface of the body and a white abdomen with large black squares. It attains an adult length of about six feet and is widely distributed from Maryland on the north westward to the Mississippi and to the Gulf and Florida.

The Coluber is a good climber, often ascending small trees and bushes in search of young birds in their nests. Besides frequenting the margins of woods and open fields the snake is often found in corn fields where there is an abundance of rodents which come to feed on the grain, hence one of its common names, "Corn Snake."

A coluber may be satisfactorily exhibited in a large box, 3' x 4' and 3' deep with a glass front, screened top and the back arranged as a door with hinges and a handle. Some upright branches can be set up for the snake to coil around and to assist in shedding its skin. Colubers frequently breed in captivity, the female laying from one to two dozen yellowish-white eggs. When these are placed in a pail of dampened wood-pulp which is kept at a temperature of about 70° F., they will usually hatch within two months.

Besides rodents, a pet coluber will take such live bird pests with the wings clipped as the English sparrow.

RATTLESNAKES, COPPERHEADS, CORAL SNAKES AND WATER MOCCASINS

Poisonous snakes ordinarily cannot be classified as pets. One is not justified in keeping them in capitivity unless they are to be definitely utilized as an educational exhibit or as subjects for research. Ventilation should be from the upper part of the rear, and the front and part of the top provided with special non-breakable plate glass. A hinged door for cleaning out the cage should be fitted in the lower part of the rear of the box. The dimensions of the box itself should be about 3' x 3' square and about 2½' deep, thus enabling the snakes to get proper exercise. All parts of the box should be tight and secure against prying fingers of curious people. You will not have to worry about watering your snakes, for none of them drink, but rather get their liquid nourishment from their animal food. The floor of the cage can be painted a cream color to show the dark colored snakes up, or a thin layer of clean sand can be put on and this changed once a week. A flat rock or two can be added for the snake to bask upon. About four hours of direct sunlight can be given daily and the temperature inside the box should not be allowed to rise above 90° F. if possible.

Venomous snakes that have recently expired in captivity should be removed in such a way that the bare hands will not be nearer than a foot from the reptile's head. This is necessary because the nerve reflexes in the head often cause this part to swing around on any point of contact and bite.

The food of the rattlesnake consists of warm-blooded prey as rats, mice, birds, squirrels, chipmunks and small rabbits. The author has fed a rattlesnake over a period of two years on a diet of mice (caught in wire traps and thrown into the snake's box alive). Eight years was the record of longevity of a Florida diamond rattler kept in the National Zoological Park, Washington, D. C. "One may venture a guess," says its distinguished director, W. M. Mann, "that this comparatively short span of life in captivity results from lack of sunshine which the snake requires. While the author recommended a box type of cage with a glass front he would supplement this by suggesting the front panel be of quartz glass and that a quartz glass top on hinges be installed if possible and the cage be kept out in the sun during the warm days of spring, summer, and fall." The quartz or "vita" glass, which has appeared very recently on the market, will admit those ultra-violet health giving rays excluded through ordinary window glass. During the winter months, snakes in captivity can benefit from exposure to the rays of sunlamps or ultra-violet lamps, the latter carefully regulated.

The food problem of the copperhead is a more complicated one and has a direct bearing on the possibility of finding certain kinds of food during different seasons when it is in a wild state. In alluding to the feeding habits of the copperhead, Ditmars remarks: "During the spring and fall, it is very fond of frogs, grasping them with lightning-like rapidity and retaining the hold until the prey is dead. The venom acts quickly upon the cold-blooded batrachian. During the later spring, these snakes prefer young birds, showing in fact such a decided preference to this food that some snakes will fast unless provided with the feathered prey. During the summer months captive specimens will eat small rodents, such as mice and rats, or chipmunks. This preference though not invariable is quite general as noted in caring for many of these snakes. After several years in captivity these reptiles assume a less particular appetite and live contentedly upon a diet of mice and frogs."

The Coral Snake, a resident of the southeast, particularly of Florida, is somewhat difficult to keep in captivity. Its food is made up of lizards, especially the blue-tailed (*Eumeses*), and other snakes. Unless given a situation in captivity that approximates very closely that of its natural habitat, it will die after a very short time. It must have a medium, or place where it can both burrow and hide itself, and this can best be made, as Ditmars explains, "by giving it a case provided with several inches depth of sphagnum moss; but it is delicate and, unless kept in a temperature of 75° F. or over, will persistently refuse food." Under the direction of Ditmars, experiments were conducted in the New York Zoological Society's reptile house for several years with the object of constructing quarters where the coral snake might both be seen and its burrowing tendencies satisfied. When it was placed on thin layers of moss and sand it succeeded in wholly secreting itself and refused all food. Ditmars adds that "specimens in cases well filled with moss lived and thrived, but were never seen by visitors. Finding it practically impossible to strike a happy medium, a few specimens were kept on hand to be uncovered occasionally for the benefit of students . . ."

One of the snakes of the southeastern section of the United States somewhat dreaded by the natives is the Water Moccasin. As the common name applies, water moccasins live in or near the water, especially in damp, swampy situations, or in low trees or bushes overhanging the water, into which they plunge when disturbed.

The water moccasin reaches a length of from four to six feet, but has a thick and clumsy body and is therefore quite heavy. Its general color is olive-brown, with 20 to 30 darker cross-bars. Favorite items in its bill of fare are fish, frogs, birds, other snakes, and small mammals. The majority of poisonous snakes only bite when stepped on or handled roughly, but the water moccasin will raise its head and open its whitish mouth, a habit which gives it the common name of "Cotton-mouth Snake" and, after several seconds' delay, will strike at any animal within reach. Its venom is not as virulent as that of certain other snakes, and few fatalities from its bite are on record. In captivity the water moccasin invariably becomes tame and gentle. A large pan of fresh water should be sunk in its quarters or terrarium so it can catch the frogs and live fish you put in.

The Story of the Snake

by A. W. ROLKER

ONE OF THE MOST INTERESTING AND ONE OF THE MOST fascinating additions of recent years to zoological exhibits is the modern reptile house. Both the animal and the vegetable world are represented in it. It is a whole world of forests, dusky swamps, barren deserts, and tangled jungles brought from North and South and East and West and crowded under one roof. And under the roof, caged among giant palms, hanging bushrope, and drooping resurrection ferns, there squirm and coil the most mysterious and uncanny and merciless of all of God's creatures, housed according to the most advanced ideas of animal science, with all the surroundings peculiar to the wild and natural state of each. This novelty of showing the animals, and the modern facilities for feeding them as once they fed themselves, for studying reptile diseases, and even for operating with the surgeon's knife, have practically revolutionized the snake house of old into the marvelous reptile house of to-day.

To the life of the snake there is no known parallel in natural history. Destruction, merciless extermination, and eternal war mark every phase of it. From the very beginning, in the very nature of its food and its manner of eating, the snake is repulsively fascinating. Among the larger reptiles the fight over food frequently leads to the most horrible of combats, each principal seeking to get into his mouth the head of his opponent, after which there remains only the cruel swallowing process. The most hideous form of cannibalism—kind eating kind *alive*—is the revolting diet of a large portion of the reptile family.

The most atrocious cannibal among all the snakes is the king cobra. The sight of this snake feeding is not one for sensitive nerves. In its natural state this monarch of reptiles contents himself with lizards when nothing better offers; but when captive he declines to touch food unless tempted by the morsel of a squirming six-foot snake. The spectacle of a frightened "black-racer" being introduced into the cage would be more pitiful were it not that he himself is a cannibal. For an instant the dread brown head peers around a corner of the water tank at the doomed one, who has not a chance in a thousand in his favor. But he makes a single frantic attempt for his life. His motion is lightning. Cornered hopelessly as he is, he whips out like a streak of light in one mighty effort to coil about the enemy's throat to choke him. But the cobra is quicker still. One dart— too quick for the human eye to follow—and the black head is between the relentless jaws, which, with their back-set teeth and alternate outward and inward motion, steadily draw the fighting, squirming thing inward. Gradually the food is swallowed, with frequent pauses for breath and with halts to repress the squirming and fighting of the prey struggling inch by inch in the throes of a living death. Such is the meal of the cannibal snake, whether he be fed with live food by the hand of man or whether he hunt in his own lair.

But in the modern reptile house it happens frequently that the naturalist himself must take a hand in devising ways and means to coax his rare and splendid specimens into eating. Often the snake man is unable to supply his cobra's demand for large blacksnakes. The specimens soon grow scarce in any one locality when hunted persistently. To the owner of a valuable cobra the situation is critical. The reptile, sometimes representing in money value the equivalent of a good road horse, refuses to eat a blacksnake not of an alluring size. Birds, frogs, fish, rats, chickens, and the tid-bits that attract other snakes in captivity, the great serpent declines. Only one alternative remains to the snake man—he must artificially produce a blacksnake to fit the requirements. The naturalist consults his blacksnake cage. Here, in the top of the cage-tree, hangs a great bunch of reptiles, knotted and twisted like rain worms into a hopeless snarl to keep one another warm. The man selects the largest snake in the collection and begins to disentangle the bunch. Sometimes an angered snake turns on the intruder and sinks its teeth into the offending hand. But the wound is not poisonous, and it is what a man must expect from time to time when handling snakes. Inch by inch the victim is pulled and twisted and looped out of the heap, until he is held squirming and dangling by the tail. Then, like the lash of a whip, the snake is whirled through the air. At the end of the sweep there is a snap and the reptile hangs lifeless, its neck broken. Then comes a stuffing process. Down the throat of the dead reptile a frog is forced. On top of this a second frog, and then, a third, and so on until the shiny black body, at first no larger than a policeman's club, has attained the diameter of a man's wrist. Distorted to these enticing dimensions he is greedily devoured by the cobra, and there has been smuggled into him sustenance enough for two weeks, though of the "stuffing" the animal would refuse to partake unless in this form of a "snake pill."

What the blacksnake is to the cobra the garter snake is to the blacksnake, and the frog and the tiny field mouse are to the garter snake. According to the estimate of one scientist, at least twenty times as many snakes as are used for exhibition purposes are needed annually to feed the "star attractions." Snake hunters scour the neighboring fields and woods and swamps, but most of the snakes used for food purposes are born and bred right in the reptile houses, and the sight of four or five cages filled with garter snakes, each pair to be depended upon to furnish from forty to eighty young each year, is a common sight in large snake collections.

Sometimes snakes quarrel over their food, and in the ensuing fight one of the combatants swallows his opponent alive. In a famous New York reptile collection a remarkable instance of this kind happened recently.

A coachwhip snake had caught the head of a black racer in his jaws and was swallowing him. The racer was more than half way down the throat of the coachwhip fellow when interference came. A snake man grasped each reptile by the tail and readily pulled the one outside of the other, when it was found that the blacksnake still held in his mouth a small frog, the object of the fight. Not being able to take the frog from its opponent, the coachwhip snake had decided to swallow the whole competing show—snake, frog, and all. The blacksnake, unharmed, finished its meal where it had been interrupted.

Among the most interesting specimens in respect to their food and their habits while eating is the great American viper— the rattlesnake. At large, the splendid brownish black reptile—there never was a fairer in a fight—roams the corn and the wheatfields of the farmer hunting rats that threaten crops. Quick and fearless in attack in his natural haunts, when in captivity he develops a dignity which if interfered with would lead even to starvation, for few full grown rattlers will deign to eat with more than a single companion in the cage. Even with a pair in one cage, but one will eat at a time, while the other remains perfectly motionless in a far corner of the den. If, while the male viper is engaged in eating, the female glides toward him, or across his body, the feeding ceases instantly. Slowly, with all the stateliness of one of the higher animals, the wicked, flat, triangular head rises, the merciless, cold, black eyes send shafts at the intruder, and, as if carved in stone, both snakes remain motionless. Only after some minutes is the meal resumed. Unless the snakes are confined in a large cage it is necessary to kill the rat before feeding him to a rattlesnake. The little brown animal of brawn and muscle is no mean antagonist for even a full grown rattler. A born athlete and quick as thought, the intended victim would feint and jump, and, landing on the neck of his foe, would bite the backbone, paralyzing the viper. In an open field the rattlesnake rarely would succumb, but in even a large-sized cage, where space forbids the free manoeuvring of the snake, the chances would be much in favor of the rat.

In captivity most snakes are fed on dead food for more reasons than the restriction of the S.P.C.A. Boa constrictors would much prefer live chickens to the dead ones thrown to them, but should a lusty rooster be let loose in a cage between a pair of boas there would soon be a snake knot which it would require half a dozen snake men a day to unravel, if indeed either of the reptiles were alive.

A most famous instance of snake feeding happened a year ago in the New York Zoölogical Park when Czarina, a twenty-foot regal python, one of the largest specimens in captivity and known all over among naturalists, was fed against her will. Like all big pythons in captivity, she was trying to starve herself to death. Imagine a creature in length the height of a two-story house; in weight 240 pounds; girth measure bigger than a large man's thigh; possessing within its tremendous frame the strength of twelve men; of a brown and purpled colored skin; with a head big as a wolf's; eyes like russet shoe buttons, and a pair of jaws capable of swallowing a full-sized Newfoundland dog.

For more than six weeks Czarina had not touched food, when Curator R. L. Ditmars, in charge of the reptile house, decided to capture the monster, to take her out of her cage, to stretch her full length, and to force food down her throat. Every keeper in every department of the Park was notified to report in the reptile house that evening, and the snake meal was prepared. Thirty pounds of rabbits were killed, bound together with

twine, and fastened to a bamboo pole ten feet long. This was set aside for
later use.

That evening when the visitors had gone the fight began—twelve men
against the snake. The creature lay coiled and re-coiled in a great three-
foot heap, in a plate-glass cage, ten by twenty feet, and as high as its
width. Through a slot in the big door at the back of the cage the Curator
peered to locate the snake. Then he threw open the door. The monster
languidly raised her head, and for an interval man and serpent glared at
each other, the one surprised, the other awed in spite of himself. A glimmer of wickedness lit the small reddish-brown eyes and a quiver seemed
to run through the dreadful body. Then the Curator, only a burlap bag in
hand and trusting to the eleven to follow, threw himself toward the monster and in an instant the bag was over her head. Blinded and with the
hands of man clutching her throat, like a giant spring Czarina hurled herself loose among the struggling men who had piled into the cage and
were trying to clutch the wonderful coils. Through the cloud of dust within
appeared glimpses of the fighting keepers and flashes of the lashing body,
while the scuffle of feet and the shouts and cries of men sounded over all.
The Curator, still clutching the throat of his great adversary, staggered
about, whipped back and forth like a jackstraw. Grabbing, groping, hug-
ging, and tugging, the others were tossed like chaff here and there only to
fall back to their work which now had grown a matter of life and death, for
to release the snake and permit all hands to escape in safety would now
have been impossible. Through the dust were seen five or six men lying side
by side on their bellies trying to pin the snake to earth, but the next instant they were up in the air, tossed by the dreadful spring of those giant
coils. The men were panting with exertion, and their shouts and cries of
encouragement to one another came from parched and strained throats.
And so another ten minutes dragged on, while photographers in front of
the cage ran about like chickens without heads for vantage points to
snap their pictures.

But even Czarina's tremendous strength was unable to withstand in-
definitely the assault of the small army of hardened and trained animal
men. At the end of another five minutes they had pinned down the snake.
Like foot-ball players they lay, side by side, panting and exhausted, while
the struggles ceased gradually in the great frame. Mr. Ditmars, still clutching the wicked head, was the first to stagger out of the cage. One by one
the others followed, each lugging a share of the snake. The python was
stretched full length on the floor of the house. The custody of the head
was turned over to an assistant, and the Curator prepared to adminster the
food. The great jaws were forced apart, and the bamboo pole with its
bologna of rabbits was shoved into the mouth and down the endless
throat. There was a final desperate squirm as the operation began, but the
python was readily held. Still, as if lifeless, she remained, while down,
down went the food, until, when nearly the entire pole was buried within

the reptile, the rabbits were wriggled loose, and the great snake had been forced to feed.

The curse of the snake still rests heavily upon man. In the dense jungles of the far South and the distant East, among savage and semi-civilized races, the annual crop of deaths due to snake venom amounts to little less than a ravage.

Venomous snakes may be divided into two classes—the cobras and the viperoids. The cobras, inhabitants of distant India, form a class apart. To the viperoids belong all other venomous species, including our own splendid rattler, the moccasin, the fer de lance of the West Indies, and the deadly bushmaster of Venezuela and the Guianas.

Diametrically opposite though equally fatal are the effects of the cobra and the viperoids poisons. Diametrically opposite also are the two methods of attack. The cobra at times is aggressive, the king cobra being said even to pursue man. Silent, without the least warning, and from a place where you would least suspect, the round head darts out of a thicket, a sharp pain causes you to exclaim, and the frightful fangs of the snake are buried in your flesh. Like the grip of a bulldog they hold fast, while from five to ten feet of animated cable come stretching out of the thicket to coil leisurely beneath the dread head.

For this eternal hold on the victim there is a natural reason. The fangs of a ten-foot cobra are but a third of an inch long. It is impossible, therefore, to squirt the venom deep in a single stroke. In order to give the venom time to absorb the snake must retain its hold. The fatal poison contains about 95 per cent of nerve destroying and about 5 per cent of blood-destroying elements. Within five minutes the pain leaves the wound and even the shock of the attack begins to wear off. There is little suffering, nor will there be to the relentless end. Only if by chance the bite is from a small snake or if a fresh supply of anti-toxin happens to be at hand is there a chance for your life. If one recovers from the immediate effects, within a week one is as healthy as ever.

While the poison of the cobra often kills within the hour, there have been cases where the "strike" of a rattlesnake and a bushmaster have caused death within ten minutes. Naturalists accept, however, that the king cobra, owing to its great size and the consequent quantity and quality of poison emitted, is the most dangerous of all the snakes.

To illustrate the effects of the poisons of the viperoids there is probably no better example than that of the rattlesnake. The viper strikes in self-defense, when angered or suddenly startled. Keen, sharp fangs, long and slender, and pointed as shad bones, make possible a quick attack which sends the venom deep into veins and arteries within the fraction of a second. Coiled, with head and forebody extended in the shape of a letter S, the rattler lies. The fat, wicked body is motionless and steady as though cast in steel, the black, beady eyes riveted on the victim. Only the tail with its warning rattles is performing an evolution. The attack is sharp and quick. Quick as thought the fangs have been buried an inch or more into the flesh. The poison is quite the opposite of the cobra's, containing about 95 per cent. of blood-destroying and about 5 per cent. of nerve-destroying elements. With all the vigor of a sharp acid the venom circulates, attacking the walls of the veins and the red corpuscles in the blood, and causing untold agony. Quick blood poisoning is the result, and all the excrutiating pain endured by a sufferer from that sickness during a two week's period is crowded into the few remaining hours of the victim's life. Unless the heart action can be kept up by stimulants the end comes within a few hours. Anti-toxin may save the victim, but the difficulty of obtaining this in a state of preservation when needed renders it practically useless to humanity in general. And even with the anti-toxin at hand, the after-effects would remain. For a long time the victim may suffer from blood diseases, carbuncles, abscesses, and, frequently, gangrene.

The young of the poisonous species—deserted from the very first by the parent snakes—are as dangerous as if full grown from the moment they enter the world. The proprietor of a Philadelphia museum learned this to his cost not long ago. In a big glass case partitioned through the middle by a wire screen there lived side by side an eleven-foot anaconda (of the constrictor family) and a colony of cotton mouth moccasins. It was impossible for the moccasins to glide through the narrow meshes of the screen or even to venture an occasional "strike" at their large and peaceful neighbor. But during the night a brood of young cotton mouths unexpectedly appeared, babies, not five inches long. They squirmed through the meshes of the partition, and before they had been two hours in this world, were gliding joyfully over the lifeless body of the huge constrictor who lay poisoned by the youngsters' fangs.

The extraction of the venom from live specimens for experimental purposes is a process of much interest. For the larger snakes a special apparatus has been devised; but in the handling of the smaller-sized vipers, like the moccasin, the experts use little ceremony. They work boldly and quickly and think little more of handling a wicked viper with the sting of death in its head than of capturing a vicious cat.

A moccasin, for example, lies in the diminutive swamp of his cage all thoughtless of trouble, when suddenly the door of his cage is thrown open. A hand holding a stout stick intrudes. In an instant the viper has coiled and struck out at the nearest object threatening—the stick. Almost before he can withdraw his fangs the stick comes down across his back, right behind the head, pinning him to the floor of the cage, while the hand reaches in, grasps the neck, and bears the snake to the operating room. To a casual observer it seems ridiculously simple and easy, but the snake man takes no chances. His thumb and forefinger tremble with the pressure on the throat of his captive, while the eyes of the viper bulge with the choking.

To collect the venom, an ordinary sheet of writing paper is used. This is folded once upon itself, cylinder fashion, and approached to the mouth of the reptile. At first it refuses to bite. It is necessary to nag it with the bait. Then the mouth opens, like the mouth of a cat, showing the long, thin poison fangs and the back-set teeth in a setting of sickly pink. As the jaws come together there is a pricking of the paper, and later only these punctures show on the exterior of the roll. But when the sheet is unwrapped the venom is found—canary yellow in color, viscous as milk, —enough to fill a tablespoon and to kill three strong men.

The reader is now in a position to appreciate a remarkable feat of snake surgery which, like the feeding of the regal python, took place in the New York Zoölogical Park under Curator Ditmars. Naigina, a splendid ten-foot king cobra, had developed an abscess next to one of her poison fangs, and unless this were removed she would die. To capture the dangerous reptile, to force her jaws apart, and to cut the abscess, was the problem. The Curator had a plan and he called for an extra fat snake pill. When the stuffed snake appeared it was distended to the bursting point. In more than a month the cobra had not touched food. Mr. Ditmars summoned five keepers, armed himself with a surgeon's pincers, and proceeded to the attack. In the center of the door, high up from the floor, where the poison-ous head would not be apt to dart through the instant an opening was shown, there was a circular aperture protected with a slide, and through this the snake pill was threaded. The hungry snake took hold of it at once. Frequently she stopped, in evident pain, but each time she resumed until the long, black thing was half way down her throat. This was the moment to act. The door was thrown open and before the cobra could disgorge herself to fight, she was seized by the head and throat, while other hands grasped her body and tail. Then the mouth was forced wide apart while the pincers did their work, and the finest specimen of cobra in captivity was thus saved to the collection.

The price asked for a snake depends on its value as a specimen, the scarcity of the species, the danger and difficulty of catching and transport-ing it, and, above all, the demand for the snake. A regal python of the size of Czarina, broken to captivity, is valued in the neighborhood of $400. A pair of fine diamond back rattlesnakes, from six to seven feet long, may be bought at prices varying from twenty-five cents to one dollar a foot. But most of all the prices depend upon the number of snake men—naturalists, museum proprietors, directors of zoölogical gardens, and snake fanciers—who are present to bid against each other for any par-ticular snake.

The white man is, perhaps, the most expert snake hunter in the world. Your practised snake man thinks but little of letting loose his rattlesnake, just to show you the method of capture. He knows he can recapture the reptile at will without danger to himself, providing always that he has a sight of the snake. Whether he captures it on the concreted floor of a rep-tile house or in the wilds of a mountain gorge, the method used is the same, and is the same as that used for the moccasin or any other viper of equal size. A six-foot pole, long enough to extend beyond the danger zone of the poison fangs and carefully aimed, pins down the prey till the hunter secures it by the neck and thrusts it unceremoniously into his snake bag.

It is only when snakes are hunted in swamps, where the yielding ground would make secure pinning down impossible, that another method—used also in the capture of the bigger poisonous snakes like the cobra—is brought into play. A long pole, supplied at one end with a wire loop controlled by the hunter from the opposite end, is the hunter's weapon. The reptile, goaded and maddened by the sight of the enemy, lies ready awaiting his approach. His eyes are fastened only upon his intended victim. With the stupidity of his family he does not notice the loop until it has "ringed" him and he is squirming in the wire tightening about his throat.

But aside from mankind the snake has many enemies. It is as if half of creation were sworn to war against him. Even the tiny, red robin fights him; so do the nightingale, and the owl, and many other birds. The mongoose, the ordinary house cat, as well as many wild species of the cat family, and the pig, domestic or wild, all fight the snake and destroy it. But the most relentless exterminator of reptiles is a member of the family itself—the beautiful, lithe, yellow and black king snake, the friend of man and the avowed enemy of anything that creeps or crawls, regardless of size or poison fang. A native of our own South, the king snake is between five and eight feet long and no thicker around than a man's thumb. Built in every muscle and bone for speed and tremendous constricting power there is not another snake on earth that can withstand his assault. He is immune to the poison of the cobra and of the rattler alike, and the strength of a thirty-foot python has no terrors for him. Within five minutes from the opening of the fight, the king snake could kill the biggest python that ever lived. Ferocious as the little constrictor is toward his own kind, toward man he is friendly, and rarely tries to escape when met afield. If picked up in the hand he will coil about his captor's arm, evidently pleased at the exhibition of friendliness.

It is natural that from time immemorial a creature so repulsive and so incomprehensible as the snake should have given excuse for many of the weirdest and most absurd myths. There is the story of the "hoop snake"—the fellow who takes his tail in his mouth, rolls hoop-like over the ground with the rapidity of a whirlwind till he fetches up against the invariable cotton-wood tree, which begins to fade within the hour, and in less than a day stands charred and black, poisoned by the frightful venom sent into the bark. No snake of the hoop snake species is known outside of mythical science. Similarly mythical is the "milk snake." When of an evening the farmer finds the output of a herd short by thirty or forty quarts, he says that the milk snake has been around. The reptile he describes as but three feet long with a proportionate girth, and yet this diminutive animal is charged with having stored away something like half a can of milk.

Many popular misconceptions regarding the lives of snakes are still prevalent. The setting of the sun, for example, has nothing to do with the death of a snake. When a snake is decapitated it is dead at once. The tail will remain sensitive and will wriggle for several hours after death, but the movement is purely spasmodic and ceases in time without reference to the position of the sun.

Another popular fallacy is that a rattlesnake will commit suicide when hopelessly cornered, by sinking its own fangs into its sides. No poisonous snake is susceptible to the poison of its own kind. Two cobras in a fight know this. Neither reptile tries to strike the other. The combat is a live swallowing match.

Another mistaken notion is partly based on fact, the only fact which seems to impute to a snake any of the higher motives. A blacksnake, the story has it, will open its mouth to swallow its young in time of danger. It is true the black racer swallows its young when threatened, but there is no record that the little ones ever see daylight again. Instead, the mother lies peaceful, much in the manner of having enjoyed a good meal—the most unnatural of all cannibals, the consumer of her own flesh and blood, and but another example of the rare and loathsome creatures that make up an uncanny world by themselves.

A Tree-Climbing Black Snake

by HENRY D. THOREAU

SAT DOWN IN THE SUN IN THE PATH THROUGH WRIGHT'S wood-lot above Goose Pond, but soon, hearing a slight rustling, I looked round and saw a very large black snake about five feet long on the dry leaves, about a rod off. When I moved, it vibrated its tail very rapidly and smartly, which made quite a loud rustling or rattling sound, reminding me of the rattlesnake, as if many snakes obeyed the same instinct as the rattlesnake when they vibrate their tails. Once I thought I heard a low hiss. It was on the edge of a young wood of oaks and a few white pines from ten to eighteen feet high, the oaks as yet bare of leaves. As I moved toward the snake, I thought it would take refuge in some hole, but it appeared that it was out on a scout and did not know of any place of refuge near. Suddenly, as it moved along, it erected itself half its length, and when I thought it was preparing to strike at me, to my surprise it glided up a slender oak sapling about an inch in diameter at the ground and ten feet high. It ascended this easily and quickly, at first, I think, slanting its body over the lowest twig of the next tree. There were seven little branches for nine feet, averaging about the size of a pipe-stem. It moved up in a somewhat zigzag manner, availing itself of the branches, yet also in part spirally about the main stem. It finds a rest (or hold if necessary) for its neck or forward part of its body, moving crosswise the small twigs, then draws up the rest of its body. From the top of this little oak it passed into the top of a white pine of the same height an inch and a half in diameter at the ground and two feet off; from this into another oak, fifteen feet high and three feet from the pine; from this to another oak, three feet from the last and about the same height; from this to a large oak about four feet off and three or four inches in diameter, in which it was about fourteen feet from the ground; thence through two more oaks, a little lower, at intervals of four feet, and so into a white pine; and at last into a smaller white pine and thence to the ground. The distance in a straight line from where it left the ground to where it descended was about twenty-five feet, and the greatest height it reached, about fourteen feet. It moved quite deliberately for the most part, choosing its course from tree to tree with great skill, and resting from time to time while it watched me, only my approach compelling it to move again. It surprised me very much to see it cross from tree to tree exactly like a squirrel, where there appeared little or no support for such a body. It would glide down the proper twig, its body resting at intervals of a foot or two, on the smaller side twigs, perchance, and then would easily cross an interval of two feet, sometimes in an ascending, sometimes a descending, direction. If the latter, its weight at last bent the first twig down nearer to the opposite one. It would extend its neck very much, as I could see by the increased width of the scales exposed, till its neck rested across the opposite twig, hold on all the while tightly to some part of the last twig by the very tip of its tail, which was curled round it just like a monkey's. I have hardly seen a squirrel *rest* on such slight twigs as it would rest on in mid-air, only two or three not bigger than a pipe-stem, while its body stretched *clear* a foot at least between two trees. It was not at all like creeping over a coarse basketwork, but suggested long practice and skill, like the rope-dancer's. There were no limbs for it to use comparable for size with its own body, and you hardly noticed the few slight twigs it rested on, as it glided through the air. When its neck rested on the opposite twig, it was, as it were, glued to it. It helped itself over or up them as surely as if it grasped with a hand. There were, no doubt, rigid kinks in its body when they were needed for support. It is a sort of endless hook, and, by its ability to bend its body in every direction, it finds some support on every side. Perhaps the edges of its scales give it a hold also. It is evident that it can take the young birds out of a sapling of any height, and no twigs are so small and pliant as to prevent it. Pendulous sprays would be the most difficult for it, where the twigs are more nearly parallel with the main one, as well as nearly vertical, but even then it might hold on by its tail while its head hung below. I have no doubt that this snake could have reached many of the oriole-nests which I have seen. I noticed that in its anger its rigid neck was very much flattened or compressed vertically. At length it coiled itself upon itself as if to strike, and, I presenting a stick, it struck it smartly and then darted away, running swiftly down the hill toward the pond.

DRAMA

The Death of Cleopatra

by WILLIAM SHAKESPEARE

SCENE—*Alexandria. The Monument.*

Enter aloft, CLEOPATRA, CHARMIAN, *and* IRAS.

Cleo. My desolation does begin to make
A better life. 'Tis paltry to be Cæsar;
Not being Fortune, he's but Fortune's knave,
A minister of her will; and it is great
To do that thing that ends all other deeds,
Which shackles accidents, and bolts up change,
Which sleeps, and never palates more the dug,
The beggar's nurse and Cæsar's.

Enter, below, PROCULEIUS, GALLUS, *and* Soldiers.

Pro. Cæsar sends greeting to the Queen of Egypt;
And bids thee study on what fair demands
Thou mean'st to have him grant thee.
    Cleo.   What's thy name?
Pro. My name is Proculeius.
    Cleo.   Antony
Did tell me of you, bade me trust you; but
I do not greatly care to be deceiv'd,
That have no use for trusting. If your master
Would have a queen his beggar, you must tell him,
That majesty, to keep decorum, must
No less beg than a kingdom: if he please
To give me conquer'd Egypt for my son,
He gives me so much of mine own as I
Will kneel to him with thanks.
    Pro.   Be of good cheer;
You're fall'n into a princely hand, fear nothing.
Make your full reference freely to my lord,
Who is so full of grace, that it flows over
On all that need; let me report to him
Your sweet dependancy, and you shall find
A conqueror that will pray in aid for kindness

287

Where he for grace is kneel'd to.

Cleo.   Pray you, tell him
I am his fortune's vassal, and I send him
The greatness he has got. I hourly learn
A doctrine of obedience, and would gladly
Look him i' the face.

Pro.   This I'll report, dear lady:
Have comfort, for I know your plight is pitied
Of him that caus'd it.

Gal. You see how easily she may be surpris'd.

> [PROCULEIUS *and two of the* Guard *ascend the monument by a lad-
> der, and come behind* CLEOPATRA. *Some of the* Guard *unbar and
> open the gates, discovering the lower room of the monument.*

[*To* PROCULEIUS *and the* Guard.] Guard her till Cæsar come.

[*Exit.*

Iras. Royal queen!

Char. O Cleopatra! thou art taken, queen.

Cleo. Quick, quick, good hands.

[*Drawing a dagger.*

Pro.   Hold, worthy lady, hold!

[*Seizes and disarms her.*

Do not yourself such wrong, who are in this
Reliev'd, but not betray'd.

Cleo.   What, of death too,
That rids our dogs of languish?

Pro.   Cleopatra,
Do not abuse my master's bounty by
The undoing of yourself; let the world see
His nobleness well acted, which your death
Will never let come forth.

Cleo.   Where art thou, death?
Come hither, come! come, come, and take a queen
Worth many babes and beggars!

Pro.   O! temperance, lady.

Cleo. Sir, I will eat no meat, I'll not drink, sir;
If idle talk will once be necessary,
I'll not sleep neither. This mortal house I'll ruin,
Do Cæsar what he can. Know, sir, that I
Will not wait pinion'd at your master's court,
Nor once be chastis'd with the sober eye
Of dull Octavia. Shall they hoist me up
And show me to the shouting varletry
Of censuring Rome? Rather a ditch in Egypt
Be gentle grave unto me! rather on Nilus' mud
Lay me stark nak'd, and let the water-flies

Blow me into abhorring! rather make
My country's high pyramides my gibbet,
And hang me up in chains!
  Pro.   You do extend
These thoughts of horror further than you shall
Find cause in Cæsar.

Enter DOLABELLA.

  Dol.   Proculeius,
What thou hast done thy master Cæsar knows,
And he hath sent for thee; as for the queen,
I'll take her to my guard.
  Pro.   So, Dolabella,
It shall content me best; be gentle to her.
[*To* CLEOPATRA.] To Cæsar I will speak what you shall please,
If you'll employ me to him.
  Cleo.   Say, I would die.
       [*Exeunt* PROCULEIUS *and* Soldiers.
  Dol. Most noble empress, you have heard of me?
  Cleo. I cannot tell.
  Dol.   Assuredly you know me.
  Cleo. No matter, sir, what I have heard or known.
You laugh when boys or women tell their dreams;
Is 't not your trick?
  Dol.   I understand not, madam.
  Cleo. I dream'd there was an Emperor Antony:
O! such another sleep, that I might see
But such another man.
  Dol.   If it might please ye,—
  Cleo. His face was as the heavens, and therein stuck
A sun and moon, which kept their course, and lighted
The little O, the earth.
  Dol.   Most sovereign creature,—
  Cleo. His legs bestrid the ocean; his rear'd arm
Crested the world; his voice was propertied
As all the tuned spheres, and that to friends;
But when he meant to quail and shake the orb,
He was as rattling thunder. For his bounty,
There was no winter in 't, an autumn 'twas
That grew the more by reaping; his delights
Were dolphin-like, they show'd his back above
The element they liv'd in; in his livery
Walk'd crowns and crownets, realms and islands were
As plates dropp'd from his pocket.
  Dol.   Cleopatra,—

Cleo. Think you there was, or might be, such a man
As this I dream'd of?
  Dol.   Gentle madam, no.
  Cleo. You lie, up to the hearing of the gods.
But, if there be, or ever were, one such,
It's past the size of dreaming; nature wants stuff
To vie strange forms with fancy; yet to imagine
An Antony were nature's piece 'gainst fancy,
Condemning shadows quite.
  Dol.   Hear me, good madam.
Your loss is as yourself, great; and you bear it
As answering to the weight: would I might never
O'ertake pursu'd success, but I do feel,
By the rebound of yours, a grief that smites
My very heart at root.
  Cleo.   I thank you, sir.
Know you what Cæsar means to do with me?
  Dol. I am loath to tell you what I would you knew.
  Cleo. Nay, pray you, sir,—
  Dol.   Though he be honourable,—
  Cleo. He'll lead me then in triumph?
  Dol. Madam, he will; I know 't.

       [*Within,* 'Make way there!—Cæsar!'

  Enter Cæsar, Gallus, Proculeius, Mecænas, Seleucus,
      and Attendants.

  Cæs. Which is the Queen of Egypt?
  Dol. It is the emperor, madam.

            [Cleopatra *kneels.*

  Cæs. Arise, you shall not kneel.
I pray you, rise; rise, Egypt.
  Cleo.   Sir, the gods
Will have it thus; my master and my lord
I must obey.
  Cæs. Take to you no hard thoughts;
The record of what injuries you did us,
Though written in our flesh, we shall remember
As things but done by chance.
  Cleo.   Sole sir o' the world,
I cannot project mine own cause so well
To make it clear; but do confess I have
Been laden with like frailties which before
Have often sham'd our sex.
  Cæs.   Cleopatra, know,
We will extenuate rather than enforce:

If you apply yourself to our intents,—
Which towards you are most gentle,—you shall find
A benefit in this change; but if you seek
To lay on me a cruelty, by taking
Antony's course, you shall bereave yourself
Of my good purposes, and put your children
To that destruction which I'll guard them from,
If thereon you rely. I'll take my leave.
   Cleo. And may through all the world: 'tis yours; and we,
Your scutcheons, and your signs of conquest, shall
Hang in what place you please. Here, my good lord.
   Cæs. You shall advise me in all for Cleopatra.
   Cleo. [*Giving a Scroll.*] This is the brief of money, plate, and jewels,
I am possess'd of: 'tis exactly valued;
Not petty things admitted. Where's Seleucus?
   Sel. Here, madam.
   Cleo. This is my treasurer; let him speak, my lord,
Upon his peril, that I have reserv'd
To myself nothing. Speak the truth, Seleucus.
   Sel. Madam,
I had rather seal my lips, than, to my peril,
Speak that which is not.
    Cleo.   What have I kept back?
   Sel. Enough to purchase what you have made known.
   Cæs. Nay, blush not, Cleopatra; I approve
Your wisdom in the deed.
    Cleo.   See! Cæsar! O, behold,
How pomp is follow'd; mine will now be yours;
And, should we shift estates, yours would be mine.
The ingratitude of this Seleucus does
Even make me wild. O slave! of no more trust
Than love that's hir'd. What! goest thou back? thou shalt
Go back, I warrant thee; but I'll catch thine eyes,
Though they had wings: slave, soulless villain, dog!
O rarely base!
   Cæs.   Good queen, let us entreat you.
   Cleo. O Cæsar! what a wounding shame is this,
That thou, vouchsafing here to visit me,
Doing the honour of thy lordliness
To one so meek, that mine own servant should
Parcel the sum of my disgraces by
Addition of his envy. Say, good Cæsar,
That I some lady trifles have reserv'd,
Immoment toys, things of such dignity
As we greet modern friends withal; and say,

Some nobler token I have kept apart
For Livia and Octavia, to induce
Their mediation; must I be unfolded
With one that I have bred? The gods! it smites me
Beneath the fall I have. [*To* SELEUCUS.] Prithee, go hence;
Or I shall show the cinders of my spirits
Through the ashes of my chance. Wert thou a man,
Thou wouldst have mercy on me.
    Cæs.   Forbear, Seleucus.

                                      [*Exit* SELEUCUS.

    Cleo. Be it known that we, the greatest, are misthought
For things that others do; and, when we fall,
We answer others' merits in our name,
Are therefore to be pitied.
    Cæs.   Cleopatra,
Not what you have reserv'd, nor what acknowledg'd,
Put we i' the roll of conquest: still be 't yours,
Bestow it at your pleasure; and believe,
Cæsar's no merchant, to make prize with you
Of things that merchants sold. Therefore be cheer'd;
Make not your thoughts your prisions: no, dear queen;
For we intend so to dispose you as
Yourself shall give us counsel. Feed, and sleep:
Our care and pity is so much upon you,
That we remain your friend; and so, adieu.
    Cleo. My master, and my lord!
    Cæs.   Not so. Adieu.

                  [*Flourish. Exeunt* CÆSAR *and his Train.*
    Cleo. He words me, girls, he words me, that I should not
Be noble to myself: but, hark thee, Charmian.

                      [*Whispers* CHARMIAN.
    Iras. Finish, good lady; the bright day is done,
And we are for the dark.
    Cleo.   Hie thee again:
I have spoke already, and it is provided;
Go, put it to the haste.
    Char.   Madam, I will.

                Re-enter DOLABELLA.

    Dol. Where is the queen?
    Char.   Behold, sir. [*Exit.*
    Cleo.   Dolabella!
    Dol. Madam, as thereto sworn by your command,
Which my love makes religion to obey,

I tell you this: Cæsar through Syria
Intends his journey; and within three days
You with your children will he send before.
Make your best use of this; I have perform'd
Your pleasure and my promise.
    Cleo.   Dolabella,
I shall remain your debtor.
    Dol.   I your servant.
Adieu, good queen; I must attend on Cæsar.
    Cleo. Farewell, and thanks.

                       [*Exit* DOLABELLA.
              Now, Iras, what think'st thou?

Thou, an Egyptian puppet, shall be shown
In Rome, as well as I; mechanic slaves
With greasy aprons, rules and hammers, shall
Uplift us to the view; in their thick breaths,
Rank of gross diet, shall we be enclouded,
And forc'd to drink their vapour.
    Iras.   The gods forbid!
    Cleo. Nay, 'tis most certain, Iras. Saucy lictors
Will catch at us, like strumpets, and scald rimers
Ballad us out o'tune; the quick comedians
Extemporally will stage us, and present
Our Alexandrian revels. Antony
Shall be brought drunken forth, and I shall see
Some squeaking Cleopatra boy my greatness
I' the posture of a whore.
    Iras.   O, the good gods!
    Cleo. Nay, that's certain.
    Iras. I'll never see it; for, I am sure my nails
Are stronger than mine eyes.
    Cleo.   Why, that's the way
To fool their preparation, and to conquer
Their most absurd intents.

             Re-enter CHARMIAN.

                    Now, Charmian,

Show me, my women, like a queen; go fetch
My best attires; I am again for Cydnus,
To meet Mark Antony. Sirrah Iras, go.
Now, noble Charmian, we'll dispatch indeed;
And, when thou hast done this chare, I'll give thee leave
To play till doomsday. Bring our crown and all. [*Exit* IRAS. *A noise heard.*
Wherefore's this noise?

Enter one of the GUARD.

Guard.   Here is a rural fellow
That will not be denied your highness' presence:
He brings you figs.
   Cleo. Let him come in. [*Exit* Guard.] What poor an instrument
May do a noble deed! he brings me liberty.
My resolution's plac'd, and I have nothing
Of woman in me; now from head to foot
I am marble-constant, now the fleeting moon
No planet is of mine.

     Re-enter Guard, *with a* Clown *bringing in a basket.*

Guard.   This is the man.
   Cleo. Avoid, and leave him.   [*Exit* Guard.
Hast thou the pretty worm of Nilus there,
That kills and pains not?
   Clo. Truly, I have him; but I would not be the party that should desire you to touch him, for his biting is immortal; those that do die of it do seldom or never recover.
   Cleo. Remember'st thou any that have died on 't?
   Clo. Very many, men and women too. I heard of one of them no longer than yesterday; a very honest woman, but something given to lie, as a woman should not do but in the way of honesty, how she died of the biting of it, what pain she felt. Truly, she makes a very good report o' the worm; but he that will believe all that they say shall never be saved by half that they do. But this is most fallible, the worm's an odd worm.
   Cleo. Get thee hence; farewell.
   Clo. I wish you all joy of the worm.

                       [*Sets down the basket.*
   Cleo. Farewell.
   Clo. You must think this, look you, that the worm will do his kind.
   Cleo. Ay, ay; farewell.
   Clo. Look you, the worm is not to be trusted but in the keeping of wise people; for indeed there is no goodness in the worm.
   Cleo. Take thou no care; it shall be heeded.
   Clo. Very good. Give it nothing, I pray you, for it is not worth the feeding.
   Cleo. Will it eat me?
   Clo. You must not think I am so simple but I know the devil himself will not eat a woman; I know that woman is a dish for the gods, if the devil dress her not. But, truly, these same whoreson devils do the gods great harm in their women, for in every ten that they make, the devils mar five.
   Cleo. Well, get thee gone; farewell.
   Clo. Yes, forsooth; I wish you joy of the worm.   [*Exit.*

Re-enter IRAS, *with a robe, crown, &c.*

Cleo. Give me my robe, put on my crown; I have
Immortal longings in me; now no more
The juice of Egypt's grape shall moist this lip.
Yare, yare, good Iras; quick. Methinks I hear
Antony call; I see him rouse himself
To praise my noble act; I hear him mock
The luck of Cæsar, which the gods give men
To excuse their after wrath: husband, I come:
Now to that name my courage prove my title!
I am fire, and air; my other elements
I give to baser life. So; have you done?
Come then, and take the last warmth of my lips.
Farewell, kind Charmian; Iras, long farewell.

              [*Kisses them.* IRAS *falls and dies.*

Have I the aspic in my lips? Dost fall?
If thou and nature can so greatly part,
The stroke of death is as a lover's pinch,
Which hurts, and is desir'd. Dost thou lie still?
If thus thou vanishest, thou tell'st the world
It is not worth leave-taking.

    Char. Dissolve, thick cloud, and rain, That I may say,
The gods themselves do weep.

    Cleo.   This proves me base:
If she first meet the curled Antony,
He'll make demand of her, and spend that kiss
Which is my heaven to have. Come, thou mortal wretch,

         [*To the asp, which she applies to her breast.*

With thy sharp teeth this knot intrinsicate
Of life at once untie; poor venomous fool,
Be angry, and dispatch. O! couldst thou speak,
That I might hear thee call great Cæsar ass
Unpolicied.

    Char.   O eastern star!

    Cleo.   Peace, peace!
Dost thou not see my baby at my breast,
That sucks the nurse asleep?

    Char.   O, break! O, break!

    Cleo. As sweet as balm, as soft as air, as gentle,—
O Antony!—Nay, I will take thee too.

         [*Applying another asp to her arm.*
                [*Dies.*
What should I stay—

    Char. In this vile world? So, fare thee well.
Now boast thee, death, in thy possession lies

A lass unparallel'd. Downy windows, close;
And golden Phœbus never be beheld
Of eyes again so royal! Your crown's awry;
I'll mend it, and then play.

Enter the Guard, *rushing in.*

First Guard. Where is the queen?
Char.   Speak softly, wake her not.
First Guard. Cæsar hath sent—
Char.   Too slow a messenger.

                                    [*Applies an asp.*

O! come apace, dispatch; I partly feel thee.
    First Guard. Approach, ho! All's not well; Cæsar's beguil'd.
    Sec. Guard. There's Dolabella sent from Cæsar; call him.
    First Guard. What work is here! Charmian, is this well done?
    Char. It is well done, and fitting for a princess
Descended of so many royal kings.
Ah! soldier.   [*Dies.*

Re-enter DOLABELLA.

    Dol. How goes it here?
    Sec. Guard.   All dead.
    Dol.   Cæsar, thy thoughts
Touch their effects in this; thyself art coming
To see perform'd the dreaded act which thou
So sought'st to hinder.

                        [*Within,* 'A way there!—a way for Cæsar!'

Re-enter CÆSAR *and all his Train.*

    Dol. O! sir, you are too sure an augurer;
That you did fear is done.
    Cæs.   Bravest at the last,
She levell'd at our purposes, and, being royal,
Took her own way. The manner of their deaths?
I do not see them bleed.
    Dol.   Who was last with them?
    First Guard. A simple countryman that brought her figs:
This was his basket.
    Cæs.   Poison'd then.
    First Guard.   O Cæsar!
This Charmian liv'd but now; she stood, and spake:
I found her trimming up the diadem
On her dead mistress; tremblingly she stood,
And on the sudden dropp'd.

Cæs.   O noble weakness!
If they had swallow'd poison 'twould appear
By external swelling; but she looks like sleep,
As she would catch another Antony
In her strong toil of grace.
    Dol.   Here, on her breast,
There is a vent of blood, and something blown;
The like is on her arm.
    First Guard. This is an aspic's trail; and these fig-leaves
Have slime upon them, such as the aspic leaves
Upon the caves of Nile.
    Cæs.   Most probable
That so she died; for her physician tells me
She hath pursu'd conclusions infinite
Of easy ways to die. Take up her bed;
And bear her women from the monument.
She shall be buried by her Antony:
No grave upon the earth shall clip in it
A pair so famous. High events as these
Strike those that make them; and their story is
No less in pity than his glory which
Brought them to be lamented. Our army shall,
In solemn show, attend this funeral,
And then to Rome. Come, Dolabella, see
High order in this great solemnity.   [*Exeunt.*

DANCE

The Hopi Snake Dance

by D. H. LAWRENCE

THE HOPI COUNTRY IS IN ARIZONA, NEXT THE NAVAJO country, and some seventy miles north of the Santa Fé railroad. The Hopis are Pueblo Indians, village Indians, so their reservation is not large. It consists of a square track of greyish, unappetising desert, out of which rise three tall arid mesas, broken off in ragged, pallid rock. On the top of the mesas perch the ragged, broken, greyish pueblos, identical with the mesas on which they stand.

The nearest village, Walpi, stands in half-ruin high, high on a narrow rock-top where no leaf of life ever was tender. It is all grey, utterly dry, utterly pallid, stone and dust, and very narrow. Below it all the stark light of the dry Arizona sun.

Walpi is called the "first mesa." And it is at the far edge of Walpi you see the withered beaks and claws and bones of sacrificed eagles, in a rock-cleft under the sky. They sacrifice an eagle each year, on the brink, by rolling him out and crushing him so as to shed no blood. Then they drop his remains down the dry cleft in the promontory's farthest grey tip.

The trail winds on, utterly bumpy and horrible, for thirty miles, past the second mesa, where Chimopova is, on to the third mesa. And on the Sunday afternoon of August 17th, black automobile after automobile lurched and crawled across the grey desert, where low, grey, sage-scrub was coming to pallid yellow. Black hood followed crawling after black hood, like a funeral cortège. The motor-cars, with all the tourists, wending their way to the third and farthest mesa, thirty miles across this dismal desert where an odd water-windmill spun, and odd patches of corn blew in the strong desert wind, like dark-green women with fringed shawls blowing and fluttering, not far from the foot of the great, grey, up-piled mesa.

The snake dance (I am told) is held once a year, on each of the three mesas in succession. This year of grace 1924 it was to be held in Hotevilla, the last village on the furthest western tip of the third mesa.

On and on bumped the cars. The lonely second mesa lay in the distance. On and on, to the ragged ghost of the third mesa.

The third mesa has two main villages, Oraibi, which is on the near edge, and Hotevilla, on the far. Up scrambles the car, on all its four legs, like a black-beetle straddling past the schoolhouse and store down below, up the bare rock and over the changeless boulders, with a surge and a sickening lurch to the sky-brim, where stands the rather foolish church. Just beyond, dry, grey, ruined, and apparently abandoned, Oraibi, its few ragged stone huts. All these cars come all this way, and apparently nobody at home.

You climb still, up the shoulder of rock, a few more miles, across the lofty, wind-swept mesa, and so you come to Hotevilla, where the dance is, and where already hundreds of motor-cars are herded in an official camping-ground, among the piñon bushes.

Hotevilla is a tiny little village of grey little houses, raggedly built with undressed stone and mud around a little oblong plaza, and partly in ruins. One of the chief two-storey houses on the small square is a ruin, with big square window-holes.

It is a parched, grey country of snakes and eagles, pitched up against the sky. And a few dark-faced, short, thickly built Indians have their few peach trees among the sand, their beans and squashes on the naked sand under the sky, their springs of brackish water.

Three thousand people came to see the little snake dance this year, over miles of desert and bumps. Three thousand, of all sorts, cultured people from New York, Californians, onward-pressing tourists, cowboys, Navajo Indians, even negroes; fathers, mothers, children, of all ages, colours, sizes of stoutness, dimensions of curiosity.

What had they come for? Mostly to see men hold *live rattlesnakes* in their mouths. *I never did see a rattlesnake, and I'm crazy to see one!* cried a girl with bobbed hair.

There you have it. People trail hundreds of miles, avidly, to see this circus-performance of men handling live rattlesnakes that may bite them any minute—even do bite them. Some show, that!

There is the other aspect, of the ritual dance. One may look on from the angle of culture, as one looks on while Anna Pavlova dances with the Russian Ballet.

Or there is still another point of view, the religious. Before the snake dance begins, on the Monday, and the spectators are packed thick on the ground round the square, and in the window-holes, and on all the roofs, all sorts of people greedy with curiosity, a little speech is made to them all, asking the audience to be silent and respectful, as this is a sacred religious ceremonial of the Hopi Indians, and not a public entertainment. Therefore, please, no clapping or cheering or applause, but remember you are, as it were, in a church.

The audience accepts the implied rebuke in good faith, and looks round with a grin at the "church." But it is a good-humoured, very decent crowd, ready to respect any sort of feelings. And the Indian with his "religion" is a sort of public pet.

From the cultured point of view, the Hopi snake dance is almost nothing, not much more than a circus turn, or the games that children play in the street. It has none of the impressive beauty of the Corn Dance at Santo Domingo, for example. The big pueblos of Zuni, Santo Domingo, Taos have a cultured instinct which is not revealed in the Hopi snake dance. The last is grotesque rather than beautiful, and rather uncouth in its touch of horror. Hence the thrill, and the crowd.

As a cultured spectacle, it is a circus turn: men actually dancing round with snakes, poisonous snakes, dangling from their mouths.

And as a religious ceremonial: well, you can either be politely tolerant like the crowd to the Hopis; or you must have some spark of understanding of the sort of religion implied.

"Oh, the Indians," I heard a woman say, "they believe we are all brothers, the snakes are the Indian's brothers, and the Indians are the snakes' brothers. The Indians would never hurt the snakes, they won't hurt any animal. So the snakes won't bite the Indians. They are all brothers, and none of them hurt anybody."

This sounds very nice, only more Hindoo than Hopi. The dance itself does not convey much sense of fraternal communion. It is not in the least like St. Francis preaching to the birds.

The animistic religion, as we call it, is not the religion of the Spirit. A religion of spirits, yes. But not of Spirit. There is no One Spirit. There is no One God. There is no Creator. There is strictly no God at all: because all is alive. In our conception of religion there exists God and His Creation: two things. We are creatures of God, therefore we pray to God as the Father, the Saviour, the Maker.

But strictly, in the religion of aboriginal America, there is no Father, and no Maker. There is the great living source of life: say the Sun of existence: to which you can no more pray than you can pray to Electricity. And emerging from this Sun are the great potencies, the invincible influences which make shine and warmth and rain. From these great interrelated potencies of rain and heat and thunder emerge the seeds of life itself, corn, and creatures like snakes. And beyond these, men, persons. But all emerge separately. There is no oneness, no sympathetic identifying oneself with the rest. The law of isolation is heavy on every creature.

Now the Sun, the rain, the shine, the thunder, they are alive. But they are not persons or people. They are alive. They are manifestations of living activity. But they are not personal Gods.

Everything lives. Thunder lives, and rain lives, and sunshine lives. But not in the personal sense.

How is man to get himself into relation with the vast living convulsions of rain and thunder and sun, which are conscious and alive and potent, but like the vastest of beasts, inscrutable and incomprehensible? How is man to get himself into relation with these, the vastest of cosmic beasts?

It is the problem of the ages of man. Our religion says the cosmos is Matter, to be conquered by the Spirit of Man. The yogi, the fakir, the saint try conquest by abnegation and by psychic powers. The real conquest of the cosmos is made by science.

The American-Indian sees no division into Spirit and Matter, God and not-God. Everything is alive, though not personally so. Thunder is neither Thor nor Zeus. Thunder is the vast living thunder asserting itself like some incomprehensible monster, or some huge reptile-bird of the pristine cosmos.

How to conquer the dragon-mouthed thunder! How to capture the feathered rain!

We make reservoirs, and irrigation ditches and artesian wells. We make lightning conductors, and build vast electric plants. We say it is a matter of science, energy, force.

But the Indian says No! It all lives. We must approach it fairly, with profound respect, but also with desperate courage. Because man must conquer the cosmic monsters of living thunder and live rain. The rain that slides down from its source, and ebbs back subtly, with a strange energy generated between its coming and going, an energy which, even to our science, is of life: this, man has to conquer. The serpent-striped, featherly Rain.

We made the conquest by dams and reservoirs and windmills. The Indian, like the old Egyptian, seeks to make the conquest from the mystic will within him, pitted against the Cosmic Dragon.

We must remember, to the animistic vision there is no perfect God behind us, who created us from his knowledge, and foreordained all things. No such God. Behind lies only the terrific, terrible, crude Source, the mystic Sun, the well-head of all things. From this mystic Sun emanate the Dragons, Rain, Wind, Thunder, Shine, Light. The Potencies or Powers. These bring forth Earth, then reptiles, birds, and fishes.

The Potencies are not Gods. They are Dragons. The Sun of Creation itself is a dragon most terrible, vast, and most powerful, yet even so, less in being than we. The only gods on earth are men. For gods, like man, do not exist beforehand. They are created and evolved gradually, with æons of effort, out of the fire and smelting of life. They are the highest thing created, smelted between the furnace of the Life-Sun, and beaten on the anvil of the rain, with hammers of thunder and bellows of rushing wind. The cosmos is a great furnace, a dragon's den, where the heroes and demi-gods, men, forge themselves into being. It is a vast and violent matrix, where souls form like diamonds in earth, under extreme pressure.

So that gods are the outcome, not the origin. And the best gods that have resulted, so far, are men. But gods frail as flowers; which have also the godliness of things that have won perfection out of the terrific dragon-clutch of the cosmos. Men are frail as flowers. Man is as a flower, rain can kill him or succour him, heat can flick him with a bright tail, and destroy him: or, on the other hand, it can softly call him into existence, out of the egg of chaos. Man is delicate as a flower, godly beyond flowers, and his lordship is a ticklish business.

He has to conquer, and hold his own, and again conquer all the time. Conquer the powers of the cosmos. To us, science is our religion of conquest. Hence through science, we are the conquerors and resultant gods of our earth. But to the Indian, the so-called mechanical processes do not exist. All lives. And the conquest is made by the means of the living will.

This is the religion of all aboriginal America, Peruvian, Aztec, Athabascan: perhaps the aboriginal religion of all the world. In Mexico, men fell into horror of the crude, pristine gods, the dragons. But to the pueblo Indian, the most terrible dragon is still somewhat gentle-hearted.

This brings us back to the Hopi. He has the hardest task, the stubbornest destiny. Some inward fate drove him to the top of these parched mesas, all rocks and eagles, sand and snakes, and wind and sun and alkali. These he had to conquer. Not merely, as we should put it, the natural conditions of the place. But the mysterious life-spirit that reigned there. The eagle and the snake.

It is a destiny as well as another. The destiny of the animistic soul of man, instead of our destiny of Mind and Spirit. We have undertaken the scientific conquest of forces, or natural conditions. It has been comparatively easy, and we are victors. Look at our black motor-cars like beetles working up the rock-face at Oraibi. Look at our three thousand tourists gathered to gaze at the twenty lonely men who dance in the tribe's snake dance!

The Hopi sought the conquest by means of the mystic, living will that is in man, pitted against the living will of the dragon-cosmos. The Egyptians long ago made a partial conquest by the same means. We have made a partial conquest by other means. Our corn doesn't fail us: we have no seven years' famine, and apparently need never have. But the other thing fails us, the strange inward sun of life; the pellucid monster of the rain never shows us his stripes. To us, heaven switches on daylight, or turns on the shower-bath. We little gods are gods of the machine only. It is our highest. Our cosmos is a great engine. And we die of ennui. A subtle dragon stings us in the midst of plenty. *Quos vult perdere Deus, dementat prius.*

On the Sunday evening is a first little dance in the plaza at Hotevilla, called the Antelope dance. There is the hot, sandy, oblong little place, with a tuft of green cotton-wood boughs stuck like a plume at the south end, and on the floor at the foot of the green, a little lid of a trap door. They say the snakes are under there.

They say that the twelve officiating men of the snake clan of the tribe have for nine days been hunting snakes in the rocks. They have been performing the mysteries for nine days, in the kiva, and for two days they have fasted completely. All these days they have tended the snakes, washed them with repeated lustrations, soothed them, and exchanged spirits with them. The spirit of man soothing and seeking and making interchange with the spirits of the snakes. For the snakes are more rudimentary, nearer to the great convulsive powers. Nearer to the nameless Sun, more knowing in the slanting tracks of the rain, the pattering of the invisible feet of the rain-monster from the sky. The snakes are man's next emissaries to the rain-gods. The snakes lie nearer to the source of potency, the dark, lurking, intense sun at the centre of the earth. For to the cultured animist, and the pueblo Indian is such, the earth's dark centre holds its dark sun, our source of isolated being, round which our world coils its folds like a great snake. The snake is nearer the dark sun, and cunning of it.

They say—people say—that rattlesnakes are not travellers. They haunt the same spots on earth, and die there. It is said also that the snake-priests (so-called) of the Hopi, probably capture the same snakes year after year.

Be that as it may. At sundown before the real dance, there is the little dance called the Antelope dance. We stand and wait on a house-roof. Behind us is tethered an eagle; rather dishevelled he sits on the coping, and looks at us in unutterable resentment. See him, and see how much "brother-hood" the Indian feels with animals—at best the silent tolerance that acknowledges dangerous difference. We wait without event. There are no drums, no announcements. Suddenly into the plaza, with rude, intense movements, hurries a little file of men. They are smeared all with grey and black, and are naked save for little kilts embroidered like the sacred dance-kilts in other pueblos, red and green and black on a white fibre-cloth. The fox-skins hang behind. The feet of the dancers are pure ash-grey. Their hair is long.

The first is a heavy old man with heavy, long, wild grey hair and heavy fringe. He plods intensely forward, in the silence, followed in a sort of circle by the other grey-smeared, long-haired, naked, concentrated men. The oldest men are first: the last is a short-haired boy of fourteen or fifteen. There are only eight men—the so-called antelope priests. They pace round in a circle, rudely, absorbedly, till the first heavy, intense old man with his massive grey hair flowing, comes to the lid on the ground, near the tuft of kiva-boughs. He rapidly shakes from the hollow of his right hand a little white meal on the lid, stamps heavily, with naked right foot, on the meal, so the wood resounds, and paces heavily forward. Each man, to the boy, shakes meal, stamps, paces absorbedly on in the circle, comes to the lid again, shakes meal, stamps, paces absorbedly on, comes a third time to the lid, or trap door, and this time spits on the lid, stamps, and goes on. And this time the eight men file away behind the lid, between it and the tuft of green boughs. And there they stand in a line, their backs to the kiva-tuft of green; silent, absorbed, bowing a little to the ground.

Suddenly paces with rude haste another file of men. They are naked, and smeared with red "medicine," with big black lozenges of smeared paint on their backs. Their wild heavy hair hangs loose, the old, heavy, grey-haired men go first, then the middle-aged, then the young men, then last, two short-haired, slim boys, schoolboys. The hair of the young men is growing after school, and is bobbed round.

The grown men are all heavily built, rather short, with heavy but shapely flesh, and rather straight sides. They have not the archaic slim waists of the Taos Indians. They have an archaic squareness, and a sensuous heaviness. Their very hair is black, massive, heavy. These are the so-called snake-priests, men of the snake clan. And to-night, they are eleven in number.

They pace rapidly round, with that heavy wild silence of concentration characteristic of them, and cast meal and stamp upon the lid, cast meal and stamp in the second round, come round and spit and stamp in the third. For the savage, the animist, to spit may be a kind of blessing, a communion, a sort of embrace.

The eleven snake-priests form silently in a row, facing the eight grey-smeared antelope-priests across the little lid, and bowing forward a little, to earth. Then the antelope-priests, bending forward, begin a low, sombre chant, or call, that sounds wordless, only a deep, low-toned, secret Ay-a! Ay-a! Ay-a! And they bend from right to left, giving two shakes to the little, flat, white rattle in their left hand, at each shake, and stamping the right foot in heavy rhythm. In their right hand, that held the meal, is grasped a little skin bag, perhaps also containing meal.

They lean from right to left, two seed-like shakes of the rattle each time and the heavy rhythmic stamp of the foot, and the low, sombre, secretive chant-call each time. It is a strange low sound, such as we never hear, and it reveals how deep, how deep the men are in the mystery they are practising, how sunk deep below our world, to the world of snakes, and dark ways in the earth, where are the roots of corn, and where the little rivers of unchannelled, uncreated life-passion run like dark, trickling lightning, to the roots of the corn and to the feet and loins of men, from the earth's innermost dark sun. They are calling in the deep, almost silent snake-language, to the snakes and the rays of dark emission from the earth's inward "Sun."

At this moment, a silence falls on the whole crowd of listeners. It is that famous darkness and silence of Egypt, the touch of the other mystery. The deep concentration of the "priests" conquers, for a few seconds, our white-faced flippancy, and we hear only the deep Háh-ha! Háh-ha! speaking to snakes and the earth's inner core.

This lasts a minute or two. Then the antelope-priests stand bowed and still, and the snake-priests take up the swaying and the deep chant, that sometimes is so low, it is like a mutter underground, inaudible. The rhythm is crude, the swaying unison is all uneven. Culturally, there is nothing. If it were not for that mystic, dark-sacred concentration.

Several times in turn, the two rows of daubed, long-haired, insunk men facing one another take up the swaying and the chant. Then that too is finished. There is a break in the formation. A young snake-priest takes up something that may be a corn-cob—perhaps an antelope-priest hands it to him—and comes forward, with an old, heavy, but still shapely snake-priest behind him dusting his shoulders with the feathers, eagle-feathers presumably, which are the Indians' hollow prayer-sticks. With the heavy, stamping hop they move round in the previous circle, the young priest holding the cob curiously, and the old priest prancing strangely at the young priest's back, in a sort of incantation, and brushing the heavy young shoulders delicately with the prayer-feathers. It is the God-vibration that enters us from behind, and is transmitted to the hands, from the hands to the corn-cob. Several young priests emerge, with the bowed head and the cob in their hands and the heavy older priests hanging over them behind. They tread round the rough curve and come back to the kiva, take perhaps another cob, and tread round again.

That is all. In ten or fifteen minutes it is over. The two files file rapidly and silently away. A brief, primitive performance.

The crowd disperses. There were not many people. There were no venomous snakes on exhibition, so the mass had nothing to come for. And therefore the curious immersed intensity of the priests was able to conquer the white crowd.

By afternoon of the next day the three thousand people had massed in the little plaza, secured themselves places on the roofs and in the window-spaces, everywhere, till the small pueblo seemed built of people instead of stones. All sorts of people, hundreds and hundreds of white women, all in breeches like half-men, hundreds and hundreds of men who had been driving motor-cars, then many Navajos, the women in their full, long skirts and tight velvet bodices, the men rather lanky, long-waisted, real nomads. In the hot sun and the wind which blows the sand every day, every day in volumes round the corners, the three thousand tourists sat for hours, waiting for the show. The Indian policeman cleared the central oblong, in front of the kiva. The front rows of onlookers sat thick on the ground. And at last, rather early, because of the masses awaiting them, suddenly, silently, in the same rude haste, the antelope-priests filed absorbedly in, and made the rounds over the lid, as before. To-day, the eight antelope-priests were very grey. Their feet ashed pure grey, like suede soft boots: and their lower jaw was pure suede grey, while the rest of the face was blackish. With that pale-grey jaw, they looked like corpse-faces with swathing-bands. And all their bodies ash-grey smeared, with smears of black, and a black cloth to-day at the loins.

They made their rounds, and took their silent position behind the lid, with backs to the green tuft: an unearthly grey row of men with little skin bags in their hands. They were the lords of shadow, the intermediate twilight, the place of after-life and before-life, where house the winds of change. Lords of the mysterious, fleeting power of change.

Suddenly, with abrupt silence, in paced the snake-priests, headed by the same heavy man with solid grey hair like iron. To-day they were twelve men, from the old one, down to the slight, short-haired, erect boy of fourteen. Twelve men, two for each of the six worlds, or quarters: east, north, south, west, above, and below. And to-day they were in a queer ecstasy. Their faces were black, showing the whites of the eyes. And they wore small black loin-aprons. They were the hot living men of the darkness, lords of the earth's inner rays, the black sun of the earth's vital core, from which dart the speckled snakes, like beams.

Round they went, in rapid, uneven, silent absorption, the three rounds. Then in a row they faced the eight ash-grey men, across the lid. All kept their heads bowed towards earth, except the young boys.

Then, in the intense, secret, muttering chant the grey men began their leaning from right to left, shaking the hand, one-two, one-two, and bowing the body each time from right to left, left to right, above the lid in the ground, under which were the snakes. And their low, deep, mysterious voices spoke to the spirits under the earth, not to men above the earth.

But the crowd was on tenterhooks for the snakes, and could hardly wait for the mummery to cease. There was an atmosphere of inattention and impatience. But the chant and the swaying passed from the grey men to the black-faced men, and back again, several times.

This was finished. The formation of the lines broke up. There was a slight crowding to the centre, round the lid. The old antelope-priest (so-called) was stooping. And before the crowd could realize anything else a young priest emerged, bowing reverently, with the neck of a pale, delicate rattlesnake held between his teeth, the little, naive, bird-like head of the rattlesnake quite still, near the black cheek, and the long, pale, yellowish, spangled body of the snake dangling like some thick, beautiful cord. On passed the black-faced priest, with the wondering snake dangling from his mouth, pacing in the original circle, while behind him, leaping almost on his shoulders, was the oldest heavy priest, dusting the young man's shoulders with the feather-prayer-sticks, in an intense, earnest anxiety of concentration such as I have only seen in the old Indian men during a religious dance.

Came another young black-faced man out of the confusion, with another snake dangling and writhing a little from his mouth, and an elder priest dusting him from behind with the feathers: and then another, and another: till it was all confusion, probably, of six, and then four young priests with snakes dangling from their mouths, going round, apparently, three times in the circle. At the end of the third round the young priest stooped and delicately laid his snake on the earth, waving him away, away, as it were, into the world. He must not wriggle back to the kiva bush.

And after wondering a moment, the pale, delicate snake steered away with a rattlesnake's beautiful movement, rippling and looping, with the small, sensitive head lifted like antennæ, across the sand to the massed audience squatting solid on the ground. Like soft, watery lightning went the wondering snake at the crowd. As he came nearer, the people began to shrink aside, half-mesmerised. But they betrayed no exaggerated fear. And as the little snake drew very near, up rushed one of the two black-faced young priests who held the snake-stick, poised a moment over the snake, in the prayer-concentration of reverence which is at the same time conquest, and snatched the pale, long creature delicately from the ground, waving him in a swoop over the heads of the seated crowd, then delicately smoothing down the length of the snake with his left hand, stroking and smoothing and soothing the long, pale, bird-like thing; and returning with it to the kiva, handed it to one of the grey-jawed antelope-priests.

Meanwhile, all the time, the other young priests were emerging with a snake dangling from their mouths. The boy had finished his rounds. He launched his rattlesnake on the ground, like a ship, and like a ship away it steered. In a moment, after it went one of those two young black-faced priests who carried snake-sticks and were the snake catchers. As it neared the crowd, very close, he caught it up and waved it dramatically, his eyes glaring strangely out of his black face. And in the interim that youngest boy had been given a long, handsome bull-snake, by the priest at the hole under the kiva boughs. The bull-snake is not poisonous. It is a constrictor. This one was six feet long, with a sumptuous pattern. It waved its pale belly, and pulled its neck out of the boy's mouth. With two hands he put it back. It pulled itself once more free. Again he got it back, and managed to hold it. And then, as he went round in his looping circle, it coiled its handsome folds twice round his knee. He stooped, quietly, and as quietly as if he were untying his garter, he unloosed the folds. And all the time, an old priest was intently brushing the boy's thin straight shoulders with the feathers. And all the time, the snakes seemed strangely gentle, naive, wondering, and almost willing, almost in harmony with the men. Which of course was the sacred aim. While the boy's expression remained quite still and simple, as it were candid, in a candour where he and the snake should be in unison. The only dancers who showed signs of being wrought-up were the two young snake-catchers, and one of these, particularly, seemed in a state of actor-like uplift, rather ostentatious. But the old priests had that immersed, religious intentness which is like a spell, something from another world.

The young boy launched his bull-snake. It wanted to go back to the kiva. The snake-catcher drove it gently forward. Away it went, towards the crowd, and at the last minute was caught up into the air. Then this snake was handed to an old man sitting on the ground in the audience, in the front row. He was an old Hopi of the Snake clan.

Snake after snake had been carried round in the circles, dangling by the neck from the mouths of one young priest or another, and writhing and swaying slowly, with the small, delicate snake-head held as if wondering and listening. There had been some very large rattlesnakes, unusually large, two or three handsome bull-snakes, and some racers, whipsnakes. All had been launched, after their circuits in the mouth, all had been caught up by the young priests with the snake-sticks, one or two had been handed to old snake-clan men in the audience, who sat holding them in their arms as men hold a kitten. The most of the snakes, however, had been handed to the grey antelope-men who stood in the row, with their backs to the kiva bush. Till some of these ash-smeared men held armfuls of snakes, hanging over their arms like wet washing. Some of the snakes twisted and knotted round one another, showing pale bellies.

Yet most of them hung very still and docile. Docile, almost sympathetic, so that one was struck only by their clean, slim length of snake nudity, their beauty, like soft, quiescent lightning. They were so clean, because they had been washed and anointed and lustrated by the priests, in the days they had been in the kiva.

At last all the snakes had been mouth-carried in the circuits, and had made their little outrunning excursion to the crowd, and had been handed back to the priests in the rear. And now the Indian policemen, Hopi and Navajo, began to clear away the crowd that sat on the ground, five or six rows deep, around the small plaza. The snakes were all going to be set free on the ground. We must clear away.

We recoiled to the further end of the plaza. There, two Hopi women were scattering white corn-meal on the sandy ground. And thither came the two snake-catchers, almost at once, with their arms full of snakes. And before we who stood had realized it, the snakes were all writhing and squirming on the ground, in the white dust of meal, a couple of yards from our feet. Then immediately, before they could writhe clear of each other and steer away, they were gently, swiftly snatched up again, and with their arms full of snakes, the two young priests went running out of the plaza.

We followed slowly, wondering, towards the western, or north-western edge of the mesa. There the mesa dropped steeply, and a broad trail wound down the vast hollow of desert brimmed up with strong evening light, up out of which jutted a perspective of sharp rock and further mesas and distant sharp mountains: the great, hollow, rock-wilderness space of that part of Arizona, submerged in light.

Away down the trail, small, dark, naked, rapid figures with arms held close, went the two young men, running swiftly down to the hollow level, and diminishing, running across the hollow towards more stark rocks of the other side. Two small, rapid, intent, dwindling little human figures. The tiny, dark sparks of men. Such specks of gods.

They disappeared, no bigger than stones, behind rocks in shadow. They had gone, it was said, to lay down the snakes before a rock called the snake-shrine, and let them all go free. Free to carry the message and thanks to the dragon-gods who can give and withhold. To carry the human spirit, the human breath, the human prayer, the human gratitude, the human command which had been breathed upon them in the mouths of the priests, transferred into them from those feather-prayer-sticks which the old wise men swept upon the shoulders of the young, snake-bearing men, to carry this back, into the vaster, dimmer, inchoate regions where the monsters of rain and wind alternated in beneficence and wrath. Carry the human prayer and will-power into the holes of the winds, down into the octopus heart of the rain-source. Carry the corn-meal which the women had scattered, back to that terrific, dread, and causeful dark sun which is at the earth's core, that which sends us corn out of the earth's nearness, sends us food or death, according to our strength of vital purpose, our power of sensitive will, our courage.

It is battle, a wrestling all the time. The Sun, the nameless Sun, source of all things, which we call sun because the other name is too fearful, this, this vast dark protoplasmic sun from which issues all that feeds our life, this original One is all the time willing and unwilling. Systole, diastole, it pulses its willingness and its unwillingness that we should live and move on, from being to being, manhood to further manhood. Man, small, vulnerable man, the farthest adventurer from the dark heart of the first of suns, into the cosmos of creation. Man, the last god won into existence. And all the time, he is sustained and threatened, menaced and sustained from the Source, the innermost sun-dragon. And all the time, he must submit and he must conquer. Submit to the strange beneficence from the Source, whose ways are past finding out. And conquer the strange malevolence of the Source, which is past comprehension also.

For the great dragons from which we draw our vitality are all the time willing and unwilling that we should have being. Hence only the heroes snatch manhood, little by little, from the strange den of the Cosmos.

Man, little man, with his consciousness and his will, must both submit to the great origin-powers of his life, and conquer them. Conquered by man who has overcome his fears, the snakes must go back into the earth with his messages of tenderness, of request, and of power. They go back as rays of love to the dark heart of the first of suns. But they go back also as arrows shot clean by man's sapience and courage, into the resistant, malevolent heart of the earth's oldest, stubborn core. In the core of the first of suns, whence man draws his vitality, lies poison as bitter as the rattlesnake's. This poison man must overcome, he must be master of its issue. Because from the first of suns come travelling the rays that make men strong and glad and gods who can range between the known and the unknown. Rays that quiver out of the earth as serpents do, naked with vitality. But each ray charged with poison for the unwary, the irreverent, and the cowardly. Awareness, wariness, is the first virtue in primitive man's morality. And his awareness must travel back and forth, back and forth, from the darkest origins out to the brightest edifices of creation.

And amid all its crudity, and the sensationalism which comes chiefly out of the crowd's desire for thrills, one cannot help pausing in reverence before the delicate, anointed bravery of the snake-priests (so-called), with the snakes.

They say the Hopis have a marvellous secret cure for snake-bites. They say the bitten are given an emetic drink, after the dance, by the old women, and that they must lie on the edge of the cliff and vomit, vomit, vomit. I saw none of this. The two snake-men who ran down into the shadow came soon running up again, running all the while, and steering off at a tangent, ran up the mesa once more, but beyond a deep, impassable cleft. And there, when they had come up to our level, we saw them across the cleft distance washing, brown and naked, in a pool; washing off the paint, the medicine, the ecstasy, to come back into daily life and eat food. Because for two days they had eaten nothing, it was said. And for nine days they had been immersed in the mystery of snakes, and fasting in some measure.

Men who have lived many years among the Indians say they do not believe the Hopi have any secret cure. Sometimes priests do die of bites, it is said. But a rattlesnake secretes his poison slowly. Each time he strikes he loses his venom, until if he strikes several times, he has very little wherewithal to poison a man. Not enough, not half enough to kill. His glands must be very fully charged with poison, as they are when he emerges from winter-sleep, before he can kill a man outright. And even then, he must strike near some artery.

Therefore, during the nine days of the kiva, when the snakes are bathed and lustrated, perhaps they strike their poison away into some inanimate object. And surely they are soothed and calmed with such things as the priests, after centuries of experience, know how to administer to them.

We dam the Nile and take the railway across America. The Hopi smooths the rattlesnake and carries him in his mouth, to send him back into the dark places of the earth, an emissary to the inner powers.

To each sort of man his own achievement, his own victory, his own conquest. To the Hopi, the origins are dark and dual, cruelty is coiled in the very beginnings of all things, and circle after circle creation emerges towards a flickering, revealed God-head. With Man as the godhead so far achieved, waveringly and for ever incomplete, in this world.

To us and to the Orientals, the Godhead was perfect to start with, and man makes but a mechanical excursion into a created and ordained universe, an excursion of mechanical achievement, and of yearning for the return to the perfect Godhead of the beginning.

To us, God was in the beginning, Paradise and the Golden Age have been long lost, and all we can do is to win back.

To the Hopi, God is not yet, and the Golden Age lies far ahead. Out of the dragon's den of the cosmos, we have wrested only the beginnings of our being, the rudiments of our godhead.

Between the two visions lies the gulf of mutual negations. But ours was the quickest way, so we are conquerors for the moment.

The American aborigines are radically, innately religious. The fabric of their life is religious. But their religion is animistic, their sources are dark and impersonal, their conflict with their "gods" is slow, and unceasing.

This is true of the settled pueblo Indians and the wandering Navajo, the ancient Maya, and the surviving Aztec. They are all involved at every moment, in their old, struggling religion.

Until they break in a kind of hopelessness under our cheerful, triumphant success. Which is what is rapidly happening. The young Indians who have been to school for many years are losing their religion, becoming discontented, bored, and rootless. An Indian with his own religion inside him *cannot* be bored. The flow of the mystery is too intense all the time, too intense, even, for him to adjust himself to circumstances which really are mechanical. Hence his failure. So he, in his great religious struggle for the Godhead of man, falls back beaten. The Personal God who ordained a mechanical cosmos gave the victory to his sons, a mechanical triumph.

Soon after the dance is over, the Navajo begin to ride down the Western trail, into the light. Their women, with velvet bodices and full, full skirts, silver and turquoise tinkling thick on their breasts, sit back on their horses and ride down the steep slope, looking wonderingly around from their pleasant, broad, nomadic, Mongolian faces. And the men, long, loose, thin, long-waisted, with tall hats on their brows and low-sunk silver belts on their hips, come down to water their horses at the spring. We say they look wild. But they have the remoteness of their religion, their animistic vision, in their eyes, they can't see as we see. And they cannot accept us. They stare at us as the coyotes stare at us: the gulf of mutual negation between us.

So in groups, in pairs, singly, they ride silently down into the lower strata of light, the aboriginal Americans riding into their shut-in reservations. While the white Americans hurry back to their motor-cars, and soon the air buzzes with starting engines, like the biggest of rattlesnakes buzzing.

Beethoven's Ninth Symphony and the King Cobra

by EDGAR LEE MASTERS

I

In the days of steaming swamps and tropic ferns,
When life was fermenting and crackling, and trying to escape
The trance of Nature, and get beyond itself,
Footless creatures chose legs, and conquered the land.
Then they abandoned the conquest, and took back to the water,
And became the drooling sea-crocodile,
The laughing mosasaur,
And the silly giant called the ichthyosaur,
And the pleisiosaur, with a mouth like a goose,
All flapping, floundering, and laughing to be back in the water,
Unenvious of their relatives who got wings,
And long tails, and bat-like rudders,
And turtle-beaks, which stood agape, grinning like Moloch,
Roosting on sun-hot rocks.

Those were the days when there was nothing but demons,
Nothing but horns, hoofs, teeth and fangs.

Somewhere here the crawling, footless, coiling
Worm of hell lost his father and mother,
And went on without ancestors, and without memory of ancestors,
Or any worship of ancestors, and ended up as hell's perfection,
Ended as the cobra, crawling forever as abandoned diabolism,
As embodied hate and sullen loneliness.
But the footless creatures who clove to the land,
And longed till their ears could catch
Something beside this sound and the next sound,
Sounds without recurring periods and pauses,
Without continuity or rhythm;
The footless creatures which longed themselves to claws,
And then longed their claws to fingers,

Which at last could set down the signs of eternity for oboes,
For clarinets, horns and strings—
These footless creatures started the breed which fathered Beethoven at
    last;
And thus came the finale, the consummation:
Beethoven and the King Cobra.

II

Nature is a sleeping spirit.
Nature is a trance, a mass drugged by eternity,
A petrifaction, a solid jelly, a self-containment,
A contemplation which cannot arise from itself,
Or get out of itself, or look upon itself.
Man has escaped from this deep catalepsy:
He has soared up, and can look down;
He has flown forward, and can glance back;
He can turn upon the past, and see the future.
But as he ages he ceases gradually to be outside himself,
Or see himself.
He becomes again all-self-contained, reduced to one mood of Nature,
Reduced to the eye which contemplates, but does not know.
So he descends to the mind of the cobra,
On the way to the unconsciousness of Nature,
Which is Death, the cobra's cousin.

Nature is spirit, but the spirit of calm swamp-slush;
Nature is unconscious, but it casts upon matter
The reflection of what has created Nature.
Nature as the whole of things lies locked in the unconsciousness
Which is the primal condition of all terraqueous things.
The same power which slumbers in the stone,
And dreams in the flower, and sends half-legged beings
Out of the water to the land, then back to the water,
And into trees, and on to rocks—
This same power awakes in the cobra;
It awakes in Beethoven.
It awakes when anything separates itself from Nature,
And becomes two instead of one;
And becomes outside as well as inside;
And becomes something more than a landscape's mood,
Something more than a motionless eye;
Becomes in truth an eye that knows enemies,
And a head that knows that pain is in the flesh,
And comes from turning from one to two;

And that pain brings something into existence
Which is an advance upon a mere stare.

It is here that a separation takes place between Nature, the creator,
And any mind created.
Pain is the penalty, and fear, both births of consciousness.
And thus with this state of being common to both Beethoven and the
    cobra
Beethoven can disturb the cobra
By shocking its ear to be aware of sounds and octaves
Too much for an ear which is a tympanum and cochlea of mere snake
    grisle and bone,
Murmurous with its swamp nativity, and fitted to listen
For enemies and food, nothing else;
For the sound of a twig snapping, not polyphones.

What but irritation, disturbance,
What but annoyance and pain,
Made the thing at one with Nature
Become the thing escaped and fighting Nature,
Both because its resists being jailed again,
And because it resents ever being turned loose?
What are irritation, disturbance, annoyance, pain?
Are they not evil?
So Beethoven's music must be evil to the cobra,
For it forces the cobra's ear to do more than listen
For enemies and for food.
The cobra evoked from the great trance
Continues as an evil, we say.
But Beethoven so evoked after long aeons
Is he not evil, too?
Is he truth and beauty, yet a sufferer, and producing suffering?
Is he truth and beauty, who awakens greater consciousness?
Or is he continued evil, bringing pain and despair,
And deeper looks into the nothingness whence we came,
And a forecast of the resumption of sleep whither we tend?
Is he then evil as he shows these things to the full?
Does he not disturb us, as he does the cobra,
Which crawls and writhes and lifts itself
As it hears Beethoven through oboes
Tell of his sorrows and sufferings,
The neglect that the world heaped upon him,
His poverty and loneliness,
Loneliness as lonely as this glass-cage of the cobra;
All of which Beethoven uttered in music, and in the cry:

"I have no friend,
"I am alone in the world.
"O God, my Rock, my All,
"Thou Unutterable, hear thy unhappy,
"Thy most unhappy of mortals."
Is not the cobra also alone and unhappy?
And these cries of Beethoven
Do they not set vibrating
The unutterable, and the unhappy,
And the loneliness which is the cobra?

III

Beethoven was miserable, in agony, in the trap of life.
But the king cobra is all misery, all agony,
All embodied evil, being by Nature trapped to be within itself,
And by man trapped to be within this glass cage.
It is trapped by being fated to be constantly aware of its venom genius,
That is the groundwork, the essence and all of its being;
And the shape of its head, the stare of its eyes show this.
With this goes the sense of enmity between the cobra and man,
And fear of man, and fear of the jungle and night; and that is being
         trapped.
Its life is poison, and that is its wisdom also; and that is being trapped.
Its wisdom is hate for the Power which has invented traps,
Hate for the Power which has trapped its thought in a shallow skull,
And locked its thought in a trap of contemplation,
Where all the traps are contemplated dimly.
It is trapped to the life of sensuous particulars,
While the whole teases, and is never known,
The whole is a slowed-down film.
It is trapped by will without knowledge;
It is trapped by a small speck of brain plasm
From which has issued narrow channels
Of sight and hearing,
Through which the world of visible and audible things:
Man the keeper before the cage, standing safe;
And Beethoven with strings, clarinets and horns
Gorges through like a freshet, and bursts the channels, and tortures the
         brain.
It is trapped when guessing the life blisses of other creatures;
It is trapped, being shut from some realer realm of life;
It is trapped, and compelled to crawl and coil,
And lick forth a tongue to aid half-eyes;
It is trapped in loneliness, not able to live loneliness as the soul can,

Not able in loneliness to sink into the trance of the ancient swamps;
But by its loneliness made more aware
Of its separateness, and of enemies and dangers without—
Such a curse upon anything that can feel!
Such loneliness at the dark bottom-point of hell's cone!
It is trapped by dim memory of heredity,
But kept from going back to water,
And kept from taking to the air,
And cut off bitterly from the lineage of man:
For man descended not from the snake,
But from old, patriarchal, drowsy, dreaming reptiles.
It is trapped to the life of the jungle forever;
It is trapped by hate of the Cause of consciousness,
And it brews venom in revenge.
It is trapped forever to the shape of a gorilla's cylindrical excrement;
It is stripped and exposed forever like the phallus of Polyphemus,
The horror and disgust of worst and best eyes!
It is trapped by regret for vanished aeons of earth
When there was peace in the pulse of the earth mood
Which made a oneness of plants, rocks, ooze, and primordial plasm.
It is trapped because the chance is now gone forever to get feet or wings,
     and fly the jungle.
It is trapped by the will which has made this elongated frightfulness,
The will—from what source?—which has made
Teeth and fangs and poison,
And the hunger of cannibalism.
For there is a Dual Thing
Which might have made the cobra half good,
Not all evil.
And this the cobra feels, and licks forth its forked tongue
In hate of this Dual Thing.
It is trapped by the power within it
From the Power without it, which has implanted in it
This insane will of dealing death.
It is trapped by being the contemplation of the motionless eye,
Where no smile lurks, no sense of voluptuous content;
But where alert malice sparkles and burns, and winks like a half-ashed
     coal,
And flashes hate and hunger and irritable watchfulness.
It is trapped by being engendered and then spurned by a superior soul;
It is trapped by being set aside and deserted by a soul becoming superior
     as man, as Beethoven;
It is trapped by being life which looks neither to what is above,
Nor to what is below,
But to what is ahead in the weeds, the gopher snake as food.

And thus barred from worlds and worlds of life,
And crushed by exultant trumpets,
By horns and strings,
And by drums that echo frightful dangers and depths
The cobra lies stretched in the cage with motionless eye.
The cobra is a monist. All is Hate,
And the cobra is all hate.
The cobra is the hate of man, made pure poison,
Condensed in one organism of flesh,
For life as horror, as cancer, as war,
As ruin and unreason and madness.

IV

It is more than a hundred years past and gone
Since Beethoven cried:
"God, O God, my Guardian, my Rock, my All!
"Thou seest my heart, and knowest how it distresses me
"To do harm to others, though doing right to my darling Karl.
"Hear, Thou Unutterable, hear Thy unhappy,
"Most unhappy of mortals:
"I have no friend, and am alone in the world."

Shall this cry never die out?
Never be hushed as the crackling of weeds is hushed
After the giant thunder-lizard has walked on?
Shall it never vanish as the rib-marks of the serpent in the sand
Are erased by the wind?
It is more than a hundred years now since Beethoven
Set down his misery and his ecstasy,
His wounded and baffled spirit,
His climbing and sun-lit and triumphant spirit
In dots and curves, in numerals and time signatures,
In key signatures, in braves and semi-braves,
In major and minor keys, and ledger lines and clefs,
In bars of duple, triple and quadruple time, in rests and scales,
In indications for winds and strings,
Flutes, horns, bassoons, and viols—
All set down, and all to say in harmony:
Alone! Alone! Alone!
All set down so to direct forever the players of instruments
How to pass from the earthquake rumble of the lost city of the soul
To the sunlight and song of the safe slopes;
How to pass with whisperings and falterings,
Almost as of children in fear,

To fathomless depths of courage and wisdom;
How to pace the harmony of the going-out,
And the returning-in of the blood of the Universe,
When the heart of the Great Law opens and closes its valves.
And how with plucked strings of summoned courage,
And the clamor of drums, to climb, to stand
Where no cobra crawls, no devil walks,
No charms of hell are worked;
And where the silence of a great summit
Opens out as a flower trembles and unfolds,
Revealing the drone of spheres, the song, the infinite music
Of light, which is also sound,
And which is impulse at the root of all motion,
And which is without end in space or time.

It is more than a hundred years since the secrets
Of Beethoven's soul, of his vision,
Were noted on paper in these cryptograms.
Yet, and because this was done
Beethoven's suffering and rapture reverberate still,
And by the instantaneous penetration of invisible fire
Can pass through granite, through steel, through measureless space;
Can pass through the glass of the cobra's cage,
And assail the stagnant, green-scum of his hate,
Lying sprawled with motionless eye,
Neither immersed in the unconsciousness of Nature,
Nor separated from it, and by that truth in mastery of it.
So by magnetic waves of fire
Does Beethoven enter the cage of the cobra,
And start to torture it with colossal mystery,
Which the cobra cannot strike.
The cobra can only weave and writhe and stretch,
And lift up long lengths of its body in the corner,
And crawl and lie with slight shivers, like the flank of a fly-plagued horse—
All before a presence invulnerable to fangs and venom.

The king cobra has much attention just now:
An oyster-white thickness has overgrown his right eye,
So that he sees only with his left eye.
The cobra has shed his skin several times,
And each time has failed to slough off
The scale from his right eye.
And now he must be helped by his keeper,
Or the eye will be wholly blind, and that will double his loneliness,
As much so as deafness increased the loneliness of Beethoven.

The oyster-white thickness is seven-layered,
Made up of semi-globular beads,
Half translucent, but massed together impenetrable to light.
And the cobra should see, says the cobra's keeper.
Hence the keeper traps him into a box,
Where the cobra's head is held while the oyster scales are snipped off.
The cobra was fierce with anger, and fought.
But when the cobra looked from that eye,
And could see the black and white of the cage,
Like squares embroidered on canvas,
(Having no yellow spot in either eye),
It acted glad, and glided happily on to the floor of the cage again,
And devoured a five-foot gopher snake
Provided for it by the keeper;
Devoured the gopher snake as a man kills and eats a hog or steer,
Or as men destroy men in business or war.
The cobra took the gopher snake by the head,
And swallowed it inch by inch, foot by foot,
All the way down, gurgitating its spasms,
Until only the end of the tail flicked,
And vanished.

V

This is the way Beethoven entered the cage of the cobra:
The next day after the seven-fold scale was removed,
The next day after the cobra swallowed the gopher snake,
The Ninth Symphony was played at the Park;
And the keeper turned on the radio in the reptile room
To see what the cobra would do,
When the sounds of the Scherzo, and the Ode to Joy
Echoed and re-echoed about the stone walls.
The cobra was lying outstretched with motionless eye;
He was not hungry—he had swallowed the gopher snake the day before.
He wanted no mate—the rutting season was past.
He could see—the seven-fold scale had been snipped.
He lay there slick as a gray, glazed cob-web,
Dulled like slimed nacre, and yellow
As the inside of a clam-shell, and gray as agate.
He was a length of dimmed iridescence of saffron and pearl,
And scaled like the permian gar-fish,
Or the legs of the ancient archaeopterix.
What but an enemy or music could disturb him?
Thus he lay calm as hate which is softly seething
When the radio began to sound,

As the musicians at the Park took the soul of Beethoven
From the dots, dashes, signs and symbols of score sheets,
And gave it voice as lettered there, forever sealed, and forever unsealed
    at will
As the echo of Beethoven's soul echoing the Great Mystery somewhere,
Not as an imitation of Nature, or of anything in Nature,
But as a response to Something,
Even as the agitation of the cobra is a response to Beethoven.

The second violins and cellos, the first violins, tenors and basses
Begin to whisper their way from the top to the bottom of the treble stave
To the bottom of the bass.
A clarinet breaks in like the call of a lonesome summer bird;
And one by one the wind-instruments enter,
And then the flutes and oboes divide the lamentation.
They are saying: "God, O God, my Guardian,
"My Rock, my All! Hear Thou, Unutterable,
"Hear Thy unhappy, most unhappy of mortals."

VI

The cobra stirs;
The cobra sends a ripple of skin down its length.
The cobra knows nothing of poverty: it has swallowed the gopher snake.
The cobra knows nothing of a nephew's ingratitude,
Or the slight of friends, or the neglect of the world,
Or the hatefulness of business.
But this is restless music, and the cobra grows restless.
This is sound which is first impatience, and then melancholy;
And the cobra grows impatient, melancholy waves stir him.
For fire can burn beings which know not what fire is.
This is tenderness, and the cobra resents tenderness,
As he would strike the hand that petted his head.
These sorrows of Beethoven have found the language of sound
Through magnetic waves, which are light and vibration,
And vibrating themselves set vibrations singing and surging
In the cobra itself, which becomes thus vibrating particles.
The waves of Beethoven's music advance through the cobra's nerves,
Making rhythmic motions of the particles in the nerves of the cobra,
And that is like a man in pain before the mystery of his fate.

The cobra shifts his place, and licks forth his tongue.
He may be shocked into hereditary memory of the steaming swamps
When the tyrannosaur and the diplodocus went mad,
And trampled the lizards and the crocodiles,

And the first snake one hundred feet long;
And when the pteranodon with twenty-four feet of outstretched wings
Flapped in fear among the fronds
Of gigantic tree ferns.
This may be the cause of the cobra's shifting and moving;
Or it may be only that this sound stirs him,
As fire would stir him, or the tap of the keeper on the glass of the cage.
But he does not crawl from his place yet.
Like a rope slightly shaken a rhythm goes through him
From head to tail, but he keeps his place
Amid the reverberating music of Beethoven.

The Scherzo changes all.
Beethoven's soul stepped from darkness to brilliant light,
From despair to the rapture of strength
Overcoming the world.
Beethoven caught the spirit of a fresh May morning,
And it inspired him to exult with trumpets and strings,
And drums and trombones.
There are no such mornings in the jungle.
The rhythm of three bars changed to the rhythm of four bars
Is nothing less than the secret ecstasy of May;
It is nothing less than the thrill of life
Making the worm feel the blisses of creation,
And making man himself a dweller with Eternity.

And now this ecstatic storm of harmony
Is not only the voices of strong men,
And the creak of great pulleys worked by them
To lift colossal blocks of granite to the terraces
Of timeless pyramids;
It is not merely discords resolved;
It is not the mere toppling and crash of colossi,
Followed by the silence of Egyptian palm groves;
It is not merely the audible silence
Which comes before the hollow sound,
And is followed by the hollow silence
When covers are lifted and placed on great earthen jars
Which have been filled with water for thirsty villages.
It is not merely the trumpeting of mastodons
Amid carboniferous thickets,
Or along level valleys of lava and giant cactus—
It is not merely these,
Nor merely Democritus laughing and shouting as he chases the discovered
    atom

Near the orbit of Uranus where time and space become one;
It is not merely any of these.
But it is the song of infinite cranes
Lifting worlds into their orbits;
It is the deep sighing of aeons of time;
It is the chuckle of vast ages;
It is the puffing and the halloos of periodic cycles
Toiling up the spirals of infinitude;
It is the sound of smooth-lipped lids of crystal
Being placed on the huge vials of despair and fear,
After their bitter waters have been poured into the flaming rivers
Of all old Hells to the roar of steam.
It is the sound of ponderable slabs
Being laid and fitted to the sarcophagi of dead demi-gorgons;
It is the happy laughter from the cradle of the infant Heracles
As he strangled the snakes sent by the enmity of Hera;
It is the shout of Heracles despising the common kingdom
Of which Hera, the jealous goddess, deprived him.
It is the howl of fire from worlds which should be burned,
Amid the drift and swirl of apocalyptic smoke;
It is the splash of the lake of fire
When death is hurled down and engulfed;
It is the thunder of mountain-high gates being opened,
Which reveal the landscapes of eternity;
It is the shout and the song of Apollo
As he races and shoots arrows after fleeing dragons.
It is the chant of the sun as god of this world,
Worthy of worship as the source of life!

VII

And now it was that the keeper returned to the cage
To see what the cobra was doing.
The cobra had crawled to the corner.
It had lifted one third of its length aloft
There in the corner;
It was reaching up with its head, licking out its tongue;
It was leaning back unsteadily being unable to hold
So much of its length aloft
There in the presence of Beethoven.

The Boy and the Snake

by CHARLES AND MARY LAMB

Henry was every morning fed
With a full mess of milk and bread.
One day the boy his breakfast took,
And eat it by a purling brook
Which through his mother's orchard ran.
From that time ever when he can
Escape his mother's eye, he there
Takes his food in th'open air.
Finding the child delight to eat
Abroad, and make the grass his seat,
His mother lets him have his way.
With free leave Henry every day
Thither repairs, until she heard
Him talking of a fine *grey bird*.
This pretty bird, he said, indeed,
Came every day with him to feed,
And it lov'd him, and lov'd his milk,
And it was smooth and soft as silk.
His mother thought she'd go and see
What sort of bird this same might be.
So the next morn she follows Harry,
And carefully she sees him carry
Through the long grass his heap'd-up mess.
What was her terror and distress,
When she saw the infant take
His bread and milk close to a snake!
Upon the grass he spreads his feast,
And sits down by his frightful guest,
Who had waited for the treat;
And now they both begin to eat.
Fond mother! shriek not, O beware
The least small noise, O have a care—
The least small noise that may be made,
The wily snake will be afraid—
If he hear the lightest sound,

He will inflict th' envenomed wound.
She speaks not, moves not, scarce does breathe,
As she stands the trees beneath;
No sound she utters; and she soon
Sees the child lift up its spoon,
And tap the snake upon the head,
Fearless of harm; and then he said,
As speaking to familiar mate,
"Keep on your own side, do, grey Pate":
The snake then to the other side,
As one rebuked, seems to glide;
And now again advancing nigh,
Again she hears the infant cry,
Tapping the snake, "Keep further, do;
Mind, grey Pate, what I say to you."
The danger's o'er—she sees the boy
(O what a change from fear to joy!)
Rise and bid the snake "Good-bye";
Says he, "Our breakfast's done, and I
Will come again tomorrow day":
Then, lightly tripping, ran away.

Cadmus and Harmonia

by MATTHEW ARNOLD

Callicles sings:

Far, far from here,
The Adriatic breaks in a warm bay
Among the green Illyrian hills; and there
The sunshine in the happy glens is fair,
And by the sea, and in the brakes.
The grass is cool, the sea-side air
Buoyant and fresh, the mountain flowers
More virginal and sweet than ours.

And there, they say, two bright and aged snakes,
Who once were Cadmus and Harmonia,

Bask in the glens or on the warm sea-shore,
In breathless quiet, after all their ills;
Nor do they see their country, nor the place
Where the Sphinx lived among the frowning hills,
Nor the unhappy palace of their race,
Nor Thebes, nor the Ismenus, any more.

There those two live, far in the Illyrian brakes!
They had stay'd long enough to see,
In Thebes, the billow of calamity
Over their own dear children roll'd,
Curse upon curse, pang upon pang,
For years, they sitting helpless in their home,
A grey old man and woman; yet of old
The Gods had to their marriage come,
And at the banquet all the Muses sang.

Therefore they did not end their days
In sight of blood; but were rapt, far away,
To where the west-wind plays,
And murmurs of the Adriatic come
To those untrodden mountain-lawns; and there
Placed safely in changed forms, the pair
Wholly forget their first sad life, and home,
And all that Theban woe, and stray
For ever through the glens, placid and dumb.

The Conqueror Worm

by EDGAR ALLAN POE

Lo! 't is a gala night
     Within the lonesome latter years.
An angel throng, bewinged, bedight
     In veils, and drowned in tears,
Sit in a theatre to see
     A play of hopes and fears,

While the orchestra breathes fitfully
    The music of the spheres.

Mimes, in the form of God on high,
    Mutter and mumble low,
And hither and thither fly;
    Mere puppets they, who come and go
At bidding of vast formless things
    That shift the scenery to and fro,
Flapping from out their condor wings
    Invisible Woe.

That motely drama—oh, be sure
    It shall not be forgot!
With its Phantom chased for evermore
    By a crowd that seize it not,
Through a circle that ever returneth in
    To the self-same spot;
And much of Madness, and more of Sin,
    And Horror the soul of the plot.

But see amid the mimic rout
    A crawling shape intrude:
A blood-red thing that writhes from out
    The scenic solitude!
It writhes—it writhes!—with mortal pangs
    The mimes become its food,
And seraphs sob at vermin fangs
    In human gore imbued.

Out—out are the lights—out all!
    And over each quivering form
The curtain, a funeral pall,
    Comes down with the rush of a storm,
While the angels, all pallid and wan,
    Uprising, unveiling, affirm
That the play is the tragedy, "Man,"
    And its hero, the Conqueror Worm.

The Copperhead

by BRET HARTE

There is peace in the swamp where the Copperhead sleeps,
Where the waters are stagnant, and white vapor creeps,
Where the musk of Magnolia hangs thick in the air,
And the lilies' phylacteries broaden in prayer.
There is peace in the swamp, though the quiet is death,
Though the mist is miasma, the upas-tree's breath,
Though no echo awakes to the cooing of doves,—
There is peace: yes, the peace that the Copperhead loves.

Go seek him: he coils in the ooze and the drip,
Like a thong idly flung from the slave-driver's whip;
But beware the false footstep,—the stumble that brings
A deadlier lash than the overseer swings.
Never arrow so true, never bullet so dread,
As the straight steady stroke of that hammer-shaped head;
Whether slave or proud planter, who braves that dull crest,
Woe to him who shall trouble the Copperhead's rest!

Then why waste your labors, brave hearts and strong men,
In tracking a trail to the Copperhead's den?
Lay your axe to the cypress, hew open the shade
To the free sky and sunshine Jehovah has made;
Let the breeze of the North sweep the vapors away,
Till the stagnant lake ripples, the freed waters play;
And then to your heel can you righteously doom
The Copperhead born of its shadow and gloom!

Christabel

by SAMUEL TAYLOR COLERIDGE

PART THE FIRST.

'Tis the middle of night by the castle clock,
And the owls have awakened the crowing cock,
Tu—whit!——Tu—whoo!
And hark, again! the crowing cock,
How drowsily it crew.

Sir Leoline, the Baron rich,
Hath a toothless mastiff, which
From her kennel beneath the rock
Maketh answer to the clock,
Four for the quarters, and twelve for the hour;
Ever and aye, by shine and shower,
Sixteen short howls, not over loud;
Some say, she sees my lady's shroud.

Is the night chilly and dark?
The night is chilly, but not dark.
The thin gray cloud is spread on high,
It covers but not hides the sky.
The moon is behind, and at the full;
And yet she looks both small and dull.
The night is chill, the cloud is gray:
'Tis a month before the month of May,
And the Spring comes slowly up this way.
The lovely lady, Christabel,
Whom her father loves so well,
What makes her in the wood so late,
A furlong from the castle gate?
She had dreams all yesternight
Of her own betrothed knight;

And she in the midnight wood will pray
For the weal of her lover that's far away.

She stole along, she nothing spoke,
The sighs she heaved were soft and low,
And nought was green upon the oak
But moss and rarest mistletoe:
She kneels beneath the huge oak tree,
And in silence prayeth she.

The lady sprang up suddenly,
The lovely lady, Christabel!
It moaned as near, as near can be,
But what it is she cannot tell.—
On the other side it seems to be,
Of the huge, broad-breasted, old oak tree.

The night is chill; the forest bare;
Is it the wind that moaneth bleak?
There is not wind enough in the air
To move away the ringlet curl
From the lovely lady's cheek—

There is not wind enough to twirl
The one red leaf, the last of its clan,
That dances as often as dance it can,
Hanging so light, and hanging so high,
On the topmast twig that looks up at the sky.
Hush, beating heart of Christabel!
Jesu, Maria, shield her well!
She folded her arms beneath her cloak,
And stole to the other side of the oak.
   What sees she there?

There she sees a damsel bright,
Drest in a silken robe of white,
That shadowy in the moonlight shone:
The neck that made that white robe wan,
Her stately neck, and arms were bare;
Her blue-veined feet unsandal'd were,
And wildly glittered here and there
The gems entangled in her hair.
I guess, 'twas frightful there to see

A lady so richly clad as she—
Beautiful exceedingly!

Mary mother, save me now!
(Said Christabel,) And who art thou?

The lady strange made answer meet,
And her voice was faint and sweet:—
Have pity on my sore distress,
I scarce can speak for weariness:
Stretch forth thy hand, and have no fear!
Said Christabel, How camest thou here?
And the lady, whose voice was faint and sweet,
Did thus pursue her answer meet:—

My sire is of a noble line,
And my name is Geraldine:
Five warriors seized me yestermorn,
Me, even me, a maid forlorn:
They choked my cries with force and fright,
And tied me on a palfrey white.
The palfrey was as fleet as wind,
And they rode furiously behind.
They spurred amain, their steeds were white:
And once we crossed the shade of night.
As sure as Heaven shall rescue me,
I have no thought what men they be;
Nor do I know how long it is
(For I have lain entranced I wis)
Since one, the tallest of the five,
Took me from the palfrey's back,
A weary woman, scarce alive.
Some muttered words his comrade spoke:
He placed me underneath this oak;
He swore they would return with haste;
Whither they went I cannot tell—
I thought I heard, some minutes past,
Sounds as of a castle bell.
Stretch forth thy hand (thus ended she),
And help a wretched maid to flee.

Then Christabel stretched forth her hand,
And comforted fair Geraldine:
O well, bright dame! may you command
The service of Sir Leoline;

And gladly our stout chivalry
Will he send forth and friends withal
To guide and guard you safe and free
Home to your noble father's hall.

She rose: and forth with steps they passed
That strove to be, and were not, fast.
Her gracious stars the lady blest,
And thus spake on sweet Christabel:
All our household are at rest,
The hall as silent as the cell;
Sir Leoline is weak in health,
And may not well awakened be,
But we will move as if in stealth,
And I beseech your courtesy,
This night, to share your couch with me.

They crossed the moat, and Christabel
Took the key that fitted well;
A little door she opened straight,
All in the middle of the gate;
The gate was ironed within and without,
Where an army in battle array had marched out.
The lady sank, belike through pain,
And Christabel with might and main
Lifted her up, a weary weight,
Over the threshold of the gate:
Then the lady rose again,
And moved, as she were not in pain.

So free from danger, free from fear,
They crossed the court: right glad they were.
And Christabel devoutly cried
To the lady by her side,
Praise we the Virgin all divine
Who hath rescued thee from thy distress!
Alas, alas! said Geraldine,
I cannot speak for weariness.
So free from danger, free from fear,
They crossed the court: right glad they were.
Outside her kennel, the mastiff old
Lay fast asleep, in moonshine cold.
The mastiff old did not awake,
Yet she an angry moan did make!

And what can ail the mastiff bitch?
Never till now she uttered yell
Beneath the eye of Christabel.
Perhaps it is the owlet's scritch:
For what can ail the mastiff bitch?

They passed the hall, that echoes still,
Pass as lightly as you will!
The brands were flat, the brands were dying,
Amid their own white ashes lying;
But when the lady passed, there came
A tongue of light, a fit of flame;
And Christabel saw the lady's eye,
And nothing else saw she thereby,
Save the boss of the shield of Sir Leoline tall,
Which hung in a murky old niche in the wall.
O softly tread, said Christabel,
My father seldom sleepeth well.

Sweet Christabel her feet doth bare,
And jealous of the listening air
They steal their way from stair to stair,
Now in glimmer, and now in gloom,
And now they pass the Baron's room,
As still as death, with stifled breath!
And now have reached her chamber door;
And now doth Geraldine press down
The rushes of the chamber floor.
The moon shines dim in the open air,
And not a moonbeam enters here.
But they without its light can see
The chamber carved so curiously,
Carved with figures strange and sweet,
All made out of the carver's brain,
For a lady's chamber meet:
The lamp with twofold silver chain
Is fastened to an angel's feet.

The silver lamp burns dead and dim;
But Christabel the lamp will trim.
She trimmed the lamp, and made it bright,
And left it swinging to and fro,

While Geraldine, in wretched plight,
Sank down upon the floor below.

O weary lady, Geraldine,
I pray you, drink this cordial wine!
It is a wine of virtuous powers;
My mother made it of wild flowers.

And will your mother pity me,
Who am a maiden most forlorn?
Christabel answered—Woe is me!
She died the hour that I was born.
I have heard the grey-haired friar tell
How on her death-bed she did say,
That she should hear the castle-bell
Strike twelve upon my wedding-day.
O mother dear! that thou wert here!
I would, said Geraldine, she were!
But soon with altered voice, said she—
'Off, wandering mother! Peak and pine!
I have power to bid thee flee.'
Alas! what ails poor Geraldine?
Why stares she with unsettled eye?
Can she the bodiless dead espy?
And why with hollow voice cries she,
'Off, woman, off! this hour is mine—
Though thou her guardian spirit be,
Off, woman, off! 'tis given to me.'

Then Christabel knelt by the lady's side,
And raised to heaven her eyes so blue—
Alas! said she, this ghastly ride—
Dear lady! it hath wildered you!
The lady wiped her moist cold brow,
And faintly said, ' 'tis over now!'

Again the wild-flower wine she drank:
Her fair large eyes 'gan glitter bright,
And from the floor whereon she sank,
The lofty lady stood upright:
She was most beautiful to see,
Like a lady of a far countree.

And thus the lofty lady spake—
'All they who live in the upper sky,

Do love you, holy Christabel!
And you love them, and for their sake
And for the good which me befel,
Even I in my degree will try,
Fair maiden, to requite you well.
But now unrobe yourself; for I
Must pray, ere yet in bed I lie.'
Quoth Christabel, So let it be!
And as the lady bade, did she.
Her gentle limbs did she undress,
And lay down in her loveliness.

But through her brain of weal and woe
So many thoughts moved to and fro,
That vain it were her lids to close;
So half-way from the bed she rose,
And on her elbow did recline
To look at the lady Geraldine.

Beneath the lamp the lady bowed,
And slowly rolled her eyes around;
Then drawing in her breath aloud,
Like one that shuddered, she unbound
The cincture from beneath her breast:
Her silken robe, and inner vest,
Dropt to her feet, and full in view,
Behold! her bosom and half her side—
A sight to dream of, not to tell!
O shield her! shield sweet Christabel!

Yet Geraldine nor speaks nor stirs;
Ah! what a stricken look was hers!
Deep from within she seems half-way
To lift some weight with sick assay,
And eyes the maid and seeks delay;
Then suddenly, as one defied,
Collects herself in scorn and pride,
And lay down by the Maiden's side!—
And in her arms the maid she took,
      Ah well-a-day!
And with low voice and doleful look
These words did say:
'In the touch of this bosom there worketh a spell,
Which is lord of thy utterance, Christabel!
Thou knowest to-night, and wilt know to-morrow,

This mark of my shame, this seal of my sorrow;
　　　　But vainly thou warrest,
　　　　　　For this is alone in
　　　　　　Thy power to declare,
　　　　　　　That in the dim forest
　　　　　Thou heard'st a low moaning,
And found'st a bright lady, surpassingly fair;
And didst bring her home with thee in love and
　　　in charity,
To shield her and shelter her from the damp air.'

THE CONCLUSION TO PART THE FIRST.

It was a lovely sight to see
The lady Christabel, when she
Was praying at the old oak tree.
　　　　Amid the jagged shadows
　　　　Of mossy leafless boughs,
　　　　Kneeling in the moonlight,
　　　　To make her gentle vows;
Her slender palms together prest,
Heaving sometimes on her breast;
Her face resigned to bliss or bale—
Her face, oh call it fair not pale,
And both blue eyes more bright than clear,
Each about to have a tear.

With open eyes (ah woe is me!)
Asleep, and dreaming fearfully,
Fearfully dreaming, yet, I wis,
Dreaming that alone, which is—
O sorrow and shame! Can this be she,
The lady, who knelt at the old oak tree?
And lo! the worker of these harms,
That holds the maiden in her arms,
Seems to slumber still and mild,
As a mother with her child.

A star hath set, a star hath risen,
O Geraldine! since arms of thine
Have been the lovely lady's prison.
O Geraldine! one hour was thine—
Thou'st had thy will! By tairn and rill,
The night-birds all that hour were still.
But now they are jubilant anew,

From cliff and tower, tu—whoo! tu—whoo!
Tu—whoo! tu—whoo! from wood and fell!

And see! the lady Christabel
Gathers herself from out her trance;
Her limbs relax, her countenance
Grows sad and soft; the smooth thin lids
Close o'er her eyes; and tears she sheds—
Large tears that leave the lashes bright!
And oft the while she seems to smile
As infants at a sudden light!

Yea, she doth smile, and she doth weep,
Like a youthful hermitess,
Beauteous in a wilderness,
Who, praying always, prays in sleep.
And, if she move unquietly,
Perchance, 'tis but the blood so free
Comes back and tingles in her feet.
No doubt, she hath a vision sweet.
What if her guardian spirit 'twere,
What if she knew her mother near?
But this she knows, in joys and woes,
That saints will aid if men will call:
For the blue sky bends over all!

PART THE SECOND.

Each matin bell, the Baron saith,
Knells us back to a world of death.
These words Sir Leoline first said,
When he rose and found his lady dead:
These words Sir Leoline will say
Many a morn to his dying day!

And hence the custom and law began
That still at dawn the sacristan,
Who duly pulls the heavy bell,
Five and forty beads must tell
Between each stroke—a warning knell,
Which not a soul can choose but hear
From Bratha Head to Wyndermere.

Saith Bracy the bard, So let it knell!
And let the drowsy sacristan

Still count as slowly as he can!
There is no lack of such, I ween,
As well fill up the space between.
In Langdale Pike and Witch's Lair,
And Dungeon-ghyll so foully rent,
With ropes of rock and bells of air
Three sinful sextons' ghosts are pent,
Who all give back, one after t'other,
The death-note to their living brother;
And oft too, by the knell offended,
Just as their one! two! three! is ended,
The devil mocks the doleful tale
With a merry peal from Borrowdale.

The air is still! through mist and cloud
That merry peal comes ringing loud;
And Geraldine shakes off her dread,
And rises lightly from the bed;
Puts on her silken vestments white,
And tricks her hair in lovely plight,
And nothing doubting of her spell
Awakens the lady Christabel.
'Sleep you, sweet lady Christabel?
I trust that you have rested well.'

And Christabel awoke and spied
The same who lay down by her side—
O rather say, the same whom she
Raised up beneath the old oak tree!
Nay, fairer yet! and yet more fair!
For she belike hath drunken deep
Of all the blessedness of sleep!
And while she spake, her looks, her air,
Such gentle thankfulness declare,
That (so it seemed) her girded vests
Grew tight beneath her heaving breasts.
'Sure I have sinn'd!" said Christabel,
'Now heaven be praised if all be well!'
And in low faltering tones, yet sweet,
Did she the lofty lady greet
With such perplexity of mind
As dreams too lively leave behind.
So quickly she rose, and quickly arrayed
Her maiden limbs, and having prayed
That He, who on the cross did groan,

Might wash away her sins unknown,
She forthwith led fair Geraldine
To meet her sire, Sir Leoline.

The lovely maid and the lady tall
Are pacing both into the hall,
And pacing on through page and groom,
Enter the Baron's presence-room.

The Baron rose, and while he prest
His gentle daughter to his breast,
With cheerful wonder in his eyes
The lady Geraldine espies,
And gave such welcome to the same,
As might beseem so bright a dame!

But when he heard the lady's tale,
And when she told her father's name,
Why waxed Sir Leoline so pale,
Murmuring o'er the name again,
Lord Roland de Vaux of Tryermaine?

Alas! they had been friends in youth;
But whispering tongues can poison truth;
And constancy lives in realms above;
And life is thorny; and youth is vain;
And to be wroth with one we love
Doth work like madness in the brain.
And thus it chanced, as I divine,
With Roland and Sir Leoline.
Each spake words of high disdain
And insult to his heart's best brother:
They parted—ne'er to meet again!
But never either found another
To free the hollow heart from paining—
They stood aloof, the scars remaining,
Like cliffs which had been rent asunder;
A dreary sea now flows between.
But neither heat, nor frost, nor thunder,
Shall wholly do away, I ween,
The marks of that which once hath been.

Sir Leoline, a moment's space,
Stood gazing on the damsel's face:

And the youthful Lord of Tryermaine
Came back upon his heart again.

O then the Baron forgot his age,
His noble heart swelled high with rage;
He swore by the wounds in Jesu's side
He would proclaim it far and wide,
With trump and solemn heraldry,
That they, who thus had wronged the dame
Were base as spotted infamy!
'And if they dare deny the same,
My herald shall appoint a week,
And let the recreant traitors seek
My tourney court—that there and then
I may dislodge their reptile souls
From the bodies and forms of men!'
He spake: his eyes in lightning rolls!
For the lady was ruthlessly seized; and he kenned
In the beautiful lady the child of his friend!
And now the tears were on his face,
And fondly in his arms he took
Fair Geraldine, who met the embrace,
Prolonging it with joyous look.
Which when she viewed, a vision fell
Upon the soul of Christabel,
The vision of fear, the touch and pain!
She shrunk and shuddered, and saw again—
(Ah, woe is me! Was it for thee,
Thou gentle maid! such sights to see?)

Again she saw that bosom old,
Again she felt that bosom cold,
And drew in her breath with a hissing sound:
Whereat the Knight turned wildly round,
And nothing saw, but his own sweet maid
With eyes upraised, as one that prayed.

The touch, the sight, had passed away,
And in its stead that vision blest,
Which comforted her after-rest,
While in the lady's arms she lay,
Had put a rapture in her breast,
And on her lips and o'er her eyes
Spread smiles like light!
                        With new surprise,

'What ails then my beloved child?'
The Baron said—His daughter mild
Made answer, 'All will yet be well!'
I ween, she had no power to tell
Aught else: so mighty was the spell.
Yet he, who saw this Geraldine,
Had deemed her sure a thing divine.
Such sorrow with such grace she blended,
As if she feared she had offended
Sweet Christabel, that gentle maid!
And with such lowly tones she prayed
She might be sent without delay
Home to her father's mansion.
                                        'Nay!
Nay, by my soul!' said Leoline.
'Ho! Bracy the bard, the charge be thine!
Go thou, with music sweet and loud,
And take two steeds with trappings proud,
And take the youth whom thou lov'st best
To bear thy harp, and learn thy song,
And clothe you both in solemn vest,
And over the mountains haste along,
Lest wandering folk, that are abroad,
Detain you on the valley road.

'And when he has crossed the Irthing flood,
My merry bard! he hastes, he hastes
Up Knorren Moor, through Halegarth Wood,
And reaches soon that castle good
Which stands and threatens Scotland's wastes.

'Bard Bracy! bard Bracy! your horses are fleet,
Ye must ride up the hall, your music so sweet,
More loud than your horses' echoing feet!
And loud and loud to Lord Roland call,
Thy daughter is safe in Langdale hall!
Thy beautiful daughter is safe and free—
Sir Leoline greets thee thus through me.
He bids thee come without delay
With all thy numerous array;
And take thy lovely daughter home:
And he will meet thee on the way
With all his numerous array
White with their panting palfreys' foam:

And, by mine honour! I will say,
That I repent me of the day
When I spake words of fierce disdain
To Roland de Vaux of Tryermaine!—
—For since that evil hour hath flown,
Many a summer's sun hath shone;
Yet ne'er found I a friend again
Like Roland de Vaux of Tryermaine.'

The lady fell, and clasped his knees,
Her face upraised, her eyes o'erflowing;
And Bracy replied, with faltering voice,
His gracious hail on all bestowing;
'Thy words, thou sire of Christabel,
Are sweeter than my harp can tell;
Yet might I gain a boon of thee,
This day my journey should not be,
So strange a dream hath come to me;
That I had vowed with music loud
To clear yon wood from thing unblest,
Warn'd by a vision in my rest!
For in my sleep I saw that dove,
That gentle bird, whom thou dost love,
And call'st by thy own daughter's name—
Sir Leoline! I saw the same,
Fluttering, and uttering fearful moan,
Among the green herbs in the forest alone.
Which when I saw and when I heard,
I wonder'd what might ail the bird;
For nothing near it could I see,
Save the grass and green herbs underneath
        the old tree.
'And in my dream, methought, I went
To search out what might there be found;
And what the sweet bird's trouble meant,
That thus lay fluttering on the ground.
I went and peered, and could descry
No cause for her distressful cry;
But yet for her dear lady's sake
I stooped, methought, the dove to take,
When lo! I saw a bright green snake
Coiled around its wings and neck,
Green as the herbs on which it couched,
Close by the dove's its head it crouched;

And with the dove it heaves and stirs,
Swelling its neck as she swelled hers!
I woke; it was the midnight hour,
The clock was echoing in the tower;
But though my slumber was gone by,
This dream it would not pass away—
It seems to live upon my eye!
And thence I vowed this self-same day
With music strong and saintly song
To wander through the forest bare,
Lest aught unholy loiter there.'

Thus Bracy said: the Baron, the while,
Half-listening heard him with a smile;
Then turned to Lady Geraldine,
His eyes made up of wonder and love;
And said in courtly accents fine,
'Sweet maid, Lord Roland's beauteous dove,
With arms more strong than harp or song,
Thy sire and I will crush the snake!'
He kissed her forehead as he spake,
And Geraldine in maiden wise
Casting down her large bright eyes,
With blushing cheek and courtesy fine
She turned her from Sir Leoline;
Softly gathering up her train,
That o'er her right arm fell again;
And folded her arms across her chest,
And couched her head upon her breast,
And looked askance at Christabel—
Jesu, Maria, shield her well!

A snake's small eye blinks dull and shy,
And the lady's eyes they shrunk in her head,
Each shrunk up to a serpent's eye,
And with somewhat of malice, and more of dread,
At Christabel she look'd askance!—
One moment—and the sight was fled!
But Christabel in dizzy trance
Stumbling on the unsteady ground
Shuddered aloud, with a hissing sound;
And Geraldine again turned round,
And like a thing, that sought relief,

Full of wonder and full of grief,
She rolled her large bright eyes divine
Wildly on Sir Leoline.

The maid, alas! her thoughts are gone,
She nothing sees—no sight but one!
The maid, devoid of guile and sin,
I know not how, in fearful wise,
So deeply had she drunken in
That look, those shrunken serpent eyes,
That all her features were resigned
To this sole image in her mind:
And passively did imitate
That look of dull and treacherous hate!
And thus she stood, in dizzy trance,
Still picturing that look askance
With forced unconscious sympathy
Full before her father's view—
As far as such a look could be
In eyes so innocent and blue!

And when the trance was o'er, the maid
Paused awhile, and inly prayed:
Then falling at the Baron's feet,
'By my mother's soul do I entreat
That thou this woman send away!'
She said: and more she could not say:
For what she knew she could not tell,
O'er-mastered by the mighty spell.

Why is thy cheek so wan and wild,
Sir Leoline? Thy only child
Lies at thy feet, thy joy, thy pride,
So fair, so innocent, so mild;
The same, for whom thy lady died!
O, by the pangs of her dear mother
Think thou no evil of thy child!
For her, and thee, and for no other,
She prayed the moment ere she died:
Prayed that the babe for whom she died,
Might prove her dear lord's joy and pride!
That prayer her deadly pangs beguiled,
Sir Leoline!

And wouldst thou wrong thy only child,
    Her child and thine?
Within the Baron's heart and brain
If thoughts, like these, had any share,
They only swelled his rage and pain,
And did but work confusion there.
His heart was cleft with pain and rage,
His cheeks they quivered, his eyes were wild,
Dishonour'd thus in his old age;
Dishonour'd by his only child,
And all his hospitality
To the insulted daughter of his friend
By more than woman's jealousy
Brought thus to a disgraceful end—
He rolled his eye with stern regard
Upon the gentle minstrel bard,
And said in tones abrupt, austere—
'Why, Bracy! dost thou loiter here?
I bade thee hence!' The bard obeyed;
And turning from his own sweet maid,
The aged knight, Sir Leoline,
Led forth the lady Geraldine!

THE CONCLUSION TO PART THE SECOND.

A little child, a limber elf,
Singing, dancing to itself,
A fairy thing with red round cheeks,
That always finds, and never seeks,
Makes such a vision to the sight
As fills a father's eyes with light;
And pleasures flow in so thick and fast
Upon his heart, that he at last
Must needs express his love's excess
With words of unmeant bitterness.

The Double-Headed Snake of Newbury

by JOHN GREENLEAF WHITTIER

"Concerning ye Amphisbæna, as soon as I received your commands, I made diligent inquiry: . . . he assures me yt had really two heads, one at each end; two mouths, two stings or tongues."—*Rev. Christopher Toppan to Cotton Mather.*

Far away in the twilight time
Of every people, in every clime,
Dragons and griffins and monsters dire,
Born of water, and air, and fire,
Or nursed, like the Python, in the mud
And ooze of the old Deucalion flood,
Crawl and wriggle and foam with rage,
Through dusk tradition and ballad age.
So from the childhood of Newbury town
And its time of fable the tale comes down
Of a terror which haunted bush and brake,
The Amphisbæna, the Double Snake!

Thou who makest the tale thy mirth,
Consider that strip of Christian earth
On the desolate shore of a sailless sea,
Full of terror and mystery,
Half redeemed from the evil hold
Of the wood so dreary, and dark, and old,
Which drank with its lips of leaves the dew
When Time was young, and the world was new,
And wove its shadows with sun and moon,
Ere the stones of Cheops were squared and hewn.

Think of the sea's dread monotone,
Of the mournful wail from the pine-wood blown,
Of the strange, vast splendors that lit the North,
Of the troubled throes of the quaking earth,
And the dismal tales the Indian told,
Till the settler's heart at his hearth grew cold,
And he shrank from the tawny wizard boasts,
And the hovering shadows seemed full of ghosts,

346

And above, below, on every side,
The fear of his creed seemed verified;—
And think, if his lot were now thine own,
To grope with terrors nor named nor known,
How laxer muscle and weaker nerve
And a feebler faith thy need might serve;
And own to thyself the wonder more
That the snake had two heads, and not a score!

Whether he lurked in the Oldtown fen
Or the gray earth-flax of the Devil's Den,
Or swam in the wooded Artichoke,
Or coiled by the Northman's Written Rock,
Nothing on record is left to show;
Only the fact that he lived, we know,
And left the cast of a double head
In the scaly mask which he yearly shed.
For he carried a head where his tail should be,
And the two, of course, could never agree,
But wriggled about with main and might,
Now to the left and now to the right;
Pulling and twisting this way and that
Neither knew what the other was at.

A snake with two heads, lurking so near!
Judge of the wonder, guess at the fear!
Think what ancient gossips might say,
Shaking their heads in their dreary way,
Between the meetings on Sabbath-day!
How urchins, searching at day's decline
The Common Pasture for sheep or kine,
The terrible double-ganger heard
In leafy rustle or whir of bird!
Think what a zest it gave to the sport,
In berry-time, if the younger sort,
As over pastures blackberry-twined,
Reuben and Dorothy lagged behind,
And closer and closer, for fear of harm,
The maiden clung to her lover's arm;

And how the spark, who was forced to stay,
By his sweetheart's fears, till the break of day,
Thanked the snake for the fond delay!

Far and wide the tale was told,
Like a snowball growing while it rolled.

The nurse hushed with it the baby's cry;
And it served, in the worthy minister's eye,
To paint the primitive serpent by.
Cotton Mather came galloping down
All the way to Newbury town,
With his eyes agog and his ears set wide,
And his marvellous inkhorn at his side;
Stirring the while in the shallow pool
Of his brains for the lore he learned at school,
To garnish the story, with here a streak
Of Latin, and there another of Greek:
And the tales he heard and the notes he took,
Behold! are they not in his Wonder-Book?

Stories, like dragons, are hard to kill.
If the snake does not, the tale runs still
In Byfield Meadows, on Pipestave Hill.
And still, whenever husband and wife
Publish the shame of their daily strife,
And, with mad cross-purpose, tug and strain
At either end of the marriage-chain,
The gossips say, with a knowing shake
Of their gray heads, "Look at the Double Snake!
One in body and two in will,
The Amphisbæna is living still!"

Lamia

by JOHN KEATS

PART I.

Upon a time, before the fairy broods
Drove Nymph and Satyr from the prosperous woods,
Before King Oberon's bright diadem,
Sceptre, and mantle, clasped with dewy gem,
Frighted away the Dryads and the Fauns
From rushes green, and brakes, and cowsliped lawns,
The ever-smitten Hermes empty left

His golden throne, bent warm on amorous theft:
From high Olympus had he stolen light,
On this side of Jove's clouds, to escape the sight
Of his great summoner, and made retreat
Into a forest on the shores of Crete.
For somewhere in that sacred island dwelt
A nymph, to whom all hoofèd Satyrs knelt;
At whose white feet the languid Tritons poured
Pearls, while on land they withered and adored.
Fast by the springs where she to bathe was wont,
And in those meads where sometimes she might haunt,
Were strewn rich gifts, unknown to any Muse,
Though Fancy's casket were unlocked to choose.
Ah, what a world of love was at her feet!
So Hermes thought, and a celestial heat
Burnt from his wingèd heels to either ear,
That from a whiteness, as the lily clear,
Blushed into roses 'mid his golden hair,
Fallen in jealous curls about his shoulders bare.
From vale to vale, from wood to wood, he flew,
Breathing upon the flowers his passion new,
And wound with many a river to its head,
To find where this sweet nymph prepared her secret bed:
In vain; the sweet nymph might nowhere be found,
And so he rested, on the lonely ground,
Pensive, and full of painful jealousies
Of the Wood-Gods, and even the very trees.
There as he stood, he heard a mournful voice,
Such as once heard, in gentle heart, destroys
All pain but pity: thus the lone voice spake:
"When from this wreathed tomb shall I awake!
When move in a sweet body fit for life,
And love, and pleasure, and the ruddy strife
Of hearts and lips! Ah, miserable me!"
The God, dove-footed, glided silently
Round bush and tree, soft-brushing, in his speed,
The taller grasses and full-flowering weed,
Until he found a palpitating snake,
Bright, and cirque-couchant in a dusky brake.

She was a gordian shape of dazzling hue,
Vermilion-spotted, golden, green, and blue;
Striped like a zebra, freckled like a pard,
Eyed like a peacock, and all crimson barred;
And full of silver moons, that, as she breathed,

Dissolved, or brighter shone, or interwreathed
Their lustres with the gloomier tapestries—
So rainbow-sided, touched with miseries,
She seemed, at once, some penanced lady elf,
Some demon's mistress, or the demon's self.
Upon her crest she wore a wannish fire
Sprinkled with stars, like Ariadne's tiar:
Her head was serpent, but ah, bitter-sweet!
She had a woman's mouth with all its pearls complete:
And for her eyes: what could such eyes do there
But weep, and weep, that they were born so fair?
As Proserpine still weeps for her Sicilian air.
Her throat was serpent, but the words she spake
Came, as through bubbling honey, for Love's sake,
And thus; while Hermes on his pinions lay,
Like a stooped falcon ere he takes his prey:

"Fair Hermes, crowned with feathers, fluttering light,
I had a splendid dream of thee last night:
I saw thee sitting, on a throne of gold,
Among the Gods, upon Olympus old,
The only sad one; for thou didst not hear
The soft, lute-fingered Muses chanting clear,
Nor even Apollo when he sang alone,
Deaf to his throbbing throat's long, long melodious moan.
I dreamt I saw thee, robed in purple flakes,
Break amorous through the clouds, as morning breaks,
And, swiftly as a bright Phœbean dart,
Strike for the Cretan isle; and here thou art!
Too gentle Hermes, hast thou found the maid?"
Whereat the star of Lethe not delayed
His rosy eloquence, and thus inquired:
"Thou smooth-lipped serpent, surely high inspired!
Thou beauteous wreath, with melancholy eyes,
Possess whatever bliss thou canst devise,
Telling me only where my nymph is fled,—
Where she doth breathe!" "Bright planet, thou hast said,"
Returned the snake, "but seal with oaths, fair God!"
"I swear," said Hermes, "by my serpent rod,
And by thine eyes, and by thy starry crown!"
Light flew his earnest words, among the blossoms blown.
Then thus again the brilliance feminine:
"Too frail of heart! for this lost nymph of thine,
Free as the air, invisibly, she strays

About these thornless wilds; her pleasant days
She tastes unseen; unseen her nimble feet
Leave traces in the grass and flowers sweet;
From weary tendrils, and bowed branches green,
She plucks the fruit unseen, she bathes unseen:
And by my power is her beauty veiled
To keep it unaffronted, unassailed
By the love-glances of unlovely eyes,
Of Satyrs, Fauns, and bleared Silenus' sighs.
Pale grew her immortality, for woe
Of all these lovers, and she grieved so
I took compassion on her, bade her steep
Her hair in weïrd syrops, that would keep
Her loveliness invisible, yet free
To wander as she loves, in liberty.
Thou shalt behold her, Hermes, thou alone,
If thou wilt, as thou swearest, grant my boon!"
Then, once again, the charmèd God began
An oath, and through the serpent's ears it ran
Warm, tremulous, devout, psalterian.
Ravished, she lifted her Circean head,
Blushed a live damask, and swift-lisping said:
"I was a woman, let me have once more
A woman's shape, and charming as before.
I love a youth of Corinth—O the bliss!
Give me my woman's form, and place me where he is.
Stoop, Hermes, let me breathe upon thy brow,
And thou shalt see thy sweet nymph even now."
The God on half-shut feathers sank serene,
She breathed upon his eyes, and swift was seen
Of both the guarded nymph near-smiling on the green.
It was no dream; or say a dream it was,
Real are the dreams of Gods, and smoothly pass
Their pleasures in a long immortal dream.
One warm, flushed moment, hovering, it might seem
Dashed by the wood-nymph's beauty, so he burned;
Then, lighting on the printless verdure, turned
To the swooned serpent, and with languid arm,
Delicate, put to proof the lithe Caducean charm.
So done, upon the nymph his eyes he bent
Full of adoring tears and blandishment,
And towards her stept: she, like a moon in wane,
Faded before him, cowered, nor could restrain
Her fearful sobs, self-folding like a flower
That faints into itself at evening hour:

But the God fostering her chilled hand,
She felt the warmth, her eyelids opened bland,
And, like new flowers at morning song of bees,
Bloomed, and gave up her honey to the lees.
Into the green-recessed woods they flew;
Nor grew they pale, as mortal lovers do.

    Left to herself, the serpent now began
To change; her elfin blood in madness ran,
Her mouth foamed, and the grass, therewith besprent,
Withered at dew so sweet and virulent;
Her eyes in torture fixed, and anguish drear,
Hot, glazed, and wide, with lid-lashes all sear,
Flashed phosphor and sharp sparks, without one cooling tear.
The colours all inflamed throughout her train,
She writhed about, convulsed with scarlet pain:
A deep volcanian yellow took the place
Of all her milder-moonèd body's grace;
And, as the lava ravishes the mead,
Spoilt all her silver mail, and golden brede;
Made gloom of all her frecklings, streaks and bars,
Eclipsed her crescents, and licked up her stars:
So that, in moments few, she was undrest
Of all her sapphires, greens, and amethyst,
And rubious-argent: of all these bereft,
Nothing but pain and ugliness were left.
Still shone her crown; that vanished, also she
Melted and disappeared as suddenly;
And in the air, her new voice luting soft,
Cried, "Lycius! gentle Lycius!"—Borne aloft
With the bright mists about the mountains hoar
These words dissolved: Crete's forests heard no more.

    Whither fled Lamia, now a lady bright,
A full-born beauty new and exquisite?
She fled into that valley they pass o'er
Who go to Corinth from Cenchreas' shore;
And rested at the foot of those wild hills,
The rugged founts of the Peræan rills,
And of that other ridge whose barren back
Stretches, with all its mist and cloudy rack,
South-westward to Cleone. There she stood
About a young bird's flutter from a wood,
Fair, on a sloping green of mossy tread,
By a clear pool, wherein she passionèd

To see herself escaped from so sore ills,
While her robes flaunted with the daffodils.

Ah, happy Lycius!—for she was a maid
More beautiful than ever twisted braid,
Or sighed, or blushed, or on spring-flowered lea
Spread a green kirtle to the minstrelsy:
A virgin purest lipped, yet in the lore
Of love deep learned to the red heart's core:
Not one hour old, yet of sciential brain
To unperplex bliss from its neighbour pain;
Define their pettish limits, and estrange
Their points of contact, and swift counterchange
Intrigue with the specious chaos, and dispart
Its most ambiguous atoms with sure art;
As though in Cupid's college she had spent
Sweet days a lovely graduate, still unshent,
And kept his rosy terms in idle languishment.

Why this fair creature chose so fairily
By the wayside to linger, we shall see;
But first 'tis fit to tell how she could muse
And dream, when in the serpent prison-house,
Of all she list, strange or magnificent:
How, ever, where she willed, her spirit went;
Whether to faint Elysium, or where
Down through tress-lifting waves the Nereids fair
Wind into Thetis' bower by many a pearly stair;
Or where God Bacchus drains his cups divine,
Stretched out, at ease, beneath a glutinous pine;
Or where in Pluto's gardens palatine
Mulciber's columns gleam in far piazzian line.
And sometimes into cities she would send
Her dream, with feast and rioting to blend;
And once, while among mortals dreaming thus,
She saw the young Corinthian Lycius
Charioting foremost in the envious race,
Like a young Jove with calm uneager face,
And fell into a swooning love of him.
Now on the moth-time of that evening dim
He would return that way, as well she knew,
To Corinth from the shore; for freshly blew
The eastern soft wind, and his galley now
Grated the quaystones with her brazen prow
In port Cenchreas, from Egina isle

Fresh anchored; whither he had been awhile
To sacrifice to Jove, whose temple there
Waits with high marble doors for blood and incense rare.
Jove heard his vows, and bettered his desire;
For by some freakful chance he made retire
From his companions, and set forth to walk,
Perhaps grown wearied of their Corinth talk:
Over the solitary hills he fared,
Thoughtless at first, but ere eve's star appeared
His fantasy was lost, where reason fades,
In the calmed twilight of Platonic shades.
Lamia beheld him coming, near, more near—
Close to her passing, in indifference drear,
His silent sandals swept the mossy green;
So neighboured to him, and yet so unseen
She stood: he passed, shut up in mysteries,
His mind wrapped like his mantle, while her eyes
Followed his steps, and her neck regal white
Turned—syllabling thus, "Ah, Lycius bright,
And will you leave me on the hills alone?
Lycius, look back! and be some pity shown."
He did; not with cold wonder fearingly,
But Orpheus-like at an Eurydice;
For so delicious were the words she sung,
It seemed he had loved them a whole summer long:
And soon his eyes had drunk her beauty up,
Leaving no drop in the bewildering cup,
And still the cup was full,—while he, afraid
Lest she should vanish ere his lip had paid
Due adoration, thus began to adore;
Her soft look growing coy, she saw his chain so sure:
"Leave thee alone! Look back! Ah! Goddess, see
Whether my eyes can ever turn from thee!
For pity do not this sad heart belie—
Even as thou vanishest so I shall die.
Stay! though a Naiad of the rivers, stay!
To thy far wishes will thy streams obey:
Stay! though the greenest woods be thy domain,
Alone they can drink up the morning rain:
Though a descended Pleiad, will not one
Of thine harmonious sisters keep in tune
Thy spheres, and as thy silver proxy shine?
So sweetly to these ravished ears of mine
Came thy swift greeting, that if thou shouldst fade
Thy memory will waste me to a shade:

For pity do not melt!"—"If I should stay,"
Said Lamia, "here upon this floor of clay,
And pain my steps upon these flowers too rough,
What canst thou say or do of charm enough
To dull the nice remembrance of my home?
Thou canst not ask me with thee here to roam
Over these hills and vales where no joy is,—
Empty of immortality and bliss!
Thou art a scholar, Lycius, and must know
That finer spirits cannot breathe below
In human climes, and live: Alas! poor youth,
What taste of purer air hast thou to soothe
My essence? What serener palaces,
Where I may all my many senses please,
And by mysterious sleights a hundred thirsts appease?
It cannot be—Adieu!" So said, she rose
Tiptoe with white arms spread. He, sick to lose
The amorous promise of her lone complain,
Swooned, murmuring of love, and pale with pain.
The cruel lady, without any show
Of sorrow for her tender favourite's woe,
But rather, if her eyes could brighter be,
With brighter eyes and slow amenity,
Put her new lips to his, and gave afresh
The life she had so tangled in her mesh:
And as he from one trance was wakening
Into another, she began to sing,
Happy in beauty, life, and love, and everything,
A song of love, too sweet for earthly lyres,
While, like held breath, the stars drew in their panting fires.
And then she whispered in such trembling tone,
As those who, safe together, met alone
For the first time through many anguished days,
Use other speech than looks; bidding him raise
His drooping head, and clear his soul of doubt,
For that she was a woman, and without
Any more subtle fluid in her veins
Than throbbing blood, and that the self-same pains
Inhabited her frail-strung heart as his.
And next she wondered how his eyes could miss
Her face so long in Corinth, where, she said,
She dwelt but half retired, and there had led
Days happy as the gold coin could invent
Without the aid of love; yet in content
Till she saw him, as once she passed him by,

Where 'gainst a column he leant thoughtfully
At Venus' temple porch, 'mid baskets heaped
Of amorous herbs and flowers, newly reaped
Late on that eve, as 'twas the night before
The Adonian feast; whereof she saw no more,
But wept alone those days, for why should she adore?
Lycius from death awoke into amaze,
To see her still, and singing so sweet lays;
Then from amaze into delight he fell
To hear her whisper woman's lore so well;
And every word she spake enticed him on
To unperplexed delight and pleasure known.
Let the mad poets say whate'er they please
Of the sweets of Fairies, Peris, Goddesses,
There is not such a treat among them all,
Haunters of cavern, lake, and waterfall,
As a real woman, lineal indeed
From Pyrrha's pebbles or old Adam's seed.
Thus gentle Lamia judged, and judged aright,
That Lycius could not love in half a fright,
So threw the goddess off, and won his heart
More pleasantly by playing woman's part,
With no more awe than what her beauty gave,
That, while it smote, still guaranteed to save.
Lycius to all made eloquent reply,
Marrying to every word a twinborn sigh;
And last, pointing to Corinth, asked her sweet,
If 'twas too far that night for her soft feet.
The way was short, for Lamia's eagerness
Made, by a spell, the triple league decrease
To a few paces; not at all surmised
By blinded Lycius, so in her comprised.
They passed the city gates, he knew not how,
So noiseless, and he never thought to know.

    As men talk in a dream, so Corinth all,
Throughout her palaces imperial,
And all her populous streets and temples lewd,
Muttered, like tempest in the distance brewed,
To the wide-spreaded night above her towers.
Men, women, rich and poor, in the cool hours,
Shuffled their sandals o'er the pavement white,
Companioned or alone; while many a light
Flared, here and there, from wealthy festivals,
And threw their moving shadows on the walls,

Or found them clustered in the corniced shade
Of some arched temple door, or dusky colonnade.

Muffling his face, of greeting friends in fear,
Her fingers he pressed hard, as one came near
With curled grey beard, sharp eyes, and smooth bald crown
Slow-stepped, and robed in philosophic gown:
Lycius shrank closer, as they met and passed,
Into his mantle, adding wings to haste,
While hurried Lamia trembled: "Ah," said he,
Why do you shudder, love, so ruefully?
Why does your tender palm dissolve in dew?"
"I'm wearied," said fair Lamia: "tell me who
Is that old man? I cannot bring to mind
His features:—Lycius! wherefore did you blind
Yourself from his quick eyes?" Lycius replied,
" 'Tis Apollonius sage, my trusty guide
And good instructor; but to-night he seems
The ghost of folly haunting my sweet dreams."

While yet he spake they had arrived before
A pillared porch, with lofty portal door,
Where hung a silver lamp, whose phosphor glow
Reflected in the slabbed steps below,
Mild as a star in water; for so new,
And so unsullied was the marble hue,
So through the crystal polish, liquid fine,
Ran the dark veins, that none but feet divine
Could e'er have touched there. Sounds Æolian
Breathed from the hinges, as the ample span
Of the wide doors disclosed a place unknown
Some time to any, but those two alone,
And a few Persian mutes, who that same year
Were seen about the markets: none knew where
They could inhabit; the most curious
Were foiled, who watched to trace them to their house:
And but the flitter-winged verse must tell,
For truth's sake, what woe afterwards befel,
'Twould humour many a heart to leave them thus,
Shut from the busy world of more incredulous.

———

PART II.

Love in a hut, with water and a crust,
Is—Love, forgive us!—cinders, ashes, dust;
Love in a palace is perhaps at last
More grievous torment than a hermit's fast:
That is a doubtful tale from fairy land,
Hard for the non-elect to understand.
Had Lycius lived to hand his story down,
He might have given the moral a fresh frown,
Or clenched it quite: but too short was their bliss
To breed distrust and hate, that make the soft voice hiss.
Besides, there, nightly, with terrific glare,
Love, jealous grown of so complete a pair,
Hovered and buzzed his wings, with fearful roar,
Above the lintel of their chamber door,
And down the passage cast a glow upon the floor.

      For all this came a ruin: side by side
They were enthronèd, in the even-tide,
Upon a couch, near to a curtaining
Whose airy texture, from a golden string,
Floated into the room, and let appear
Unveiled the summer heaven, blue and clear,
Betwixt two marble shafts:—there they reposed,
Where use had made it sweet, with eyelids closed,
Saving a tithe which love still open kept,
That they might see each other while they almost slept;
When from the slope side of a suburb hill,
Deafening the swallow's twitter, came a thrill
Of trumpets—Lycius started—the sounds fled,
But left a thought, a buzzing in his head.
For the first time, since first he harboured in
That purple-lined palace of sweet sin,
His spirit passed beyond its golden bourne
Into the noisy world almost foresworn.
The lady, ever watchful, penetrant,
Saw this with pain, so arguing a want
Of something more, more than her empery
Of joys; and she began to moan and sigh
Because he mused beyond her, knowing well
That but a moment's thought is passion's passing bell.
"Why do you sigh, fair creature?" whispered he:
"Why do you think?" returned she tenderly:
"You have deserted me;—where am I now?

Not in your heart while care weighs on your brow:
No, no, you have dismissed me; and I go
From your breast houseless: ay, it must be so."
He answered, bending to her open eyes,
Where he was mirrowed small in paradise:
"My silver planet, both of eve and morn!
Why will you plead yourself so sad forlorn,
While I am striving how to fill my heart
With deeper crimson, and a double smart?
How to entangle, trammel up and snare
Your soul in mine, and labyrinth you there
Like the hid scent in an unbudded rose?
Ay, a sweet kiss—you see your mighty woes.
My thoughts! shall I unveil them? Listen then!
What mortal hath a prize, that other men
May be confounded and abashed withal,
But lets it sometimes pace abroad majestical,
And triumph, as in thee I should rejoice
Amid the hoarse alarm of Corinth's voice.
Let my foes choke, and my friends shout afar,
While through the thronged streets your bridal car
Wheels round its dazzling spokes."—The lady's cheek
Trembled; she nothing said, but, pale and meek,
Arose and knelt before him, wept a rain
Of sorrows at his words; at last with pain
Beseeching him, the while his hand she wrung,
To change his purpose. He thereat was stung,
Perverse, with stronger fancy to reclaim
Her wild and timid nature to his aim:
Besides, for all his love, in self-despite,
Against his better self, he took delight
Luxurious in her sorrows, soft and new.
His passion, cruel grown, took on a hue
Fierce and sanguineous as 'twas possible
In one whose brow had no dark veins to swell.
Fine was the mitigated fury, like
Apollo's presence when in act to strike
The serpent—Ha, the serpent! certes, she
Was none. She burnt, she loved the tyranny,
And, all subdued, consented to the hour
When to the bridal he should lead his paramour.
Whispering in midnight silence, said the youth,
"Sure some sweet name thou hast, though, by my truth,
I have not asked it, ever thinking thee
Not mortal, but of heavenly progeny,

As still I do. Hast any mortal name,
Fit appellation for this dazzling frame?
Or friends or kinsfolk on the citied earth,
To share our marriage feast and nuptial mirth?"
"I have no friends," said Lamia, "no, not one;
My presence in wide Corinth hardly known:
My parents' bones are in their dusty urns
Sepulchred, where no kindled incense burns,
Seeing all their luckless race are dead, save me,
And I neglect the holy rite for thee.
Even as you list invite your many guests;
But if, as now it seems, your vision rests
With any pleasure on me, do not bid
Old Apollonius—from him keep me hid."
Lycius, perplexed at words so blind and blank,
Made close inquiry; from whose touch she shrank,
Feigning a sleep; and he to the dull shade
Of deep sleep in a moment was betrayed.

It was the custom then to bring away
The bride from home at blushing shut of day,
Veiled, in a chariot, heralded along
By strewn flowers, torches, and a marriage song,
With other pageants: but this fair unknown
Had not a friend. So being left along
(Lycius was gone to summon all his kin),
And knowing surely she could never win
His foolish heart from its mad pompousness,
She set herself, high-thoughted, how to dress
The misery in fit magnificence.
She did so, but 'tis doubtful how and whence
Came, and who were her subtle servitors.
About the halls, and to and from the doors,
There was a noise of wings, till in short space
The glowing banquet-room shone with wide-arched grace.
A haunting music, sole perhaps and lone
Supportress of the fairy-roof, made moan
Throughout, as fearful the whole charm might fade.
Fresh carved cedar, mimicking a glade
Of palm and plantain, met from either side,
High in the midst, in honour of the bride:
Two palms and then two plantains, and so on,
From either side their stems branched one to one
All down the aisled place; and beneath all
There ran a stream of lamps straight on from wall to wall.

So canopied, lay an untasted feast
Teeming with odours. Lamia, regal drest,
Silently paced about, and as she went,
In pale contented sort of discontent,
Missioned her viewless servants to enrich
The fretted splendour of each nook and niche.
Between the tree-stems, marbled plain at first,
Came jasper panels; then, anon, there burst
Forth creeping imagery of slighter trees,
And with the larger wove in small intricacies.
Approving all, she faded at self-will,
And shut the chamber up, close, hushed and still,
Complete and ready for the revels rude,
When dreadful guests would come to spoil her solitude.
    The day appeared, and all the gossip rout.
O senseless Lycius! Madman! wherefore flout
The silent-blessing fate, warm cloistered hours,
And show to common eyes these secret bowers?
The herd approached; each guest, with busy brain,
Arriving at the portal, gazed amain,
And entered marvelling: for they knew the street,
Remembered it from childhood all complete
Without a gap, yet ne'er before had seen
That royal porch, that high-built fair demesne;
So in they hurried all, mazed, curious and keen:
Save one, who looked thereon with eye severe,
And with calm-planted steps walked in austere;
'Twas Apollonius: something too he laughed,
As though some knotty problem that had daft
His patient thought, had now begun to thaw,
And solve and melt:—'twas just as he foresaw.

    He met within the murmurous vestibule
His young disciple. "'Tis no common rule,
"Lycius," said he, "for uninvited guest
To force himself upon you, and infest
With an unbidden presence the bright throng
Of younger friends; yet must I do this wrong,
And you forgive me." Lycius blushed, and led
The old man through the inner doors broad-spread;
With reconciling words and courteous mien
Turning into sweet milk the sophist's spleen.

    Of wealthy lustre was the banquet-room,
Filled with pervading brilliance and perfume

Before each lucid panel fuming stood
A censer fed with myrrh and spiced wood,
Each by a sacred tripod held aloft,
Whose slender feet wide-swerved upon the soft
Wool-woofed carpets: fifty wreaths of smoke
From fifty censers their light voyage took
To the high roof, still mimicked as they rose
Along the mirrored walls by twin-clouds odorous.
Twelve sphered tables, by silk seats insphered,
High as the level of a man's breast reared
On libbard's paws, upheld the heavy gold
Of cups and goblets, and the store thrice told
Of Ceres' horn, and, in huge vessels, wine
Came from the gloomy tun with merry shine.
Thus loaded with a feast the tables stood,
Each shrining in the midst the image of a God.

When in an ante-chamber every guest
Had felt the cold full sponge to pleasure pressed,
By minist'ring slaves, upon his hands and feet,
And fragrant oils with ceremony meet
Poured on his hair, they all moved to the feast
In white robes, and themselves in order placed
Around the silken couches, wondering
Whence all this mighty cost and blaze of wealth could spring.

Soft went the music the soft air along,
While fluent Greek a vowelled undersong
Kept up among the guests, discoursing low
At first, for scarcely was the wine at flow;
But when the happy vintage touched their brains,
Louder they talk, and louder come the strains
Of powerful instruments:—the gorgeous dyes
The space, the splendour of the draperies,
The roof of awful richness, nectarous cheer
Beautiful slaves, and Lamia's self, appear.
Now, when the wine has done its rosy deed,
And every soul from human trammels freed,
No more so strange; for merry wine, sweet wine,
Will make Elysian shades not too fair, too divine.
Soon was God Bacchus at meridian height;
Flushed were their cheeks, and bright eyes double bright:
Garlands of every green, and every scent
From vales deflowered, or forest-trees branch-rent,
In baskets of bright osiered gold were brought

High as the handles heaped, to suit the thought
Of every guest; that each, as he did please,
Might fancy-fit his brows, silk-pillowed at his ease.

What wreath for Lamia? What for Lycius?
What for the sage, old Apollonius?
Upon her aching forehead be there hung
The leaves of willow and of adder's tongue,
And for the youth, quick, let us strip for him
The thyrsus, that his watching eyes may swim
Into forgetfulness; and for the sage,
Let spear-grass and the spiteful thistle wage
War on his temples. Do not all charms fly
At the mere touch of cold philosophy?
There was an awful rainbow once in heaven:
We know her woof, her texture; she is given
In the dull catalogue of common things.
Philosophy will clip an angel's wings,
Conquer all mysteries by rule and line,
Empty the haunted air, and gnomed mine—
Unweave a rainbow, as it erewhile made
The tender-personed Lamia melt into a shade.

By her glad Lycius sitting, in chief place,
Scarce saw in all the room another face,
Till, checking his love trance, a cup he took
Full brimmed, and opposite sent forth a look
'Cross the broad table, to beseech a glance
From his old teacher's wrinkled countenance,
And pledge him. The bald-head philosopher
Had fixed his eye, without a twinkle or stir
Full on the alarmed beauty of the bride,
Brow-beating her fair form, and troubling her sweet pride.
Lycius then pressed her hand, with devout touch,
As pale it lay upon the rosy couch:
'Twas icy, and the cold ran through his veins;
Then sudden it grew hot, and all the pains
Of an unnatural heat shot to his heart.
"Lamia, what means this? Wherefore dost thou start?
Know'st thou that man?" Poor Lamia answered not.
He gazed into her eyes, and not a jot
Owned they the love-lorn piteous appeal:
More, more he gazed: his human senses reel:
Some hungry spell that loveliness absorbs;
There was no recognition in those orbs.

"Lamia!" he cried—and no soft-toned reply.
The many heard, and the loud revelry
Grew hush; the stately music no more breathes;
The myrtle sickened in a thousand wreaths.
By faint degrees, voice, lute, and pleasure ceased;
A deadly silence step by step increased,
Until it seemed a horrid presence there,
And not a man but felt the terror in his hair.
"Lamia!" he shrieked; and nothing but the shriek
With its sad echo did the silence break.
"Begone, foul dream!" he cried, gazing again
In the bride's face, where now no azure vein
Wandered on fair-spaced temples; no soft bloom
Misted the cheek; no passion to illume
The deep-recessed vision:—all was blight;
Lamia, no longer fair, there sat a deadly white.
"Shut, shut those juggling eyes, thou ruthless man!
Turn them aside, wretch! or the righteous ban
Of all the Gods, whose dreadful images
Here represent their shadowy presences,
May pierce them on the sudden with the thorn
Of painful blindness; leaving thee forlorn,
In trembling dotage to the feeblest fright
Of conscience, for their long offended might,
For all thine impious proud-heart sophistries,
Unlawful magic, and enticing lies.
Corinthians! look upon that grey-beard wretch!
Mark how, possessed, his lashless eyelids stretch
Around his demon eyes! Corinthians, see!
My sweet bride withers at their potency."
"Fool!" said the sophist, in an under-tone
Gruff with contempt; which a death-nighing moan
From Lycius answered, as heart-struck and lost,
He sat supine beside the aching ghost.
"Fool! Fool!" repeated he, while his eyes still
Relented not, nor moved; "from every ill
Of life have I preserved thee to this day,
And shall I see thee made a serpent's prey?"
Then Lamia breathed death breath; the sophist's eye,
Like a sharp spear, went through her utterly,
Keen, cruel, perceant, stinging: she, as well
As her weak hand could any meaning tell,
Motioned him to be silent; vainly so,
He looked and looked again a level—No!
A Serpent!" echoed he; no sooner said,

Than with a frightful scream she vanished:
And Lycius' arms were empty of delight,
As were his limbs of life, from that same night.
On the high couch he lay!—his friends came round—
Supported him—no pulse, or breath they found,
And, in its marriage robe, the heavy body wound.

Nature Poem

by EMILY DICKINSON

A narrow fellow in the grass
Occasionally rides;
You may have met him,—do you not?
His notice sudden is.

The grass divides as with a comb,
A spotted shaft is seen;
And then it closes at your feet
And opens further on.

He likes a boggy acre,
A floor too cool for corn.
Yet when a child, and barefoot,
I more than once at morn,

Have passed, I thought, a whip-lash
Unbraiding in the sun,—
When, stooping to secure it,
It wrinkled, and was gone.

Several of nature's people
I know, and they know me;
I feel for them a transport
Of cordiality;

But never met this fellow,
Attended or alone,
Without a tighter breathing,
And zero at the bone.

Paradise Lost Because of the Serpent

by JOHN MILTON

Say first, for heaven hides nothing from thy view,
Nor the deep tract of hell; say first, what cause
Moved our grand Parents in that happy state,
Favour'd of heaven so highly, to fall off
From their Creator, and transgress his will
For one restraint, lords of the world besides?
Who first seduced them to that foul revolt?
The infernal serpent: he it was, whose guile,
Stirr'd up with envy and revenge, deceived
The mother of mankind, what time his pride
Had cast him out from heaven, with all his host
Of rebel angels; by whose aid aspiring
To set himself in glory above his peers,
He trusted to have equal'd the Most High,
If he opposed; and with ambitious aim
Against the throne and monarchy of God
Raised impious war in heaven and battel proud
With vain attempt. Him the Almighty Power
Hurl'd headlong flaming from the ethereal sky,
With hideous ruin and combustion, down
To bottomless perdition, there to dwell
In adamantine chains and penal fire,
Who durst defy the Omnipotent to arms.

*   *   *   *   *

No more of talk where God or angel guest
With man, as with his friend, familiar used
To sit indulgent, and with him partake
Rural repast; permitting him the while

Venial discourse unblamed. I now must change
Those notes to tragic; foul distrust, and breach
Disloyal on the part of man, revolt
And disobedience: on the part of Heaven
Now alienated, distance and distaste,
Anger and just rebuke, and judgment given,
That brought into this world a world of woe,
Sin and her shadow Death, and Misery,
Death's harbinger: sad task!

*   *   *   *   *

The sun was sunk, and after him the star
Of Hesperus, whose office is to bring
Twilight upon the earth, short arbiter
'Twixt day and night; and now from end to end
Night's hemisphere had veil'd the horizon round;
When Satan, who late fled before the threats
Of Gabriel out of Eden, now improved
In meditated fraud and malice, bent
On man's destruction, maugre what might hap
Of heavier on himself, fearless return'd.
By night he fled, and at midnight return'd
From compassing the earth; cautious of day,
Since Uriel, regent of the sun, descried
His entrance, and forewarn'd the cherubim
That kept their watch; thence full of anguish driven,
The space of seven continued nights he rode
With darkness; thrice the equinoctial line
He circled; four times cross'd the car of night
From pole to pole, travérsing each colure;
On the eighth return'd; and, on the coast averse
From entrance or cherubic watch, by stealth
Found unsuspected way. There was a place,
Now not, though sin, not time, first wrought the change,
Where Tigris, at the foot of Paradise,
Into a gulf shot underground; till part
Rose up a fountain by the tree of life:
In with the river sunk, and with it rose,
Satan, involved in rising mist; then sought
Where to lie hid: sea he had search'd, and land
From Eden over Pontus, and the pool
Mæotis, up beyond the river Ob;
Downward as far antarctic; and in length,
West from Orontes to the ocean barr'd
At Darien; thence to the land where flows

Ganges and Indus: thus the orb he roam'd
With narrow search; and with inspection deep
Consider'd every creature, which of all
Most opportune might serve his wiles; and found
The serpent subtlest beast of all the field.
Him, after long debate irresolute
Of thoughts revolved, his final sentence chose;
Fit vessel, fittest imp of fraud, in whom
To enter, and his dark suggestions hide
From sharpest sight; for, in the wily snake
Whatever sleights, none would suspicious mark,
As from his wit and native subtlety
Proceeding; which, in other beasts observed,
Doubt might beget of diabolic power
Active within, beyond the sense of brute.
Thus he resolved; but first from inward grief
His bursting passion into plaints thus pour'd:
    O earth, how like to heaven, if not preferr'd
More justly, seat worthier of gods, as built
With second thoughts, reforming what was old!
For what God, after better, worse would build?
Terrestrial heaven, danced round by other heavens
That shine, yet bear their bright officious lamps,
Light above light, for thee alone, as seems;
In thee concentring all their precious beams
Of sacred influence! As God in heaven
Is centre, yet extends to all; so thou,
Centring, receiv'st from all those orbs: in thee,
Not in themselves, all their known virtue appears
Productive in herb, plant, and nobler birth
Of creatures animate with gradual life,
Of growth, sense, reason, all summ'd up in man.
With what delight could I have walk'd thee round,
If I could joy in aught! sweet interchange
Of hill, and valley, rivers, woods, and plains,
Now land, now sea, and shores with forest crown'd,
Rocks, dens, and caves! But I in none of these
Find place or refuge; and the more I see
Pleasures about me, so much more I feel
Torment within me, as from the hateful siege
Of contraries: all good to me becomes
Bane, and in heaven much worse would be my state.
But neither here seek I, no, nor in heaven
To dwell, unless by mastering heaven's Supreme:
Nor hope to be myself less miserable

By what I seek, but others to make such
As I, though thereby worse to me redound:
For only in destroying I find ease
To my relentless thoughts; and, him destroy'd,
Or won to what may work his utter loss,
For whom all this was made; all this will soon
Follow, as to him link'd in weal or woe:
In woe then; that destruction wide may range.
To me shall be the glory sole among
The infernal powers, in one day to have marr'd
What he, Almighty styled, six nights and days
Continued making; and who knows how long
Before had been contriving? though perhaps
Not longer than since I, in one night, freed
From servitude inglorious well nigh half
The angelic name, and thinner left the throng
Of his adorers: he, to be avenged,
And to repair his numbers thus impair'd,
Whether such virtue spent of old now fail'd
More angels to create, if they at least
Are his created; or, to spite us more,
Determined to advance into our room
A creature form'd of earth; and him endow,
Exalted from so base original,
With heavenly spoils, our spoils: what he decreed,
He effected; man he made, and for him built
Magnificent this world, and earth his seat,
Him lord pronounced; and, O indignity!
Subjected to his service angel-wings,
And flaming ministers to watch and tend
Their earthy charge: of these the vigilance
I dread; and, to elude, thus wrapp'd in mist
Of midnight vapour glide obscure; and pry
In every bush and brake, where hap may find
The serpent sleeping; in whose mazy folds
To hide me, and the dark intent I bring.
O foul descent that I, who erst contended
With gods to sit the highest, am now constrain'd
Into a beast; and, mix'd with bestial slime,
This essence to incarnate and imbrute,
That to the highth of deity aspired!
But what will not ambition and revenge
Descend to? Who aspires, must down as low
As high he soar'd; obnoxious, first to last,
To basest things. Revenge, at first though sweet,

Bitter ere long, back on itself recoils:
Let it; I reck not, so it light well aim'd,
Since higher I fall short, on him who next
Provokes my envy, this new favourite
Of Heaven, this man of clay, son of despite;
Whom, us the more to spite, his Maker raised
From dust: spite then with spite is best repaid.
  So saying, through each thicket dank or dry,
Like a black mist low-creeping, he held on
His midnight search, where soonest he might find
The serpent: him fast sleeping soon he found
In labyrinth of many a round self-roll'd,
His head the midst, well stored with subtle wiles:
Not yet in horrid shade or dismal den,
Nor nocent yet; but, on the grassy herb,
Fearless unfear'd he slept: in at his mouth
The devil enter'd; and his brutal sense,
In heart or head, possessing, soon inspired
With act intelligential; but his sleep
Disturb'd not, waiting close the approach of morn.
  Now, when as sacred light began to dawn
In Eden on the humid flowers, that breathed
Their morning incense, when all things, that breathe,
From the earth's great altar send up silent praise
To the Creator, and his nostrils fill
With grateful smell, forth came the human pair,
And join'd their vocal worship to the quire
Of creatures wanting voice; that done, partake
The season, prime for sweetest scents and airs:
Then commune, how that day they best may ply
Their growing work; for much their work outgrew
The hands' dispatch of two, gardening so wide;
And Eve first to her husband thus began:
  Adam, well may we labour still to dress
This garden, still to tend plant, herb, and flower,
Our pleasant task enjoin'd; but, till more hands
Aid us, the work under our labour grows,
Luxurious by restraint: what we by day
Lop overgrown, or prune, or prop, or bind,
One night or two with wanton growth derides,
Tending to wild. Thou therefore now advise,
Or hear what to my mind first thoughts present:
Let us divide our labours; thou, where choice
Leads thee, or where most needs; whether to wind
The woodbine round this arbour, or direct

The clasping ivy where to climb: while I,
In yonder spring of roses intermix'd
With myrtle, find what to redress till noon:
For, while so near each other thus all day
Our task we choose, what wonder if so near
Looks intervene and smiles, or object new
Casual discourse draw on; which intermits
Our day's work, brought to little, though begun
Early, and the hour of supper comes unearn'd?
    To whom mild answer Adam thus return'd:
Sole Eve, associate sole, to me beyond
Compare above all living creatures dear!
Well hast thou motion'd, well thy thoughts employ'd
How we might best fulfil the work which here
God hath assign'd us; nor of me shalt pass
Unpraised; for nothing lovelier can be found
In woman, than to study household good,
And good works in her husband to promote.
Yet not so strictly hath our Lord imposed
Labour, as to debar us when we need
Refreshment, whether food, or talk between,
Food of the mind, or this sweet intercourse
Of looks and smiles; for smiles from reason flow,
To brute denied, and are of love the food;
Love, not the lowest end of human life.
For not to irksome toil, but to delight,
He made us, and delight to reason join'd.
These paths and bowers doubt not but our joint hands
Will keep from wilderness with ease, as wide
As we need walk; till younger hands ere long
Assist us: but if much converse perhaps
Thee satiate, to short absence I could yield;
For solitude sometimes is best society,
And short retirement urges sweet return.
But other doubt possesses me, lest harm
Befall thee sever'd from me; for thou know'st
What hath been warn'd us; what malicious foe,
Envying our happiness, and of his own
Despairing, seeks to work us woe and shame
By sly assault; and somewhere nigh at hand
Watches, no doubt, with greedy hope to find
His wish and best advantage, us asunder;
Hopeless to circumvent us join'd, where each
To other speedy aid might lend at need:
Whether his first design be to withdraw

Our fealty from God; or to disturb
Conjugal love, than which perhaps no bliss
Enjoy'd by us excites his envy more;
Or this, or worse, leave not the faithful side
That gave thee being, still shades thee, and protects.
The wife, where danger or dishonour lurks,
Safest and seemliest by her husband stays,
Who guards her, or with her the worst endures.
    To whom the virgin majesty of Eve,
As one who loves, and some unkindness meets,
With sweet austere composure thus replied:
    Offspring of heaven and earth, and all earth's lord!
That such an enemy we have, who seeks
Our ruin, both by thee inform'd I learn,
And from the parting angel overheard,
As in a shady nook I stood behind,
Just then return'd at shut of evening flowers.
But that thou shouldst my firmness therefore doubt
To God or thee, because we have a foe
May tempt it, I expected not to hear.
His violence thou fear'st not; being such
As we, not capable of death or pain,
Can either not receive, or can repel.
His fraud is then thy fear; which plain infers
Thy equal fear, that my firm faith and love
Can by his fraud be shaken or seduced;
Thoughts, which how found they harbour in thy breast,
Adam, misthought of her to thee so dear?
    To whom with healing words Adam replied:
Daughter of God and man, immortal Eve!
For such thou art; from sin and blame entire:
Not diffident of thee, do I dissuade
Thy absence from my sight; but to avoid
The attempt itself, intended by our foe.
For he who tempts, though in vain, at least asperses
The tempted with dishonour foul; supposed
Not incorruptible of faith, not proof
Against temptation: thou thyself with scorn
And anger wouldst resent the offer'd wrong,
Though ineffectual found: misdeem not then,
If such affront I labour to avert
From thee alone, which on us both at once
The enemy, though bold, will hardly dare;
Or daring, first on me the assault shall light.
Nor thou his malice and false guile contemn:

Subtle he needs must be, who could seduce
Angels; nor think superfluous others' aid.
I, from the influence of thy looks, receive
Access in every virtue; in thy sight
More wise, more watchful, stronger, if need were
Of outward strength; while shame, thou looking on,
Shame to be overcome or overreach'd,
Would utmost vigour raise, and raised unite.
Why shouldst not thou like sense within thee feel
When I am present, and thy trial choose
With me, best witness of thy virtue tried?
   So spake domestic Adam in his care
And matrimonial love; but Eve, who thought
Less áttributed to her faith sincere,
Thus her reply with accent sweet renew'd:
   If this be our condition, thus to dwell
In narrow circuit straiten'd by a foe,
Subtle or violent, we not endued
Single with like defence, wherever met;
How are we happy, still in fear of harm?
But harm precedes not sin: only our foe,
Tempting, affronts us with his foul esteem
Of our integrity: his foul esteem
Sticks no dishonour on our front, but turns
Foul on himself; then wherefore shunn'd or fear'd
By us? who rather double honour gain
From his surmise proved false; find peace within,
Favour from Heaven, our witness, from the event.
And what is faith, love, virtue, unassay'd
Alone, without exteriour help sustain'd?
Let us not then suspect our happy state
Left so imperfect by the Maker wise,
As not secure to single or combined.
Frail is our happiness, if this be so;
And Eden were no Eden, thus exposed.
   To whom thus Adam fervently replied:
O woman, best are all things as the will
Of God ordain'd them: his creating hand
Nothing imperfect or deficient left
Of all that he created: much less man,
Or aught that might his happy state secure,
Secure from outward force: within himself
The danger lies, yet lies within his power:
Against his will he can receive no harm:
But God left free the will; for what obeys

Reason, is free; and reason he made right,
But bid her well be ware, and still erect;
Lest, by some fair-appearing good surprised,
She dictate false, and misinform the will
To do what God expressly hath forbid.
Not then mistrust, but tender love enjoins,
That I should mind thee oft; and mind thou me.
Firm we subsist, yet possible to swerve;
Since reason not impossibly may meet
Some specious object by the foe suborn'd,
And fall into deception unaware,
Not keeping strictest watch, as she was warn'd.
Seek not temptation then, which to avoid
Were better, and most likely if from me
Thou sever not: trial will come unsought.
Wouldst thou approve thy constancy? approve
First thy obedience; the other who can know?
Not seeing thee attempted, who attest?
But if thou think trial unsought may find
Us both securer than thus warn'd thou seem'st
Go; for thy stay, not free, absents thee more;
Go in thy native innocence, rely
On what thou hast of virtue; summon all:
For God towards thee hath done his part; do thine.
    So spake the patriarch of mankind; but Eve
Persisted; yet submiss, though last, replied:
    With thy permission then, and thus forewarn'd
Chiefly by what thy own last reasoning words
Touch'd only; that our trial, when least sought,
May find us both perhaps far less prepared;
The willinger I go, nor much expect
A foe so proud will first the weaker seek;
So bent, the more shall shame him his repulse.
    Thus saying, from her husband's hand her hand
Soft she withdrew, and, like a wood-nymph light,
Oread or Dryad, or of Delia's train,
Betook her to the groves; but Delia's self
In gait surpass'd, and goddess-like deport,
Though not as she with bow and quiver arm'd,
But with such gardening-tools as art, yet rude,
Guiltless of fire, had form'd, or angels brought.
To Pales, or Pomona, thus adorn'd,
Likest she seem'd; Pomona, when she fled
Vertumnus; or to Ceres in her prime,
Yet virgin of Proserpina from Jove.

Her long with ardent look his eye pursued
Delighted, but desiring more her stay.
Oft he to her his charge of quick return
Repeated: she to him as oft engaged
To be return'd by noon amid the bower,
And all things in best order to invite
Noontide repast, or afternoon's repose.
O, much deceived, much failing, hapless Eve,
Of thy presumed return! event perverse!
Thou never from that hour in Paradise
Found'st either sweet repast or sound repose;
Such ambush, hid among sweet flowers and shades,
Waited with hellish rancour imminent
To intercept thy way, or send thee back
Despoil'd of innocence, of faith, of bliss!
For now, and since first break of dawn, the fiend,
Mere serpent in appearance, forth was come;
And on his quest, where likeliest he might find
The only two of mankind, but in them
The whole included race, his purposed prey.
In bower and field he sought, where any tuft
Of grove or garden-plot more pleasant lay,
Their tendance, or plantation for delight;
By fountain or by shady rivulet
He sought them both, but wish'd his hap might find
Eve separate; he wish'd, but not with hope
Of what so seldom chanced; when to his wish,
Beyond his hope, Eve separate he spies,
Veil'd in a cloud of fragrance, where she stood,
Half spied, so thick the roses bushing round
About her glow'd, oft stooping to support
Each flower of slender stalk, whose head, though gay
Carnation, purple, azure, or speck'd with gold,
Hung drooping unsustain'd; them she upstay
Gently with myrtle band, mindless the while
Herself, though fairest unsupported flower,
From her best prop so far, and storm so nigh.
Nearer he drew, and many a walk travérs'd
Of stateliest covert, cedar, pine, or palm;
Then voluble and bold, now hid, now seen,
Among thick-woven arborets, and flowers
Imborder'd on each bank, the hand of Eve:
Spot more delicious than those gardens feign'd
Or of revived Adonis, or renown'd
Alcinous, host of old Laertes' son;

Or that, not mystic, where the sapient king
Held dalliance with his fair Egyptian spouse.
Much he the place admired, the person more.
As one who, long in populous city pent,
Where houses thick and sewers annoy the air,
Forth issuing on a summer's morn, to breathe
Among the pleasant villages and farms
Adjoin'd, from each thing met conceives delight,
The smell of grain, or tedded grass, or kine,
Or dairy, each rural sight, each rural sound;
If chance, with nymph-like step, fair virgin pass
What pleasing seem'd, for her now pleases more;
She most, and in her look sums all delight:
Such pleasure took the serpent to behold
This flowery plat, the sweet recess of Eve
Thus early, thus alone: her heavenly form
Angelic, but more soft, and feminine,
Her graceful innocence, her every air
Of gesture, or least action, overawed
His malice, and with rapine sweet bereaved
His fierceness of the fierce intent it brought:
That space the evil one abstracted stood
From his own evil, and for the time remain'd
Stupidly good; of enmity disarm'd,
Of guile, of hate, of envy, of revenge:
But the hot hell that always in him burns,
Though in mid heaven, soon ended his delight,
And tortures him now more, the more he sees
Of pleasure, not for him ordain'd: then soon
Fierce hate he recollects: and all his thoughts
Of mischief, gratulating, thus excites:
　　　Thoughts, whither have ye led me? with what sweet
Compulsion thus transported, to forget
What hither brought us? hate, not love; nor hope
Of Paradise for hell, hope here to taste
Of pleasure; but all pleasure to destroy,
Save what is in destroying: other joy
To me is lost. Then, let me not let pass
Occasion which now smiles; behold alone
The woman, opportune to all attempts,
Her husband (for I view far round) not nigh,
Whose higher intellectual more I shun,
And strength, of courage haughty, and of limb
Heroic built, though of terrestrial mould;
Foe not informidable! exempt from wound,

I not; so much hath hell debased, and pain
Enfeebled me, to what I was in heaven.
She fair, divinely fair, fit love for gods!
Not terrible, though terrour be in love
And beauty, not approach'd by stronger hate,
Hate stronger, under show of love well feign'd;
The way which to her ruin now I tend.

  So spake the enemy of mankind, enclosed
In serpent, inmate bad! and toward Eve
Address'd his way: not with indented wave,
Prone on the ground, as since; but on his rear,
Circular base of rising folds, that tower'd
Fold above fold, a surging maze! his head
Crested aloft, and carbuncle his eyes;
With burnish'd neck of verdant gold, erect
Amidst his circling spires, that on the grass
Floated redundant: pleasing was his shape
And lovely; never since of serpent-kind
Lovelier, not those that in Illyria changed
Hermione and Cadmus, or the god
In Epidaurus; nor to which transform'd
Ammonian Jove or Capitoline was seen;
He with Olympias; this with her who bore
Scipio, the highth of Rome. With tract oblique
At first, as one who sought access, but fear'd
To interrupt, sidelong he works his way.
As when a ship, by skilful steersman wrought
Nigh river's mouth, or foreland, where the wind
Veers oft, as oft so steers, and shifts her sail:
So varied he, and of his tortuous train
Curl'd many a wanton wreath in sight of Eve,
To lure her eye; she, busied, heard the sound
Of rustling leaves, but minded not, as used
To such disport before her through the field,
From every beast; more duteous at her call,
Than at Circean call the herd disguised.
He, bolder now, uncall'd before her stood,
But as in gaze admiring: oft he bow'd
His turret crest, and sleek enamell'd neck,
Fawning; and lick'd the ground whereon she trod.
His gentle dumb expression turn'd at length
The eye of Eve, to mark his play; he, glad
Of her attention gain'd, with serpent-tongue
Organic, or impulse of vocal air,
His fraudulent temptation thus began:

Wonder not, sovran mistress, if perhaps
Thou canst, who art sole wonder! much less arm
Thy looks, the heaven of mildness, with disdain,
Displeased that I approach thee thus, and gaze
Insatiate; I thus single; nor have fear'd
Thy awful brow, more awful thus retired.
Fairest resemblance of thy Maker fair,
Thee all things living gaze on, all things thine
By gift, and thy celestial beauty adore
With ravishment beheld! there best beheld,
Where universally admired; but here
In this enclosure wild, these beasts among,
Beholders rude, and shallow to discern
Half what in thee is fair, one man except,
Who sees thee? (and what is one?) who shouldst be seen
A goddess among gods, adored and served
By angels numberless, thy daily train.
　　So glozed the tempter, and his proem tuned:
Into the heart of Eve his words made way,
Though at the voice much marvelling; at length,
Not unamazed, she thus in answer spake:
　　What may this mean? language of man pronounced
By tongue of brute, and human sense express'd?
The first, at least, of these I thought denied
To beasts; whom God, on their creation-day,
Created mute to all articulate sound:
The latter I demur; for in their looks
Much reason, and in their actions, oft appears.
Thee, serpent, subtlest beast of all the field
I knew, but not with human voice endued:
Redouble then this miracle, and say,
How cam'st thou speakable of mute; and how
To me so friendly grown above the rest
Of brutal kind, that daily are in sight?
Say, for such wonder claims attention due.
　　To whom the guileful tempter thus replied:
Empress of this fair world, resplendent Eve!
Easy to me it is to tell thee all
What thou command'st; and right thou shouldst be obey'd:
I was at first as other beasts that graze
The trodden herb, of abject thoughts and low,
As was my food; nor aught but food discern'd,
Or sex, and apprehended nothing high:
Till, on a day roving the field, I chanced
A goodly tree far distant to behold

Loaden with fruit of fairest colours mix'd,
Ruddy and gold: I nearer drew to gaze;
When from the boughs a savoury odour blown,
Grateful to appetite, more pleased my sense
Than smell of sweetest fennel, or the teats
Of ewe or goat dropping with milk at even,
Unsuck'd of lamb or kid, that tend their play.
To satisfy the sharp desire I had
Of tasting those fair apples, I resolved
Not to defer; hunger and thirst at once,
Powerful persuaders, quicken'd at the scent
Of that alluring fruit, urged me so keen.
About the mossy trunk I wound me soon;
For, high from ground, the branches would require
Thy utmost reach or Adam's: round the tree
All other beasts that saw, with like desire
Longing and envying stood, but could not reach.
Amid the tree now got, where plenty hung
Tempting so nigh, to pluck and eat my fill
I spared not; for such pleasure till that hour,
At feed or fountain, never had I found.
Sated at length, ere long I might perceive
Strange alteration in me, to degree
Of reason in my inward powers; and speech
Wanted not long; though to this shape retain'd.
Thenceforth to speculations high or deep
I turn'd my thoughts, and with capacious mind
Consider'd all things visible in heaven,
Or earth, or middle; all things fair and good:
But all that fair and good in thy divine
Semblance, and in thy beauty's heavenly ray,
United I beheld; no fair to thine
Equivalent or second! which compell'd
Me thus, though importune perhaps, to come
And gaze, and worship thee, of right declared
Sovran of creatures, universal dame!
  So talk'd the spirited sly snake; and Eve,
Yet more amazed, unwary thus replied:
  Serpent, thy overpraising leaves in doubt
The virtue of that fruit, in thee first proved:
But say, where grows the tree? from hence how far?
For many are the trees of God that grow
In Paradise, and various, yet unknown
To us; in such abundance lies our choice,
As leaves a greater store of fruit untouch'd

Still hanging incorruptible, till men
Grow up to their provision, and more hands
Help to disburden Nature of her birth.
    To whom the wily adder, blithe and glad:
Empress, the way is ready, and not long;
Beyond a row of myrtles, on a flat,
Fast by a fountain, one small thicket past
Of blowing myrrh and balm: if thou accept
My conduct, I can bring thee thither soon.
    Lead then, said Eve. He, leading, swiftly roll'd
In tangles, and made intricate seem straight,
To mischief swift. Hope elevates, and joy
Brightens his crest. As when a wandering fire,
Compact of unctuous vapour, which the night
Condenses, and the cold environs round,
Kindled through agitation to a flame,
Which oft, they say, some evil spirit attends,
Hovering and blazing with delusive light,
Misleads the amaz'd night-wanderer from his way
To bogs and mires, and oft through pond or pool;
There swallow'd up and lost, from succour far:
So glister'd the dire snake, and into fraud
Led Eve, our credulous mother, to the tree
Of prohibition, root of all our woe;
Which when she saw, thus to her guide she spake:
    Serpent, we might have spared our coming hither,
Fruitless to me, though fruit be here to excess,
The credit of whose virtue rest with thee;
Wondrous indeed, if cause of such effects!
But of this tree we may not taste nor touch;
God so commanded, and left that command
Sole daughter of his voice: the rest, we live
Law to ourselves; our reason is our law.
    To whom the tempter guilefully replied:
Indeed! hath God then said that of the fruit
Of all these garden-trees ye shall not eat,
Yet lords declared of all in earth or air?
    To whom thus Eve, yet sinless: Of the fruit
Of each tree in the garden we may eat;
But of the fruit of this fair tree amidst
The garden, God hath said, Ye shall not eat
Thereof, nor shall ye touch it, lest ye die.
    She scarce had said, though brief, when now **more bold**
The tempter, but with show of zeal and love
To man, and indignation at his wrong,

New part puts on; and, as to passion moved,
Fluctuates disturb'd, yet comely and in act
Raised, as of some great matter to begin.
As when of old some orator renown'd,
In Athens, or free Rome, where eloquence
Flourish'd, since mute, to some great cause address'd,
Stood in himself collected, while each part,
Motion, each act, won audience ere the tongue,
Sometimes in highth began, as no delay
Of preface brooking, through his zeal of right:
So standing, moving, or to highth upgrown,
The tempter, all impassion'd, thus began:
    O sacred, wise, and wisdom-giving plant,
Mother of science! now I feel thy power
Within me clear; not only to discern
Things in their causes, but to trace the ways
Of highest agents, deem'd however wise.
Queen of this universe! do not believe
Those rigid threats of death: ye shall not die;
How should you? by the fruit? it gives you life
To knowledge; by the threatener? look on me,
Me, who have touch'd and tasted; yet both live,
And life more perfect have attain'd than fate
Meant me, by venturing higher than my lot.
Shall that be shut to man, which to the beast
Is open? or will God incense his ire
For such a petty trespass? and not praise
Rather your dauntless virtue, whom the pain
Of death denounced, whatever thing death be,
Deterr'd not from achieving what might lead
To happier life, knowledge of good and evil;
Of good, how just? of evil, if what is evil
Be real, why not known, since easier shunn'd?
God therefore cannot hurt ye, and be just:
Not just, not God; not fear'd then, nor obey'd:
Your fear itself of death removes the fear.
Why then was this forbid? why, but to awe?
Why, but to keep ye low and ignorant,
His worshippers? He knows, that in the day
Ye eat thereof, your eyes, that seem so clear,
Yet are but dim, shall perfectly be then
Open'd and clear'd, and ye shall be as gods,
Knowing both good and evil, as they know.
That ye shall be as gods, since I as man,
Internal man, is but proportion meet;

I, of brute, human; ye, of human, gods.
So ye shall die perhaps, by putting off
Human, to put on gods; death to be wish'd,
Though threaten'd, which no worse than this can bring.
And what are gods, that man may not become
As they, participating godlike food?
The gods are first, and that advantage use
On our belief, that all from them proceeds:
I question it; for this fair earth I see,
Warm'd by the sun, producing every kind;
Them, nothing: if they all things, who enclosed
Knowledge of good and evil in this tree,
That whoso eats thereof, forthwith attains
Wisdom without their leave? and wherein lies
The offence, that man should thus attain to know?
What can your knowledge hurt him, or this tree
Impart against his will, if all be his?
Or is it envy? and can envy dwell
In heavenly breasts? These, these, and many more
Causes import your need of this fair fruit.
Goddess humane, reach then, and freely taste.
    He ended; and his words, replete with guile,
Into her heart too easy entrance won:
Fix'd on the fruit she gazed, which to behold
Might tempt alone; and in her ears the sound
Yet rung of his persuasive words, impregn'd
With reason, to her seeming, and with truth:
Meanwhile the hour of noon drew on, and waked
An eager appetite, raised by the smell
So savoury of that fruit, which with desire,
Inclinable now grown to touch or taste,
Solicited her longing eye; yet first
Pausing awhile, thus to herself she mused:
    Great are thy virtues, doubtless, best of fruits,
Though kept from man, and worthy to be admired;
Whose taste, too long forborne, at first assay
Gave elocution to the mute, and taught
The tongue not made for speech to speak thy praise.
Thy praise he also, who forbids thy use,
Conceals not from us, naming thee the tree
Of knowledge, knowledge both of good and evil;
Forbids us then to taste: but his forbidding
Commends thee more, while it infers the good
By thee communicated, and our want:
For good unknown sure is not had; or, had

And yet unknown, is as not had at all.
In plain then, what forbids he but to know,
Forbids us good, forbids us to be wise?
Such prohibitions bind not. But, if death
Bind us with after-bands, what profits then
Our inward freedom? In the day we eat
Of this fair fruit, our doom is, we shall die!
How dies the serpent? he hath eaten and lives,
And knows, and speaks, and reasons, and discerns,
Irrational till then. For us alone
Was death invented? or to us denied
This intellectual food, for beasts reserved?
For beasts it seems: yet that one beast which first
Hath tasted envies not, but brings with joy
The good befallen him, authour unsuspect,
Friendly to man, far from deceit or guile.
What fear I then? rather, what know to fear
Under this ignorance of good or evil,
Of God or death, of law or penalty?
Here grows the cure of all, this fruit divine,
Fair to the eye, inviting to the taste,
Of virtue to make wise: what hinders then
To reach, and feed at once both body and mind?
　So saying, her rash hand in evil hour
Forth reaching to the fruit, she pluck'd, she eat!
Earth felt the wound; and Nature from her seat,
Sighing through all her works, gave signs of woe,
That all was lost. Back to the thicket slunk
The guilty serpent.

The Sea-Serpent

by PLANCHÉ

All bones but yours will rattle when I say
I'm the sea-serpent from America.
Mayhap you've heard that I've been round the world;
I guess I'm round it now, Mister, twice curled.

Of all the monsters through the deep that splash,
I'm "number one" to all immortal smash.
When I lie down and would my length unroll,
There ar'n't half room enough 'twixt pole and pole.
In short, I grow so long that I've a notion
I must be measured soon for a new ocean.

The Serpent That Dances

by CHARLES BAUDELAIRE

(translated by Arthur F. Kraetzer, M.D.)

How sweet to see, dear lazy one,
　　On your body fine,
Like satin in the shimm'ring sun
　　Your fair skin shine!

Upon your hair's profundity,
　　With pungent smells,
A fragrant vagabonding sea
　　Of blue-brown swells.

Just as a ship gets under weigh
　　In the morning breeze,
My dreaming soul sails far away
　　For distant skies.

Your eyes, where naught is e'er revealed
　　Of warmth or cold,
Are frozen gems where are congealed
　　Iron and gold.

To see you rhythmic'lly advance
　　With madcap look,
One thinks of serpents that can dance
　　To baton's stroke.

Beneath your idleness's weight,
   Your childlike head
With a young elephant's soft grace
   Is balancèd.

Then sways your body and draws out
   Like lovely ship
Which on its beam end rolls about
   Its yards to dip.

As waves made mighty by the thaws
   Of glaciers grim
When your mouth's sweet saliva pours
   To your teeth's white rim,

I taste Bohemian wine aglow,
   Potent and tart,
A liquid heaven that can sow
   Stars in my heart.

Snake

by JOHN RUSSELL MC CARTHY

Poor unpardonable length,
All belly to the mouth,
Writhe then, and wriggle,
If there's joy in it!

My heel, at least, shall spare you.

A little sun on a stone,
A mouse or two,
And all that unreasonable belly
Is happy.

No wonder God wasn't satisfied—
And went on creating.

The Snake-Charmer

by THOMAS GORDON HAKE

I

The forest rears on lifted arms
   A world of leaves, whence verdurous light
Shakes through the shady depths and warms
   Proud tree and stealthy parasite,
There where those cruel coils enclasp
The trunks they strangle in their grasp.

II

An old man creeps from out the woods,
   Breaking the vine's entangling spell;
He thrids the jungle's solitudes
   O'er bamboos rotting where they fell;
Slow down the tiger's path he wends
Where at the pool the jungle ends.

III

No moss-greened alley tells the trace
   Of his lone step, no sound is stirred,
Even when his tawny hands displace
   The boughs, that backward sweep unheard:
His way as noiseless as the trail
Of the swift snake and pilgrim snail.

IV

The old snake-charmer,—once he played
   Soft music for the serpent's ear,
But now his cunning hand is stayed;
   He knows the hour of death is near.
And all that live in brake and bough,
All know the brand is on his brow.

V

Yet where his soul is he must go:
  He crawls along from tree to tree.
The old snake-charmer, doth he know
  If snake or beast of prey he be?
Bewildered at the pool he lies
And sees as through a serpent's eyes.

VI

Weeds wove with white-flowered lily crops
  Drink of the pool, and serpents hie
To the thin brink as noonday drops,
  And in the froth-daubed rushes lie.
There rests he now with fastened breath
'Neath a kind sun to bask in death.

VII

The pool is bright with glossy dyes
  And cast-up bubbles of decay:
A green death-leaven overlies
  Its mottled scum, where shadows play
As the snake's hollow coil, fresh shed,
Rolls in the wind across its bed.

VIII

No more the wily note is heard
  From his full flute—the riving air
That tames the snake, decoys the bird,
  Worries the she-wolf from her lair.
Fain would he bid its parting breath
Drown in his ears the voice of death.

IX

Still doth his soul's vague longing skim
  The pool beloved: he hears the hiss
That siffles at the sedgy rim,
  Recalling days of former bliss,
And the death-drops, that fall in showers,
Seem honied dews from shady flowers.

X

There is a rustle of the breeze
  And twitter of the singing bird;

He snatches at the melodies
   And his faint lips again are stirred;
The olden sounds are in his ears;
But still the snake its crest uprears.

XI

His eyes are swimming in the mist
   That films the earth like serpent's breath:
And now,—as if a serpent hissed,—
   The husky whisperings of Death
Fill ear and brain—he looks around—
Serpents seem matted o'er the ground.

XII

Soon visions of past joys bewitch
   His crafty soul; his hands would set
Death's snare, while now his fingers twitch
   The tasselled reed as 'twere his net.
But his thin lips no longer fill
The woods with song; his flute is still.

XIII

Those lips still quaver to the flute,
   But fast the life-tide ebbs away;
Those lips now quaver and are mute,
   But nature throbs in breathless play:
Birds are in open song, the snakes
Are watching in the silent brakes.

XIV

In sudden fear of snares unseen
   The birds like crimson sunset swarm,
All gold and purple, red and green,
   And seek each other for the charm.
Lizards dart up the feathery trees
Like shadows of a rainbow breeze.

XV

The wildered birds again have rushed
   Into the charm,—it is the hour
When the shrill forest-note is hushed,
   And they obey the serpent's power,—

Drawn to its gaze with troubled whirr,
As by the thread of falconer.

XVI

As 'twere to feed, on slanting wings
    They drop within the serpent's glare:
Eyes flashing fire in burning rings
    Which spread into the dazzled air;
They flutter in the glittering coils;
The charmer dreads the serpent's toils.

XVII

While Music swims away in death
    Man's spell is passing to his slaves:
The snake feeds on the charmer's breath,
    The vulture screams, the parrot raves,
The lone hyena laughs and howls,
The tiger from the jungle growls.

XVIII

Then mounts the eagle—flame-flecked folds
    Belt its proud plumes; a feather falls:
He hears the death-cry, he beholds
    The king-bird in the serpent's thralls,
He looks with terror on the feud,—
And the sun shines through dripping blood.

XIX

The deadly spell a moment gone—
    Birds, from a distant Paradise,
Strike the winged signal and have flown,
    Trailing rich hues through azure skies:
The serpent falls; like demon wings
The far-out branching cedar swings.

XX

The wood swims round; the pool and skies
    Have met; the death-drops down that cheek
Fall faster; for the serpent's eyes
    Grow human, and the charmer's seek.
A gaze like man's directs the dart
Which now is buried at his heart.

XXI

The monarch of the world is cold:
　　The charm he bore has passed away:
The serpent gathers up its fold
　　To wind about its human prey.
The red mouth darts a dizzy sting,
And clenches the eternal ring.

The Snakes

by EUGENE FIELD

These are the snakes that Rowdy saw:
　　Some were green and some were white,
　　Some were black as the spawn of night;
　　　　Some were yellow;
　　　　And one big fellow
　　Had monstrous blotches of angry red,
　　And a scarlet welt on his shiny head;
And other snakes that Rowdy saw
　　　　Were of every hue
　　　　From pink to blue
And the longer he looked the bigger they grew!

An old he-snake with a frowsy head
Was one of the snakes that Rowdy saw.
　　This old he-snake he grinned and leered
　　When he saw that Rowdy was afeard;
　　And he ran out his tongue in frightful wise
　　As he batted his fireless dead-fish eyes;
　　　　And he lashed his tail
　　　　In the moonlight pale,
And he tickled his jaw with his left hind paw—
Did this old he-snake that Rowdy saw!

These hideous snakes that Rowdy saw
　　　　Wriggled and twisted

Wherever they listed,
Straightway glided
Or ambled one-sided.
There were some of those things
That had fiery wings—
Yes, some of the snakes that Rowdy saw
Hummed round in the air
With their eyeballs aglare
And their whiskers aflare;
And they hissed their approval of Rowdy's despair!

And some of the snakes that Rowdy saw
Had talons like bats,
And looked like a cross between buzzards and rats!
They crawled from his boots, and they sprawled on the floor;
They sat on the mantel, and perched on the door,
And grinned all the fiercer the louder he swore!

Out, out of his boots
Came the damnable brutes—
These murdersome snakes that Rowdy saw!
Strange cries they uttered,
And poison they sputtered
As they crawled or they fluttered,
This way and that
Their venom they spat,
Till Rowdy had doubts as to where he was at.
They twined round his legs, and encircled his waist;
His arms and his neck and his breast they embraced;
They hissed in his ears, and spat in his eyes,
And with their foul breaths interrupted his cries.
Blue serpents and green,
Red, yellow, and black,
Of as hideous mien
As ever was seen,
Girt him round, fore and back,
And higgling
And wiggling,
With their slimy and grimy preponderance they bore
Rowdy down to the floor. He remembers no more.

The sequel is this: The snakes that he saw
Were such hideous snakes, were such torturesome things,
With their poison-tipped fangs and their devil-claw wings,
That he speaks of them now with a meaningful awe;

And when in the bar-room the bottle goes round,
And wassail and laughter and "boodle" abound,
Poor Rowdy he turns down his glass with a sigh.
"Come, Rowdy, drink hearty!" the aldermen cry.
His palate is yearning, his fauces are dry,
The bottle appeals to his gullet and eye;
But he thinks of the snakes, and he—lets it go by.

The Vision of Hell

by DANTE ALIGHIERI

In the year's early nonage, when the sun
Tempers his tresses in Aquaries' urn,
And now towards equal day the nights recede;
When as the rime upon the earth puts on
Her dazzling sister's image, but not long
Her milder sway endures; then riseth up
The village hind, whom fails his wintry store,
And looking out beholds the plain around
All whiten'd; whence impatiently he smites
His thighs, and to his hut returning in,
There paces to and fro, wailing his lot,
As a discomfited and helpless man;
Then comes he forth again, and feels new hope
Spring in his bosom, finding e'en thus soon
The world hath changed its countenance, grasps his crook,
And forth to pasture drives his little flock:
So me my guide dishearten'd, when I saw
His troubled forehead; and so speedily
That ill was cured; for at the fallen bridge
Arriving, towards me with a look as sweet,
He turn'd him back, as that I first beheld
At the steep mountain's foot. Regarding well
The ruin, and some counsel first maintain'd
With his own thought, he open'd wide his arm
And took me up. As one, who, while he works,
Computes his labor's issue, that he seems

Still to foresee the effect; so lifting me
Up to the summit of one peak, he fix'd
His eye upon another. Grapple that,"
Said he, "but first make proof, if it be such
As will sustain thee." For one capp'd with lead
This were no journey. Scarcely he, though light,
And I, though onward push'd from crag to crag,
Could mount. And if the precinct of this coast
Were not less ample than the last, for him
I know not, but my strength had surely fail'd.
But Malebolge all toward the mouth
Inclining of the nethermost abyss,
The site of every valley hence requires,
That one side upward slope, the other fall.

At length the point from whence the utmost stone
Juts down, we reach'd; soon as to that arrived,
So was the breath exhausted from my lungs
I could no further, but did seat me there.

"Now needs thy best of man;" so spake my guide:
"For not on downy plumes, nor under shade
Of canopy reposing, fame is won;
Without which whosoe'er consumes his days,
Leaveth such vestige of himself on earth,
As smoke in air or foam upon the wave.
Thou therefore rise: vanquish thy weariness
By the mind's effort, in each struggle form'd
To vanquish, if she suffer not the weight
Of her corporeal frame to crush her down.
A longer ladder yet remains to scale.
From these to have escaped sufficeth not,
If well thou note me, profit by my words."

I straightway rose, and show'd myself less spent
Than I in truth did feel me. "On," I cried,
"For I am stout and fearless." Up the rock
Our way we held, more rugged than before,
Narrower, and steeper far to climb. From talk
I ceased not, as we journey'd, so to seem
Least faint; whereat a voice from the other foss
Did issue forth, for utterance suited ill.
Though on the arch that crosses there I stood,
What were the words I knew not, but who spake
Seem'd moved in anger. Down I stoop'd to look;
But my quick eye might reach not to the depth
For shrouding darkness; wherefore thus I spake:
"To the next circle, teacher, bend thy steps,

And from the wall dismount we; for as hence
I hear and understand not, so I see
Beneath, and naught discern."—"I answer not,"
Said he, "but by thy deed. To fair request
Silent performance maketh best return."
  We from the bridge's head descended, where
To the eighth mount it joins; and then, the chasm
Opening to view, I saw a crowd within
Of serpents terrible, so strange of shape
And hideous, that remembrance in my veins
Yet shrinks the vital current. Of her sands
Let Libya vaunt no more: if Jaculus,
Pareas and Chelyder be her brood,
Cenchris and Amphisbæna, plagues so dire
Or in such numbers swarming ne'er she show'd,
Not with all Ethiopia, and whate'er
Above the Erythræan sea is spawn'd.
  Amid this dread exuberance of woe
Ran naked spirits wing'd with horrid fear,
Nor hope had they of crevice where to hide,
Or heliotrope to charm them out of view.
With serpents were their hands behind them bound,
Which through their reins infix'd the tail and head,
Twisted in folds before. And lo! on one
Near to our side, darted an adder up,
And, where the neck is on the shoulders tied,
Transpierced him. Far more quickly than e'er pen
Wrote O or I, be kindled, burn'd, and changed
To ashes all, pour'd out upon the earth.
When there dissolved he lay, the dust again
Uproll'd spontaneous, and the self-same form
Instant resumed. So mighty sages tell
The Arabian Phœnix, when five hundred years
Have well nigh circled, dies, and springs forthwith
Renascent: blade nor herb throughout his life
He tastes, but tears of frankincense alone
And odorous amomum: swaths of nard
And myrrh his funeral shroud. As one that falls,
He knows not how, by force demoniac dragg'd
To earth, or through obstruction fettering up
In chains invisible the powers of man,
Who, risen from his trance, gazeth around,
Bewilder'd with the monstrous agony
He hath endured, and wildly staring sighs;
So stood aghast the sinner when he rose.

Oh! how severe God's judgment, that deals out
Such blows in stormy vengeance. Who he was,
My teacher next inquired; and thus in few
He answer'd: "Vanni Fucci am I call'd,
Not long since rained down from Tuscany
To this dire gullet. Me the bestial life
And not the human pleased, mule that I was.
Who in Pistoia found my worthy den."

 I then to Virgil: "Bid him stir not hence;
And ask what crime did thrust him hither: once
A man I knew him, choleric and bloody."

 The sinner heard and feign'd not, but towards me
His mind directing and his face, wherein
Was dismal shame depictured, thus he spake:
"It grieves me more to have been caught by thee
In this sad plight, which thou beholdest, than
When I was taken from the other life.
I have no power permitted to deny
What thou inquirest. I am doom'd thus low
To dwell, for that the sacristy by me
Was rifled of its goodly ornaments,
And with the gilt another falsely charged.
But that thou mayst not joy to see me thus,
So as thou e'er shalt 'scape this darksome realm.
Open thine ears and hear what I forbode.
Reft of the Neri first Pistoia pines;
Then Florence changeth citizens and laws;
From Valdimagra, drawn by wrathful Mars,
A vapor rises, wrapt in turpid mists,
And sharp and eager driveth on the storm
With arrowy hurtling o'er Piceno's field,
Whence suddenly the cloud shall burst, and strike
Each helpless Bianco prostrate to the ground.
This have I told, that grief may rend thy heart."

   * * * * *

When he had spoke, the sinner raised his hands
Pointed in mockery, and cried: "Take them, God!
I level them at thee." From that day forth
The serpents were my friends; for round his neck
One of them rolling twisted, as it said,
"Be silent, tongue!" Another, to his arms
Upgliding, tied them, riveting itself
So close, it took from them the power to move.
 Pistoia! ah, Pistoia! why dost doubt

To turn thee into ashes, cumbering earth
No longer, since in evil act so far
Thou hast outdone thy seed? I did not mark,
Through all the gloomy circles of the abyss,
Spirit, that swell'd so proudly 'gainst his God;
Not him, who headlong fell from Thebes. He fled,
Nor utter'd more; and after him there came
A centaur full of fury, shouting, "Where,
Where is the caitiff?" On Maremma's marsh
Swarm not the serpent tribe, as on his haunch
They swarm'd, to where the human face begins.
Behind his head, upon the shoulders, lay
With open wings a dragon, breathing fire
On whomsoe'er he met. To me my guide:
"Cacus is this, who underneath the rock
Of Aventine spread oft a lake of blood.
He, from his brethren parted, here must tread
A different journey, for his fraudful theft
Of the great herd that near him stall'd; whence found
His felon deeds their end, beneath the mace
Of stout Alcides, that perchance laid on
A hundred blows, and not the tenth was felt."
    While yet he spake, the centaur sped away:
And under us three spirits came, of whom
Nor I nor he was ware, till they exclaim'd,
"Say who are ye?" We then brake off discourse,
Intent on these alone. I knew them not:
But, as it chanceth oft, befell, that one
Had need to name another. "Where," said he,
"Doth Cianfa lurk?" I, for a sign my guide
Should stand attentive, placed against my lips
The finger lifted. If, Oh reader! now
Thou be not apt to credit what I tell,
No marvel; for myself do scarce allow
The witness of mine eyes. But as I look'd
Toward them, lo! a serpent with six feet
Springs forth on one, and fastens full upon him:
His midmost grasp'd the belly, a forefoot
Seized on each arm (while deep in either cheek
He flesh'd his fangs); the hinder on the thighs
Were spread, 'twixt which the tail inserted curl'd
Upon the reins behind. Ivy ne'er clasp'd
A dodder'd oak, as round the other's limbs
The hideous monster intertwined his own.
Then, as they both had been of burning wax,

Each melted into other, mingling hues,
That which was either now was seen no more.
Thus up the shrinking paper, ere it burns,
A brown tint glides, not turning yet to black,
And the clean white expires. The other two
Look'd on, exclaiming, "Ah! how dost thou change,
Agnello! See! Thou art nor double now,
Nor only one." The two heads now became
One, and two figures blended in one form
Appear'd, where both were lost, Of the four lengths
Two arms were made: the belly and the chest,
The thighs and legs, into such members changed
As never eye hath seen. Of former shape
All trace was vanish'd. Two, yet neither, seem'd
That image miscreate, and so pass'd on
With tardy steps. As underneath the scourge
Of the fierce dog-star that lays bare the fields,
Shifting from brake to brake the lizard seems
A flash of lightning, if he thwart the road;
So toward the entrails of the other two
Approaching seem'd an adder all on fire,
As the dark pepper-grain livid and swart.
In that part, whence our life is nourish'd first,
One he transpierced; then down before him fell
Stretch'd out. The pierced spirit look'd on him,
But spake not; yea, stood motionless and yawn'd,
As if by sleep or feverous fit assail'd.
He eyed the serpent, and the serpent him.
One from the wound, the other from the mouth
Breathed a thick smoke, whose vapory column join'd.

    Lucan in mute attention now may hear,
Nor thy disastrous fate, Sabellus, tell,
Nor thine, Nasidius. Ovid now be mute.
What if in warbling fiction he record
Cadmus and Arethusa to a snake
Him changed, and her into a fountain clear,
I envy not; for never face to face
Two natures thus transmuted did he sing,
Wherein both shapes were ready to assume
The other's substance. They in mutual guise
So answer'd, that the serpent split his train
Divided to a fork, and the pierced spirit
Drew close his steps together, legs and thighs
Compacted, that no sign of juncture soon
Was visible: the tail, disparted, took

The figure which the spirit lost; its skin
Softening, his indurated to a rind.
The shoulders next I mark'd, that entering join'd
The monster's arm-pits, whose two shorter feet
So lengthen'd, as the others dwindling shrunk.
The feet behind them twisting up became
That part that man conceals, which in the wretch
Was cleft in twain. While both the shadowy smoke
With a new color veils, and generates
The excrescent pile on one, peeling it off
From the other body, lo! upon his feet
One upright rose; and prone the other fell.
Nor yet their glaring and malignant lamps
Were shifted, though each feature changed beneath.
Of him who stood erect, the mounting face
Retreated towards the temples, and what there
Superfluous matter came, shot out in ears,
From the smooth cheeks; the rest, not backward dragg'd
Of its excess did shape the nose; and swell'd
Into due size protuberant the lips.
He, on the earth who lay, meanwhile extends
His sharpen'd visage, and draws down the ears
Into the head, as doth the slug his horns.
His tongue, continuous before and apt
For utterance, severs; and the other's fork
Closing unites. That done, the smoke was laid.
The soul, transform'd into the brute, glides off,
Hissing along the vale, and after him
The other talking sputters; but soon turn'd
His new-grown shoulders on him, and in few
Thus to another spake: "Along this path
Crawling, as I have done, speed Buoso now!"
     So saw I fluctuate in successive change
The unsteady ballast of the seventh hold:
And here if aught my pen have swerved, events
So strange may be its warrant. O'er mine eyes
Confusion hung, and on my thoughts amaze.
     Yet scaped they not so covertly, but well
I mark'd Sciancato: he alone it was
Of the three first that came, who changed not: thou
The other's fate, Gaville! still dost rue.

INDEX